Mike Holt's Illustrated
ELECTRICAL
APPRENTICESHIP
SUPPLEMENT

Extracted from Mike Holt's Ultimate Training Library

YEAR 1   **Based on the 2017 NEC®**

Mike Holt Enterprises

888.NEC.CODE (632.2633) • www.MikeHolt.com

NOTICE TO THE READER

Mike Holt's Illustrated Electrical Apprenticeship Year 1 Supplement, Based on the 2017 NEC®

Second Printing: September 2018

Author: Mike Holt
Technical Illustrator: Mike Culbreath
Cover Design: Bryan Burch
Layout Design and Typesetting: Cathleen Kwas

COPYRIGHT © 2017 Charles Michael Holt
ISBN 978-0-9975452-6-5

Produced and Printed in the USA

If you are an instructor and would like to request an examination copy of this or other Mike Holt Publications:

Call: 888.NEC.CODE (632.2633) • Fax: 352.360.0983
E-mail: Info@MikeHolt.com • Visit: www.MikeHolt.com/Instructors

You can download a sample PDF of all our publications by visiting www.MikeHolt.com.

I dedicate this book to the
Lord Jesus Christ, *my mentor and teacher.*

Proverbs 16:3

We Care...

Since the day we started our business over 40 years ago, we have been working hard to produce products that get results, and to help individuals in their pursuit of learning more about this exciting industry. I have built my business on the idea that customers come first, and that everyone on my team will do everything they possibly can to take care of you. I want you to know that we value you, and are honored that you have chosen us to be your partner in electrical training.

I believe that you are the future of this industry and that it is you who will make the difference in years to come. My goal is to share with you everything that I know and to encourage you to pursue your education on a continuous basis. That not only will you learn theory, code, calculations or how to pass an exam, but that in the process you will become the expert in the field and the person who others know to trust.

We are dedicated to providing quality electrical training that will help you take your skills to the next level and we genuinely care about you. Thanks for choosing Mike Holt Enterprises for your electrical training needs.

God bless and much success,

Mike Holt

TABLE OF CONTENTS

Table of Contents

ABOUT THIS TEXTBOOK

Mike Holt's Illustrated Electrical Apprenticeship Year 1 Supplement, Based on the 2017 NEC®

Welcome to *Mike Holt's Illustrated Electrical Apprenticeship Year 1 Supplement*, based on the 2017 *NEC®*. This textbook is intended to provide you with the additional training you'll need to be an effective apprentice both in school and on the job. Your first year of apprenticeship is primarily focused on understanding the theories behind electricity and the mechanics behind the *National Electrical Code®* rules. Each of these lessons will build on the last to develop a comprehensive knowledge of the *NEC®*.

While learning theory is critical, we understand you might be on the job working from the start. Your work will probably start with the mechanical aspects of electrical installation, so you'll need some practical knowledge of the *Code*. You may need to know things like how many wires can fit in a box, the ampacity of a certain size conductor, or how big a conduit needs to be for the conductor you're going to install. With that in mind, we've selected a few *Code*-related skills you can use as you begin your electrical career.

Don't worry if you don't feel like you have these topics mastered the first time you see them. We'll come back and build on what you learn this year and each subsequent year until you've mastered even the most difficult concepts.

We hope you enjoy studying one of the most exciting trades in the industry. Be safe!

The Scope of this Textbook

This textbook, *Mike Holt's Illustrated Electrical Apprenticeship Year 1 Supplement*, based on the 2017 *NEC®*, covers the general installation requirements contained in the *NEC* from Article 90 through 362 (*NEC* Chapters 1 through 3).

This program is based on solidly grounded alternating-current systems, 1,000V or less, using 90°C insulated copper conductors sized to 60°C rated terminals for 100A and less rated circuits, and 75°C rated terminals for over 100A rated circuits, unless indicated otherwise.

How to Use This Textbook

This textbook is to be used along with the *NEC* and not as a replacement for it. Be sure to have a copy of the 2017 *National Electrical Code* handy. You'll notice that we've paraphrased a great deal of the wording, and some of the article and section titles appear different from the text in the actual *Code* book. We believe doing so makes it easier to understand the content of the rule, so keep this in mind when comparing this textbook to the actual *NEC*.

Always compare what's being explained in this textbook to what the *Code* book says. Get with others who are knowledgeable about the *NEC* to discuss any topics that you find difficult to understand, or join our free Code Forum www.MikeHolt.com/Forum to post your question.

This textbook follows the *Code* format, but it doesn't cover every change or requirement. For example, it doesn't include every article, section, subsection, exception, or Informational Note. So don't be concerned if you see that the textbook contains Exception 1 and Exception 3, but not Exception 2.

Cross-References. *NEC* cross-references to other related *Code* requirements are included to help you develop a better understanding of how the *NEC* rules relate to one another. These cross-references are indicated by *Code* section numbers in brackets, an example of which is "[90.4]."

Informational Notes. Informational Notes contained in the *NEC* will be identified in this textbook as "Note."

Exceptions. Exceptions contained in this textbook will be identified as "Ex" and not spelled out.

As you read through this textbook, allow yourself sufficient time to review the text along with the outstanding graphics and examples, to give yourself the opportunity for a deeper understanding of the *Code*.

Technical Questions

As you progress through this textbook, you might find that you don't understand every explanation, example, calculation, or comment. Don't become frustrated, and don't get down on yourself. Remember, this is the *National Electrical Code*, and sometimes the best attempt to explain a concept isn't enough to make it perfectly clear. If you're still confused, visit www.MikeHolt.com/Forum, and post your question on our free *Code* Forum. The forum is a moderated community of electrical professionals.

Book Corrections

We're committed to providing the finest product with the fewest errors, and take great care to ensure our books are correct. But we're realistic and know that errors might be found after printing. The last thing we want is for you to have problems finding, communicating, or accessing this information, so we list any corrections on our website.

If you believe there's an error of any kind (typographical, grammatical, technical, etc.) in this book or in the Answer Key, and it's not listed on the website, send an e-mail and be sure to include the book title, page number, and any other pertinent information.

To check for known errors, visit www.MikeHolt.com/corrections.

To report an error, e-mail corrections@MikeHolt.com.

Key Features of Mike Holt Textbooks

The layout and design of Mike Holt textbooks incorporate special features and icons designed to help you navigate easily through the material, and enhance your understanding.

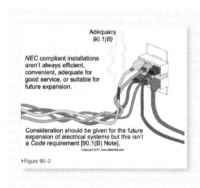

▶Figure 90–2

Full-Color, Detailed Educational Graphics

Industry-leading graphics help you visualize the sometimes complex language of the *Code*, and illustrate the rule in real-world application(s). This is a great aid to reinforce learning.

90.1 Purpose of the *NEC*

(A) Practical Safeguarding. The purpose of the *NEC* is to ensure that electrical systems are installed in a manner that protects people and property by minimizing the risks associated with the use of electricity. It isn't a design specification standard or instruction manual for the untrained and unqualified. ▶Figure 90–1

Author's Comment:

■ The *Code* is intended to be used by those skilled and knowledgeable in electrical theory, electrical systems, construction, and the installation and operation of electrical equipment.

(E) Supplemental Rod Electrode. The grounding electrode conductor to a rod(s) that serves as a supplemental electrode isn't required to be larger than 6 AWG copper.

(F) Ground Ring. A bare 2 AWG or larger copper conductor installed not less than 30 in. below the surface of the earth encircling the building [250.52(A)(4)]. ▶Figure 250–30

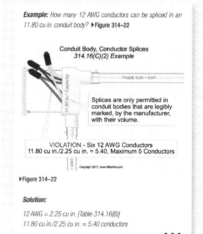

Example: How many 12 AWG conductors can be spliced in an 11.80 cu in. conduit body? ▶Figure 314–22

▶Figure 314–22

Solution:

12 AWG = 2.25 cu in. [Table 314.16(B)]
11.80 cu in./2.25 cu in. = 5.40 conductors

• • •

Code Rule Headers

The *Code* rule being taught is identified with a chapter color bar and white text.

Author's Comments

The author provides additional information to clarify the rule, and help you understand the background and context of the information.

Underlined *Code* Changes

All changes to the text in the *Code* for the 2017 *NEC* are identified by underlining in the chapter color.

Examples

Practical application questions and examples are contained in framed yellow boxes. These support the rules and help you understand how to do the calculations. If you see an ellipsis (• • •) at the bottom of the example, it's continued on the following page.

Objectionable Current

Objectionable neutral current occurs because of improper neutral-to-case connections or wiring errors that violate 250.142(B).

Improper Neutral-to-Case Connection [250.142]

Panelboards. Objectionable neutral current will flow on metal parts and the equipment grounding conductor when the neutral conductor is connected to the metal case of a panelboard on the load side of service equipment. ▶Figure 250–27

Separately Derived Systems. Objectionable neutral current will flow on metal parts if the neutral conductor is connected to the circuit equipment grounding conductor on the load side of the system bonding jumper for a separately derived system. ▶Figure 250–28

Generator. Objectionable neutral current will flow on metal parts and the equipment grounding conductor if a generator is connected to a transfer switch with a solidly connected neutral and a neutral-to-case connection is made at the generator. ▶Figure 250–29

Additional Background Information Boxes

Where the author believes that information unrelated to the specific rule will help you understand the concept being taught, he includes these topics, easily identified in boxes outlined in the chapter color.

Danger, Caution, and Warning Icons

These icons highlight areas of concern.

 Caution—Possible damage to property or equipment.

 Warning—Severe property damage or personal injury.

 Danger—Severe injury or death.

ARTICLE **300** GENERAL REQUIREMENTS FOR WIRING METHODS AND MATERIALS

Modular Color Coded Page Layout

Chapters are color coded and modular to make it easy to navigate through each section of the textbook.

$$P = I \times E$$

Formulas

Formulas are easily identifiable in green text on a gray bar.

 ## QR Codes

A few **QR Codes** are found throughout the textbook, and can be scanned with a smartphone app to take you to a sample video clip to watch Mike and the DVD panel discuss this topic.

Notes

HOW TO USE THE *NATIONAL ELECTRICAL CODE*

The original *NEC* document was developed in 1897 as a result of the united efforts of various insurance, electrical, architectural, and other allied interests. The National Fire Protection Association (NFPA) has sponsored the *National Electrical Code* since 1911.

The purpose of the *Code* is the practical safeguarding of persons and property from hazards arising from the use of electricity. It isn't intended as a design specification or an instruction manual for untrained persons. It is, in fact, a standard that contains the minimum requirements for electrical installations. Learning to understand and use the *Code* is critical to you working safely, whether you're training to become an electrician, or are already an electrician, electrical contractor, inspector, engineer, designer, or instructor.

The *NEC* was written for those who understand electrical terms, theory, safety procedures, and electrical trade practices. Learning to use the *Code* is a lengthy process and can be frustrating if you don't approach it the right way. First of all, you'll need to understand electrical theory and if you don't have theory as a background when you get into the *NEC*, you're going to be struggling—so take one step back if you need to, and learn electrical theory. You must also understand the concepts and terms, and know grammar and punctuation in order to understand the complex structure of the rules and their intended purpose(s). Our goal for the next few pages is to give you some guidelines and suggestions on using your *Code* book to help you understand what you're trying to accomplish, and how to get there.

Language Considerations for the *NEC*

Terms and Concepts

The *NEC* contains many technical terms, so it's crucial for *Code* users to understand their meanings and applications. If you don't understand a term used in a rule, it will be impossible to properly apply the *NEC* requirement. Article 100 defines the terms that are used in two or more *Code* articles; for example, the term "Dwelling Unit" is found in many articles. If you don't know the *NEC* definition for a "dwelling unit" you can't properly identify the *Code* requirements for it.

Many articles have terms unique to that specific article, and the definitions of those terms are only applicable to that given article. These definitions are usually found in the beginning of the article. For example, Section 250.2 contains the definitions of terms that only apply to Article 250—Grounding and Bonding.

Small Words, Grammar, and Punctuation

It's not only the technical words that require close attention since simple words can make a big difference to the application of a rule. Was there a comma; was it "or," "and," "other than," "greater than," or "smaller than"? The word "or" can imply alternate choices for wiring methods. A word like "or" gives us choices while the word "and" can mean an additional requirement must be met.

An example of these words being used in the *NEC* is found in 110.26(C)(2), where it says equipment containing overcurrent, switching, "or" control devices that are 1,200A or more "and" over 6 ft wide that require a means of egress at each end of the working space. In this section, the word "or" clarifies that equipment containing any of the three types of devices listed must follow this rule. The word "and" clarifies that 110.26(C)(2) only applies if the equipment is both 1,200A or more and over 6 ft wide.

Grammar and punctuation play an important role in establishing the meaning of a rule. The location of a comma can dramatically change the requirement of a rule such as in 250.28(A), where it says a main bonding jumper must be a wire, bus, screw, or similar suitable conductor. If the comma between "bus" and "screw" was removed, only a "bus screw" could be used. That comma makes a big change in the requirements of the rule.

Slang Terms or Technical Jargon

Trade-related professionals in different areas of the country often use local "slang" terms that aren't shared by all. This can make it difficult to communicate if it isn't clear what the meaning of those slang terms are. Use the proper terms by finding out what their definitions and applications are before you use them. For example, the term "pigtail" is often used to describe the short piece of conductor used to connect a device to a splice, but a "pigtail" is also a term used for a rubberized light socket with pre-terminated conductors. Although the term is the same, the meaning is very different and could cause confusion.

NEC Style and Layout

It's important to understand the structure and writing style of the *Code* if you want to use it effectively. The *National Electrical Code* is organized using eleven major components.

1. Table of Contents
2. Chapters—Chapters 1 through 9 (major categories)
3. Articles—Chapter subdivisions that cover specific subjects
4. Parts—Divisions used to organize article subject matter
5. Sections—Divisions used to further organize article subject matter
6. Tables and Figures—Represent the mandatory requirements of a rule
7. Exceptions—Alternatives to the main *Code* rule
8. Informational Notes—explanatory material for a specific rule (not a requirement)
9. Tables—Applicable as referenced in the *NEC*
10. Annexes—Additional explanatory information such as tables and references (not a requirement)
11. Index

1. Table of Contents. The Table of Contents displays the layout of the chapters, articles, and parts as well as the page numbers. It's an excellent resource and should be referred to periodically to observe the interrelationship of the various *NEC* components. When attempting to locate the rules for a particular situation, knowledgeable *Code* users often go first to the Table of Contents to quickly find the specific *NEC* rule that applies.

2. Chapters. There are nine chapters, each of which is divided into articles. The articles fall into one of four groupings: General Requirements (Chapters 1 through 4), Specific Requirements (Chapters 5 through 7), Communications Systems (Chapter 8), and Tables (Chapter 9).

Chapter 1—General
Chapter 2—Wiring and Protection
Chapter 3—Wiring Methods and Materials
Chapter 4—Equipment for General Use
Chapter 5—Special Occupancies
Chapter 6—Special Equipment
Chapter 7—Special Conditions

Chapter 8—Communications Systems (Telephone, Data, Satellite, Cable TV, and Broadband)
Chapter 9—Tables–Conductor and Raceway Specifications

3. Articles. The *NEC* contains approximately 140 articles, each of which covers a specific subject. It begins with Article 90, the introduction to the *Code*, and contains the purpose of the *NEC*, what's covered and what isn't covered, along with how the *Code* is arranged. It also gives information on enforcement and how mandatory and permissive rules are written and how explanatory material is included. Article 90 also includes information on formal interpretations, examination of equipment for safety, wiring planning, and information about formatting units of measurement. Here are some other examples of articles you'll find in the *NEC*:

Article 110—Requirements for Electrical Installations
Article 250—Grounding and Bonding
Article 300—General Requirements for Wiring Methods and Materials
Article 430—Motors and Motor Controllers
Article 500—Hazardous (Classified) Locations
Article 680—Swimming Pools, Fountains, and Similar Installations
Article 725—Remote-Control, Signaling, and Power-Limited Circuits
Article 800—Communications Circuits

4. Parts. Larger articles are subdivided into parts. Because the parts of a *Code* article aren't included in the section numbers, we have a tendency to forget what "part" an *NEC* rule is relating to. For example, Table 110.34(A) contains working space clearances for electrical equipment. If we aren't careful, we might think this table applies to all electrical installations, but Table 110.34(A) is located in Part III, which only contains requirements for "Over 1,000 Volts, Nominal" installations. The rules for working clearances for electrical equipment for systems 1,000V, nominal, or less are contained in Table 110.26(A)(1), which is located in Part II—1,000 Volts, Nominal, or Less.

5. Sections. Each *NEC* rule is called a "*Code* Section." A *Code* section may be broken down into subsections by letters in parentheses like (A), numbers in parentheses like (1), and lowercase letters like (a), (b), and so on, to further break the rule down to the second and third level. For example, the rule requiring all receptacles in a dwelling unit bathroom to be GFCI protected is contained in Section 210.8(A)(1) which is located in Chapter 2, Article 210, Section 8, Subsection (A), Sub-subsection (1).

Many in the industry incorrectly use the term "Article" when referring to a *Code* section. For example, they say "Article 210.8," when they should say "Section 210.8." Section numbers in this textbook are shown without the word "Section," unless they begin a sentence. For example, Section 210.8(A) is shown as simply 210.8(A).

6. Tables and Figures. Many *NEC* requirements are contained within tables, which are lists of *Code* rules placed in a systematic arrangement. The titles of the tables are extremely important; you must read them carefully in order to understand the contents, applications and limitations of each table. Many times notes are provided in or below a table; be sure to read them as well since they're also part of the requirement. For example, Note 1 for Table 300.5 explains how to measure the cover when burying cables and raceways, and Note 5 explains what to do if solid rock is encountered.

7. Exceptions. Exceptions are *Code* requirements or permissions that provide an alternative method to a specific rule. There are two types of exceptions—mandatory and permissive. When a rule has several exceptions, those exceptions with mandatory requirements are listed before the permissive exceptions.

Mandatory Exceptions. A mandatory exception uses the words "shall" or "shall not." The word "shall" in an exception means that if you're using the exception, you're required to do it in a particular way. The phrase "shall not" means it isn't permitted.

Permissive Exceptions. A permissive exception uses words such as "shall be permitted," which means it's acceptable (but not mandatory) to do it in this way.

8. Informational Notes. An Informational Note contains explanatory material intended to clarify a rule or give assistance, but it isn't a *Code* requirement.

9. Tables. Chapter 9 consists of tables applicable as referenced in the *NEC*. The tables are used to calculate raceway sizing, conductor fill, the radius of raceway bends, and conductor voltage drop.

10. Annexes. Annexes aren't a part of the *NEC* requirements, and are included in the *Code* for informational purposes only.

Annex A. Product Safety Standards
Annex B. Application Information for Ampacity Calculation
Annex C. Raceway Fill Tables for Conductors and Fixture Wires of the Same Size
Annex D. Examples
Annex E. Types of Construction
Annex F. Critical Operations Power Systems (COPS)
Annex G. Supervisory Control and Data Acquisition (SCADA)
Annex H. Administration and Enforcement
Annex I. Recommended Tightening Torques
Annex J. ADA Standards for Accessible Design

11. Index. The Index at the back of the *Code* book is helpful in locating a specific rule.

Author's Comment:

■ Changes in the 2017 *Code* book are indicated as follows:
  ♦ Changed rules are identified by shading the text that was changed since the previous edition.
  ♦ New rules aren't shaded like a change, instead they have a shaded "N" in the margin to the left of the section number.
  ♦ Relocated rules are treated like new rules with a shaded "N" in the left margin by the section number.
  ♦ Deleted rules are indicated by a bullet symbol "•" located in the left margin where the rule was in the previous edition.

How to Locate a Specific Requirement

How to go about finding what you're looking for in the *Code* book depends, to some degree, on your experience with the *NEC*. Experts typically know the requirements so well that they just go to the correct rule. Very experienced people might only need the Table of Contents to locate the requirement they're looking for. On the other hand, average users should use all of the tools at their disposal, including the Table of Contents, the Index, and the search feature on electronic versions of the *Code* book.

Let's work through a simple example: What *NEC* rule specifies the maximum number of disconnects permitted for a service?

Table of Contents. If you're an experienced *Code* user, you might use the Table of Contents. You'll know Article 230 applies to "Services," and because this article is so large, it's divided up into multiple parts (actually eight parts). With this knowledge, you can quickly go to the Table of Contents and see it lists the Service Equipment Disconnecting Means requirements in Part VI.

Author's Comment:

■ The number 70 precedes all page numbers because the *NEC* is NFPA Standard Number 70.

Index. If you use the Index, which lists subjects in alphabetical order, to look up the term "service disconnect," you'll see there's no listing. If you try "disconnecting means," then "services," you'll find that the Index indicates the rule is located in Article 230, Part VI. Because the *NEC* doesn't give a page number in the Index, you'll need to use the Table of Contents to find it, or flip through the *Code* book to Article 230, then continue to flip through pages until you find Part VI.

Many people complain that the *NEC* only confuses them by taking them in circles. Once you gain experience in using the *Code* and deepen your understanding of words, terms, principles, and practices, you'll find the *NEC* much easier to understand and use than you originally thought.

Customizing Your *Code* Book

One way to increase your comfort level with the *Code* book is to customize it to meet your needs. You can do this by highlighting and underlining important *NEC* requirements. Preprinted adhesive tabs are also an excellent aid to quickly find important articles and sections that are regularly referenced. Be aware that if you're using your *Code* book to prepare to take an exam, some exam centers don't allow markings of any type. Visit www.MikeHolt.com/tabs for more information.

Highlighting. As you read through textbooks or find answers to your questions, be sure you highlight those requirements in the *NEC* that are the most important or relevant to you. Use one color, like yellow, for general interest and a different one for important requirements you want to find quickly. Be sure to highlight terms in the Index and the Table of Contents as you use them.

Underlining. Underline or circle key words and phrases in the *Code* with a red or blue pen (not a lead pencil) using a short ruler or other straightedge to keep lines straight and neat. This is a very handy way to make important requirements stand out. A short ruler or other straightedge also comes in handy for locating the correct information in a table.

Different Interpretations

Industry professionals often enjoy the challenge of discussing the *NEC* requirements. This discussion is important to the process of better understanding the *Code* requirements and application(s). If you decide you're going to participate in one of these discussions, don't spout out what you think without having the actual *NEC* book in your hand. The professional way of discussing a *Code* requirement is by referring to a specific section, rather than talking in vague generalities. This will help everyone involved clearly understand the point and become better educated.

Become Involved in the *NEC* Process

The actual process of changing the *Code* takes about two years and involves hundreds of individuals making an effort to have the *NEC* as current and accurate as possible. As you study and learn how to use it, you'll find it very interesting, enjoy it more, and realize that you can also be a part of the process. Rather than sitting back and just reading it and learning it, you can participate by making proposals and being a part of its development. For the 2017 *Code*, there were 4,000 public inputs and 1,500 comments. Hundreds of updates and five new articles were added to keep the *NEC* up to date with new technologies, and pave the way to a safer and more efficient electrical future.

Let's review how this process works:

STEP 1—Public Input Stage

Public Input. The revision cycle begins with the acceptance of Public Input (PI): the public notice asking for anyone interested to submit input on an existing standard or a committee-approved new draft standard. Following the closing date, the Committee conducts a First Draft Meeting to respond to all public inputs.

First Draft Meeting. At the First Draft (FD) Meeting, the Technical Committee considers and provides a response to all Public Input. The Technical Committee may use the input to develop First Revisions to the standard. The First Draft documents consist of the initial meeting consensus of the committee by simple majority. However, the final position of the Technical Committee must be established by a ballot which follows.

Committee Ballot on First Draft. The First Draft developed at the First Draft Meeting is balloted: to appear in the First Draft, a revision must be approved by at least two-thirds of the Technical Committee.

First Draft Report Posted. First revisions which pass ballot are ultimately compiled and published as the First Draft Report on the document's NFPA web page. This report serves as documentation for the Input Stage and is published for review and comment. The public may review the First Draft Report to determine whether to submit Public Comments on the First Draft.

STEP 2—Public Comment Stage

Public Comment. Once the First Draft Report becomes available, there's a public comment period during which anyone can submit a Public Comment on the First Draft. After the Public Comment closing date, the Technical Committee conducts/holds their Second Draft Meeting.

Second Draft Meeting. After the Public Comment closing date, if Public Comments are received or the committee has additional proposed revisions, a Second Draft Meeting is held. At the Second Draft Meeting, the Technical Committee reviews the First Draft and may make additional revisions to the draft Standard. All Public Comments are considered, and the Technical Committee provides an action and response to each Public Comment. These actions result in the Second Draft.

Committee Ballot on Second Draft. The Second Revisions developed at the Second Draft Meeting are balloted. To appear in the Second Draft, a revision must be approved by at least two-thirds of the Technical Committee.

Second Draft Report Posted. Second Revisions which pass ballot are ultimately compiled and published as the Second Draft Report on the document's NFPA website. This report serves as documentation of the Comment Stage and is published for public review.

Once published, the public can review the Second Draft Report to decide whether to submit a Notice of Intent to Make a Motion (NITMAM) for further consideration.

STEP 3—NFPA Technical Meeting (Tech Session)

Following completion of the Public Input and Public Comment stages, there's further opportunity for debate and discussion of issues through the NFPA Technical Meeting that takes place at the NFPA Conference & Expo®. These motions are attempts to change the resulting final Standard from the committee's recommendations published as the Second Draft.

STEP 4—Council Appeals and Issuance of Standard

Issuance of Standards. When the Standards Council convenes to issue an NFPA standard, it also hears any related appeals. Appeals are an important part of assuring that all NFPA rules have been followed and that due process and fairness have continued throughout the standards development process. The Standards Council considers appeals based on the written record and by conducting live hearings during which all interested parties can participate. Appeals are decided on the entire record of the process, as well as all submissions and statements presented.

After deciding all appeals related to a standard, the Standards Council, if appropriate, proceeds to issue the Standard as an official NFPA Standard. The decision of the Standards Council is final subject only to limited review by the NFPA Board of Directors. The new NFPA standard becomes effective twenty days following the Standards Council's action of issuance.

Author's Comment:

- Proposals and comments can be submitted online at the NFPA website at www.nfpa.org/doc# (for NFPA 70, go to www.nfpa.org/70 for example). From the homepage, look for "Codes & Standards," then find "How the Process Works." If you'd like to see something changed in the *Code*, you're encouraged to participate in the process.

2017 *Code* Book and Tabs

The ideal way to use your *Code* book is to tab it for quick reference—Mike's best-selling tabs make organizing the *NEC* easy. If you're using your *Code* book for an exam, please confirm with your testing authority that a tabbed *Code* book is allowed into the exam room.

To order your *Code* book and tabs visit www.MikeHolt.com/Code, or call 1.888.NEC.CODE (632.2633).

INTRODUCTION TO THE *NATIONAL ELECTRICAL CODE*

Introduction to Article 90—Introduction to the *National Electrical Code*

Many *NEC* violations and misunderstandings wouldn't occur if people doing the work simply understood Article 90. For example, many people see *Code* requirements as performance standards. In fact, the *NEC* requirements are bare minimums for safety. This is exactly the stance electrical inspectors, insurance companies, and courts take when making a decision regarding electrical design or installation.

Article 90 opens by saying the *NEC* isn't intended as a design specification or instruction manual. The *National Electrical Code* has one purpose only, and that's the "practical safeguarding of persons and property from hazards arising from the use of electricity." The necessity of carefully studying the *NEC* rules can't be overemphasized, and the role of textbooks such as this one are to help in that undertaking. Understanding where to find the rules in the *Code* that apply to the installation is invaluable. Rules in several different articles often apply to even a simple installation.

Article 90 then describes the scope and arrangement of the *NEC*. The balance of this article provides the reader with information essential to understanding the *Code* rules.

Typically, electrical work requires you to understand the first four chapters of the *NEC* which apply generally, plus have a working knowledge of the Chapter 9 tables. That understanding begins with Article 90. Chapters 5, 6, and 7 make up a large portion of the *Code*, but they apply to special occupancies, special equipment, or other special conditions. They build on, modify, or amend the rules in the first four chapters. Chapter 8 contains the requirements for communications systems, such as twisted pair conductors for telephone and data systems, satellite receivers, antenna systems, and coaxial cable wiring. Communications systems (twisted wire, antennas, and coaxial cable) aren't subject to the general requirements of Chapters 1 through 4, or the special requirements of Chapters 5 through 7, unless there's a specific reference in Chapter 8 to a rule in Chapters 1 through 7.

90.1 Purpose of the *NEC*

(A) Practical Safeguarding. The purpose of the *NEC* is to ensure that electrical systems are installed in a manner that protects people and property by minimizing the risks associated with the use of electricity. It isn't a design specification standard or instruction manual for the untrained and unqualified. ▶Figure 90–1

Author's Comment:

- The *Code* is intended to be used by those skilled and knowledgeable in electrical theory, electrical systems, construction, and the installation and operation of electrical equipment.

(B) Adequacy. The *Code* contains requirements considered necessary for a safe electrical installation. If an electrical system is installed in compliance with the *NEC*, it will be essentially free from electrical hazards. The *Code* is a safety standard, not a design guide.

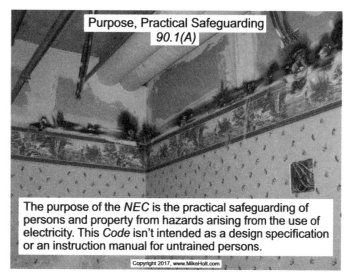

Purpose, Practical Safeguarding
90.1(A)

The purpose of the *NEC* is the practical safeguarding of persons and property from hazards arising from the use of electricity. This *Code* isn't intended as a design specification or an instruction manual for untrained persons.

Copyright 2017, www.MikeHolt.com

▶Figure 90–1

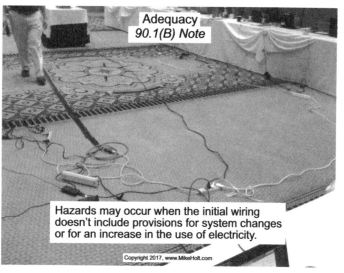

Adequacy
90.1(B) Note

Hazards may occur when the initial wiring doesn't include provisions for system changes or for an increase in the use of electricity.

Copyright 2017, www.MikeHolt.com

▶Figure 90–3

NEC requirements aren't intended to ensure the electrical installation will be efficient, convenient, adequate for good service, or suitable for future expansion. Specific items of concern, such as electrical energy management, maintenance, and power quality issues aren't within the scope of the *Code*. ▶Figure 90–2

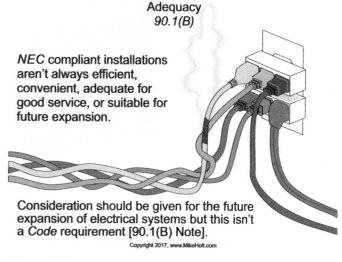

Adequacy
90.1(B)

NEC compliant installations aren't always efficient, convenient, adequate for good service, or suitable for future expansion.

Consideration should be given for the future expansion of electrical systems but this isn't a *Code* requirement [90.1(B) Note].

Copyright 2017, www.MikeHolt.com

▶Figure 90–2

Note: Hazards in electrical systems often occur because circuits are overloaded or not properly installed in accordance with the *NEC*. These often occur if the initial wiring didn't provide reasonable provisions for system changes or for the increase in the use of electricity. ▶Figure 90–3

Author's Comment:

- See the definition of "Overload" in Article 100.
- The *NEC* doesn't require electrical systems to be designed or installed to accommodate future loads. However, the electrical designer (typically an electrical engineer) is concerned with not only ensuring electrical safety (*Code* compliance), but also with ensuring the system meets the customers' needs, both of today and in the near future. To satisfy customers' needs, electrical systems are often designed and installed above the minimum requirements contained in the *NEC*. But just remember, if you're taking an exam, licensing exams are based on your understanding of the minimum *Code* requirements.

(C) Relation to International Standards. The requirements of the *NEC* address the fundamental safety principles contained in the International Electrotechnical Commission (IEC) Standard, including protection against electric shock, adverse thermal effects, overcurrent, fault currents, and overvoltage. ▶Figure 90–4

Author's Comment:

- The *NEC* is used in Chile, Ecuador, Peru, and the Philippines. It's also the *Electrical Code* for Colombia, Costa Rica, Mexico, Panama, Puerto Rico, and Venezuela. Because of these adoptions, it's available in Spanish from the National Fire Protection Association, 617.770.3000, or www.NFPA.org.

NEC Relation to International Standards
90.1(C) and Note
The *NEC* addresses the safety principles
contained in the IEC Standard such as:
• Protection against electric shock
• Adverse thermal effects
• Overcurrent
• Fault currents
• Overvoltage

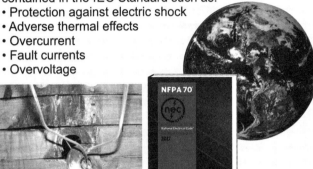

▶Figure 90–4

90.2 Scope of the *NEC*

(A) What Is Covered by the *NEC*. The *NEC* contains requirements necessary for the proper installation and removal of electrical conductors, equipment, cables, and raceways for power, signaling, fire alarm, optical cable, and communications systems (twisted wire, antennas, and coaxial cable) for: ▶Figure 90–5

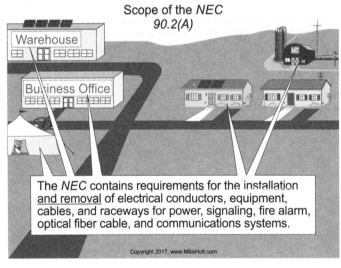

Scope of the *NEC*
90.2(A)

The *NEC* contains requirements for the installation and removal of electrical conductors, equipment, cables, and raceways for power, signaling, fire alarm, optical fiber cable, and communications systems.

▶Figure 90–5

Author's Comment:

■ The *NEC* contains the following requirements on the removal of equipment and cables; temporary wiring [590.3] and abandoned cables for Audio [640.6(B)], Signaling [725.25], Fire Alarm [760.25], Optical Fiber [770.25], Twisted Pair [800.25], and Coaxial [820.25].

(1) Public and private premises, including buildings, mobile homes, recreational vehicles, and floating buildings. ▶Figure 90–6

Scope of the *NEC*, Public and Private Premises
90.2(A)(1) and (2)

Public lighting on private property must be installed in accordance with the *NEC* even if installed by an electric utility.

The *Code* covers installation and removal in or on:
(1) Public and private premises, and
(2) Yards, lots, parking lots, carnivals, and industrial structures.

▶Figure 90–6

(2) Yards, lots, parking lots, carnivals, and industrial substations.

(3) Conductors and equipment connected to the electric utility supply.

(4) Installations used by an electric utility, such as office buildings, warehouses, garages, machine shops, recreational buildings, and other electric utility buildings that aren't an integral part of a utility's generating plant, substation, or control center. ▶Figure 90–7

(B) What Isn't Covered by the *NEC*. The *NEC* doesn't apply to the installation of electrical or communications systems (twisted wire, antennas, and coaxial cable) for:

(1) Transportation Vehicles. The *NEC* doesn't apply to installations in cars, trucks, boats, ships and watercraft, planes, or electric trains.

(2) Mining Equipment. The *NEC* doesn't apply to installations underground in mines and self-propelled mobile surface mining machinery and its attendant electrical trailing cables.

(3) Railways. The *NEC* doesn't apply to railway power, signaling, energy storage, and communications wiring.

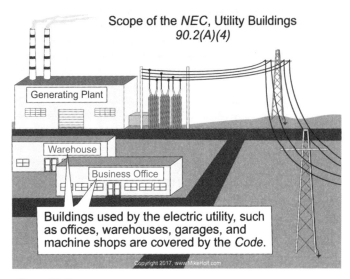

Scope of the *NEC*, Utility Buildings
90.2(A)(4)

Generating Plant

Warehouse

Business Office

Buildings used by the electric utility, such as offices, warehouses, garages, and machine shops are covered by the *Code*.

Copyright 2017, www.MikeHolt.com

▶Figure 90–7

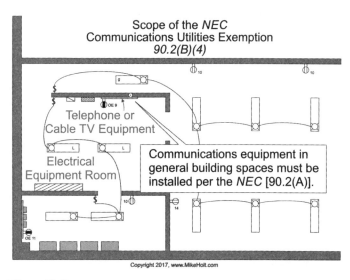

Scope of the *NEC*
Communications Utilities Exemption
90.2(B)(4)

Telephone or Cable TV Equipment

Electrical Equipment Room

Communications equipment in general building spaces must be installed per the *NEC* [90.2(A)].

Copyright 2017, www.MikeHolt.com

▶Figure 90–9

(4) Communications Utilities. If the installation is under the exclusive control of the communications utility, the installation requirements of the *NEC* don't apply to the communications (telephone) or network-powered broadband utility equipment located in building spaces used exclusively for these purposes, or located outdoors if the installation is under the exclusive control of the communications utility. ▶Figure 90–8 and ▶Figure 90–9

(5) Electric Utilities. The *NEC* doesn't apply to electrical installations under the exclusive control of an electric utility, where such installations:

a. Consist of electric utility installed service drops or service laterals under their exclusive control. ▶Figure 90–10

b. Are on property owned or leased by the electric utility for the purpose of generation, transformation, transmission, energy storage, distribution, or metering of electric energy. ▶Figure 90–11

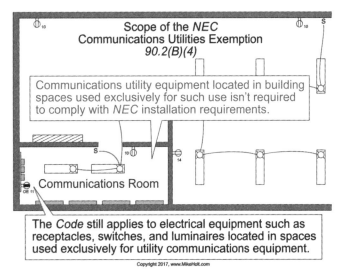

Scope of the *NEC*
Communications Utilities Exemption
90.2(B)(4)

Communications utility equipment located in building spaces used exclusively for such use isn't required to comply with *NEC* installation requirements.

Communications Room

The *Code* still applies to electrical equipment such as receptacles, switches, and luminaires located in spaces used exclusively for utility communications equipment.

Copyright 2017, www.MikeHolt.com

▶Figure 90–8

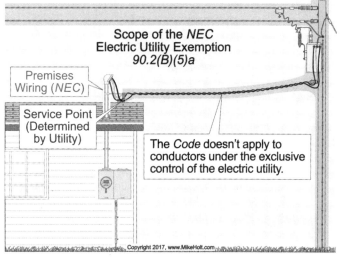

Scope of the *NEC*
Electric Utility Exemption
90.2(B)(5)a

Premises Wiring (*NEC*)

Service Point (Determined by Utility)

The *Code* doesn't apply to conductors under the exclusive control of the electric utility.

Copyright 2017, www.MikeHolt.com

▶Figure 90–10

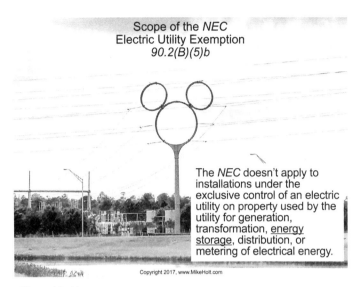

Scope of the *NEC*
Electric Utility Exemption
90.2(B)(5)b

The *NEC* doesn't apply to installations under the exclusive control of an electric utility on property used by the utility for generation, transformation, <u>energy storage</u>, distribution, or metering of electrical energy.

Copyright 2017, www.MikeHolt.com

▶Figure 90–11

Author's Comment:

- Luminaires located in legally established easements, or rights-of-way, such as at poles supporting transmission or distribution lines, are exempt from the *NEC*. However, if the electric utility provides site and public lighting on private property, then the installation must comply with the *Code* [90.2(A)(4)].

c. Are located on legally established easements or rights-of-way. ▶Figure 90–12

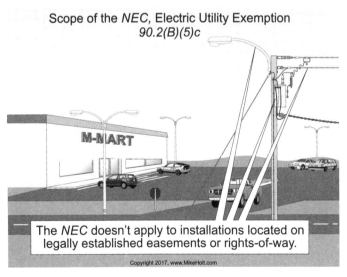

Scope of the *NEC*, Electric Utility Exemption
90.2(B)(5)c

M-MART

The *NEC* doesn't apply to installations located on legally established easements or rights-of-way.

Copyright 2017, www.MikeHolt.com

▶Figure 90–12

d. Are located by other written agreements either designated by or recognized by public service commissions, electric utility commissions, or other regulatory agencies having jurisdiction for such installations; limited to installations for the purpose of communications, metering, generation, control, transformation, transmission, <u>energy storage,</u> or distribution of electric energy where legally established easements or rights-of-way can't be obtained. These installations are limited to federal lands, Native American reservations through the U.S. Department of the Interior Bureau of Indian Affairs, military bases, lands controlled by port authorities and state agencies and departments, and lands owned by railroads.

Note to 90.2(B)(4) and (5): Utilities include entities that install, operate, and maintain communications systems (twisted wire, antennas, and coaxial cable) or electric supply (generation, transmission, or distribution systems) and are designated or recognized by governmental law or regulation by public service/utility commissions. Utilities may be subject to compliance with codes and standards covering their regulated activities as adopted under governmental law or regulation.

90.3 *Code* Arrangement

General Requirements. The *Code* is divided into an introduction and nine chapters followed by informational annexes. Chapters 1, 2, 3, and 4 are general conditions. ▶Figure 90–13

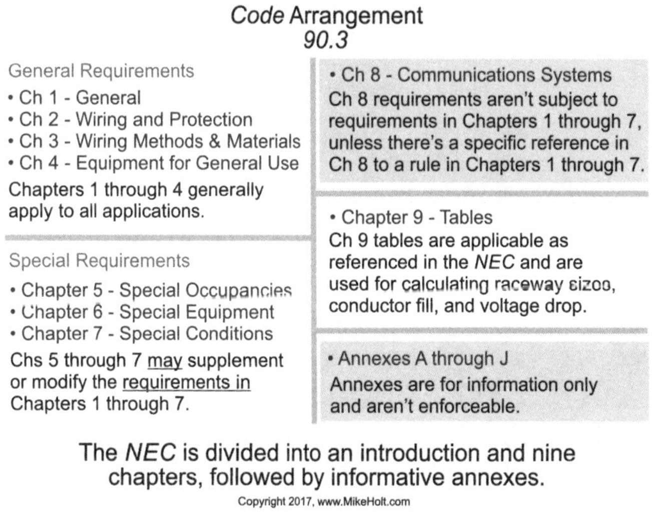

Code Arrangement
90.3

General Requirements
- Ch 1 - General
- Ch 2 - Wiring and Protection
- Ch 3 - Wiring Methods & Materials
- Ch 4 - Equipment for General Use
Chapters 1 through 4 generally apply to all applications.

Special Requirements
- Chapter 5 - Special Occupancies
- Chapter 6 - Special Equipment
- Chapter 7 - Special Conditions
Chs 5 through 7 <u>may</u> supplement or modify the <u>requirements in</u> Chapters 1 through 7.

- Ch 8 - Communications Systems
Ch 8 requirements aren't subject to requirements in Chapters 1 through 7, unless there's a specific reference in Ch 8 to a rule in Chapters 1 through 7.

- Chapter 9 - Tables
Ch 9 tables are applicable as referenced in the *NEC* and are used for calculating raceway sizes, conductor fill, and voltage drop.

- Annexes A through J
Annexes are for information only and aren't enforceable.

The *NEC* is divided into an introduction and nine chapters, followed by informative annexes.
Copyright 2017, www.MikeHolt.com

▶Figure 90–13

Author's Comment:

- These first four chapters may be thought of as the foundation for the rest of the *Code*.

Special Requirements. The requirements contained in Chapters 5, 6, and 7 apply to special occupancies, special equipment, or other special conditions, which <u>may supplement</u> or modify the <u>requirements</u> contained in Chapters 1 <u>through 7</u>, but not Chapter 8.

Communications Systems. Chapter 8 contains the requirements for communications systems (twisted wire, antennas, and coaxial cable) which aren't subject to the general requirements of Chapters 1 through 4, or the special requirements of Chapters 5 through 7, unless there's a specific reference in Chapter 8 to a rule in Chapters 1 through 7.

Author's Comment:

- An example of how Chapter 8 works is in the rules for working space about equipment. The typical 3-ft working space isn't required in front of communications equipment, because Table 110.26(A)(1) isn't referenced in Chapter 8.

Tables. Chapter 9 consists of tables applicable as referenced in the *NEC*. The tables are used to calculate raceway sizing, conductor fill, the radius of raceway bends, and conductor voltage drop.

Annexes. Annexes aren't part of the *Code*, but are included for informational purposes. There are ten annexes:

- Annex A. Product Safety Standards
- Annex B. Application Information for Ampacity Calculation
- Annex C. Raceway Fill Tables for Conductors and Fixture Wires of the Same Size
- Annex D. Examples
- Annex E. Types of Construction
- Annex F. Critical Operations Power Systems (COPS)
- Annex G. Supervisory Control and Data Acquisition (SCADA)
- Annex H. Administration and Enforcement
- Annex I. Recommended Tightening Torques
- Annex J. ADA Standards for Accessible Design

90.4 Enforcement

 Scan this QR code to watch Mike explain this topic; it's a sample video clip from Mike's *Understanding the NEC Volume 1* DVDs.

The *Code* is intended to be suitable for enforcement by governmental bodies that exercise legal jurisdiction over electrical installations for power, lighting, signaling circuits, and communications systems, such as: ▶Figure 90–14

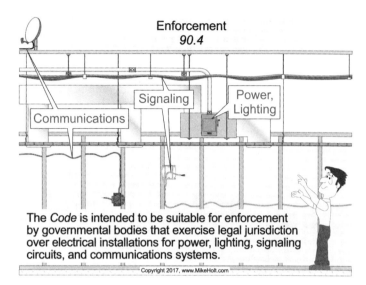

Enforcement
90.4

Communications Signaling Power, Lighting

The *Code* is intended to be suitable for enforcement by governmental bodies that exercise legal jurisdiction over electrical installations for power, lighting, signaling circuits, and communications systems.

Copyright 2017, www.MikeHolt.com

▶Figure 90–14

Signaling circuits which include:

- Article 725 Class 1, Class 2, and Class 3 Remote-Control, Signaling, and Power-Limited Circuits
- Article 760 Fire Alarm Systems
- Article 770 Optical Fiber Cables and Raceways

Communications systems which include:

- Article 810 Radio and Television Equipment (satellite dish and antenna)
- Article 820 Community Antenna Television and Radio Distribution Systems (coaxial cable)

Author's Comment:

- The installation requirements for signaling circuits and communications circuits are covered in Mike Holt's *Understanding the National Electrical Code, Volume 2* textbook.

The enforcement of the *NEC* is the responsibility of the authority having jurisdiction (AHJ), who is responsible for interpreting requirements, approving equipment and materials, waiving *Code* requirements, and ensuring equipment is installed in accordance with listing instructions.

Author's Comment:

- See the definition of "Authority Having Jurisdiction" in Article 100.

Interpretation of the Requirements. The authority having jurisdiction is responsible for interpreting the *NEC*.

Author's Comment:

■ The AHJ's decisions must be based on a specific *Code* requirement. If an installation is rejected, the authority having jurisdiction is legally responsible for informing the installer of the specific *NEC* rule that was violated. ▶Figure 90–15

Interpretation of the Requirements
90.4 Comment

The AHJ is responsible for interpreting the *NEC*, but the decision must be based on a specific *Code* requirement.

Copyright 2017, www.MikeHolt.com

▶Figure 90–15

Author's Comment:

■ The art of getting along with the authority having jurisdiction consists of doing good work and knowing what the *Code* actually says (as opposed to what you only think it says). It's also useful to know how to choose your battles when the inevitable disagreement does occur.

Approval of Equipment and Materials. Only the authority having jurisdiction has authority to approve the installation of equipment and materials. Typically, the authority having jurisdiction will approve equipment listed by a product testing organization, such as Underwriters Laboratories, Inc. (UL). The *NEC* doesn't require all equipment to be listed, but many state and local AHJs do. See 90.7, 110.2, 110.3, and the definitions for "Approved," "Identified," "Labeled," and "Listed" in Article 100. ▶Figure 90–16

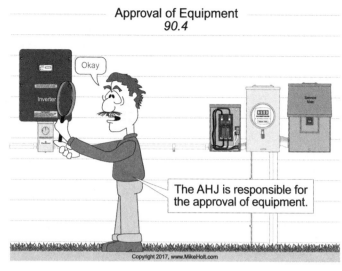

Approval of Equipment
90.4

Okay

The AHJ is responsible for the approval of equipment.

Copyright 2017, www.MikeHolt.com

▶Figure 90–16

Author's Comment:

■ According to the *NEC*, the authority having jurisdiction determines the approval of equipment. This means he or she can reject an installation of listed equipment and can approve the use of unlisted equipment. Given our highly litigious society, approval of unlisted equipment is becoming increasingly difficult to obtain.

Approval of Alternate Means. By special permission, the authority having jurisdiction may approve alternate methods where it's assured equivalent safety can be achieved and maintained.

Author's Comment:

■ Special permission is defined in Article 100 as the written consent of the authority having jurisdiction.

Waiver of New Product Requirements. If the current *NEC* requires products that aren't yet available at the time the *Code* is adopted, the authority having jurisdiction can allow products that were acceptable in the previous *Code* to continue to be used.

Author's Comment:

■ Sometimes it takes years before testing laboratories establish product standards for new *NEC* requirements, and then it takes time before manufacturers can design, manufacture, and distribute those products to the marketplace.

90.5 Mandatory Requirements and Explanatory Material

(A) Mandatory Requirements. In the *NEC* the words "shall" or "shall not," indicate a mandatory requirement.

Author's Comment:

- For the ease of reading this textbook, the word "shall" has been replaced with the word "must," and the words "shall not" have been replaced with "must not." Remember that in many places, we'll paraphrase the *Code* instead of providing exact quotes, to make it easier to read and understand.

(B) Permissive Requirements. When the *NEC* uses "shall be permitted" it means the identified actions are permitted but not required, and the authority having jurisdiction isn't permitted to restrict an installation from being completed in that manner. A permissive rule is often an exception to the general requirement.

Author's Comment:

- For ease of reading, the phrase "shall be permitted," as used in the *Code*, has been replaced in this textbook with the phrase "is permitted" or "are permitted."

(C) Explanatory Material. References to other standards or sections of the *NEC*, or information related to a *Code* rule, are included in the form of Informational Notes. Such notes are for information only and aren't enforceable as requirements of the *NEC*.

For example, Informational Note 4 in 210.19(A)(1) recommends that the voltage drop of a circuit not exceed 3 percent. This isn't a requirement; it's just a recommendation.

Author's Comment:

- For convenience and ease of reading in this textbook, Informational Notes will simply be identified as "Note."

- Informational Notes aren't enforceable, but Table Notes are. This textbook will call notes found in a table "Table Notes."

(D) Informative Annexes. Nonmandatory information annexes contained in the back of the *Code* book are for information only and aren't enforceable as requirements of the *NEC*.

90.6 Formal Interpretations

To promote uniformity of interpretation and application of the provisions of the *NEC*, formal interpretation procedures have been established and are found in the NFPA Regulations Governing Committee Projects.

Author's Comment:

- This is rarely done because it's a very time-consuming process, and formal interpretations from the NFPA aren't binding on the authority having jurisdiction.

90.7 Examination of Equipment for Product Safety

Product evaluation for safety is typically performed by a nationally recognized testing laboratory that's approved by the authority having jurisdiction. The suitability of equipment use is determined by the application of product safety listing standards that are compatible with the *NEC*.

Author's Comment:

- See Article 100 for the definition of "Approved."

Except to detect alterations or damage, listed factory-installed internal wiring and construction of equipment need not be inspected at the time of installation [300.1(B)]. ▶Figure 90–17

Examination of Equipment for Product Safety
90.7

Except to detect alterations or damage, listed factory-installed internal wiring and construction of equipment need not be inspected.

Copyright 2017, www.MikeHolt.com

▶Figure 90–17

Note 1: See 110.3 on the required use of listed products.

Note 2: "Listed" is defined in Article 100.

Note 3: Annex A contains a list of product safety standards that comply with the *NEC*.

90.9 Units of Measurement

(B) Dual Systems of Units. Both the metric and inch-pound measurement systems are shown in the *NEC*, with the metric units appearing first and the inch-pound system immediately following in parentheses.

Author's Comment:

- This is the standard practice in all NFPA standards, even though the U.S. construction industry uses inch-pound units of measurement. You'll need to be cautious when using the tables in the *Code* because the additional units can make the tables more complex and more difficult to read.

(D) Compliance. Installing electrical systems in accordance with the metric system or the inch-pound system is considered to comply with the *Code*.

Author's Comment:

- Since the use of either the metric or the inch-pound system of measurement constitutes compliance with the *NEC*, this textbook uses only inch-pound units.

ARTICLE 90 PRACTICE QUESTIONS

Please use the 2017 *Code* book to answer the following questions.

1. The *NEC* is _____.

   (a) intended to be a design manual
   (b) meant to be used as an instruction guide for untrained persons
   (c) for the practical safeguarding of persons and property
   (d) published by the Bureau of Standards

2. The *NEC* isn't intended as a design specification standard or instruction manual for untrained persons.

   (a) True
   (b) False

3. Compliance with the provisions of the *NEC* will result in _____.

   (a) good electrical service
   (b) an efficient electrical system
   (c) an electrical system essentially free from hazard
   (d) all of these

4. The *NEC* contains provisions considered necessary for safety, which will not necessarily result in _____.

   (a) efficient use
   (b) convenience
   (c) good service or future expansion of electrical use
   (d) all of these

5. Hazards often occur because of _____.

   (a) overloading of wiring systems by methods or usage not in conformity with the *NEC*
   (b) initial wiring not providing for increases in the use of electricity
   (c) a and b
   (d) none of these

6. Which of the following systems shall be installed and removed in accordance with the *NEC* requirements?

   (a) Signaling conductors, equipment, and raceways.
   (b) Communications conductors, equipment, and raceways.
   (c) Electrical conductors, equipment, and raceways.
   (d) all of these

7. The *NEC* applies to the installation of _____.

   (a) electrical conductors and equipment within or on public and private buildings
   (b) outside conductors and equipment on the premises
   (c) optical fiber cables and raceways
   (d) all of these

8. This *NEC* covers the installation of _____ for public and private premises, including buildings, structures, mobile homes, recreational vehicles, and floating buildings.

   (a) optical fiber cables
   (b) electrical equipment
   (c) raceways
   (d) all of these

9. The *NEC* does not cover electrical installations in ships, watercraft, railway rolling stock, aircraft, or automotive vehicles.

   (a) True
   (b) False

10. The *NEC* covers underground mine installations and self-propelled mobile surface mining machinery and its attendant electrical trailing cable.

   (a) True
   (b) False

11. Installations of communications equipment that are under the exclusive control of communications utilities, and located outdoors or in building spaces used exclusively for such installations _____ covered by the *NEC*.

    (a) are
    (b) are sometimes
    (c) are not
    (d) may be

12. Electric utilities may include entities that install, operate, and maintain _____.

    (a) communications systems (telephone, CATV, Internet, satellite, or data services)
    (b) electric supply systems (generation, transmission, or distribution systems)
    (c) local area network wiring on the premises
    (d) a or b

13. Utilities may be subject to compliance with codes and standards covering their regulated activities as adopted under governmental law or regulation.

    (a) True
    (b) False

14. The *NEC* does not apply to electric utility-owned wiring and equipment _____.

    (a) installed by an electrical contractor
    (b) installed on public property
    (c) consisting of service drops or service laterals
    (d) in a utility office building

15. Utilities may include entities that are designated or recognized by governmental law or regulation by public service/utility commissions.

    (a) True
    (b) False

16. Chapters 1 through 4 of the *NEC* apply _____.

    (a) generally to all electrical installations
    (b) only to special occupancies and conditions
    (c) only to special equipment and material
    (d) all of these

17. Chapters 5, 6, and 7 apply to special occupancies, special equipment, or other special conditions and may supplement or modify the requirements in Chapters 1 through 7.

    (a) True
    (b) False

18. Communications wiring such as telephone, antenna, and CATV wiring within a building shall not be required to comply with the installation requirements of Chapters 1 through 7, except where specifically referenced in Chapter 8.

    (a) True
    (b) False

19. Installations shall comply with the material located in the *NEC* Annexes because they are part of the requirements of the *Code*.

    (a) True
    (b) False

20. The authority having jurisdiction shall not be allowed to enforce any requirements of Chapter 7 (Special Conditions) or Chapter 8 (Communications Systems).

    (a) True
    (b) False

21. The _____ has the responsibility for deciding on the approval of equipment and materials.

    (a) manufacturer
    (b) authority having jurisdiction
    (c) testing agency
    (d) none of these

22. By special permission, the authority having jurisdiction may waive specific requirements in this *NEC* where it is assured that equivalent objectives can be achieved by establishing and maintaining effective safety.

    (a) True
    (b) False

23. The authority having jurisdiction has the responsibility for _____.

    (a) making interpretations of rules
    (b) deciding upon the approval of equipment and materials
    (c) waiving specific requirements in the *NEC* and permitting alternate methods and material if safety is maintained
    (d) all of these

24. If the *NEC* requires new products that are not yet available at the time a new edition is adopted, the _____ may permit the use of the products that comply with the most recent previous edition of the *NEC* adopted by that jurisdiction.

    (a) electrical engineer
    (b) master electrician
    (c) authority having jurisdiction
    (d) permit holder

25. In the *NEC*, the word(s) "_____" indicate a mandatory requirement.

    (a) shall
    (b) shall not
    (c) shall be permitted
    (d) a or b

26. When the *NEC* uses "_____," it means the identified actions are allowed but not required, and they may be options or alternative methods.

    (a) shall
    (b) shall not
    (c) shall be permitted
    (d) a or b

27. Explanatory material, such as references to other standards, references to related sections of the *NEC*, or information related to a *NEC* rule, are included in the form of Informational Notes.

    (a) True
    (b) False

28. Nonmandatory Informative Annexes contained in the back of the *NEC* book are _____.

    (a) for information only
    (b) not enforceable as a requirement of the *NEC*
    (c) enforceable as a requirement of the *NEC*
    (d) a and b

29. Factory-installed _____ wiring of listed equipment need not be inspected at the time of installation of the equipment, except to detect alterations or damage.

    (a) external
    (b) associated
    (c) internal
    (d) all of these

30. Compliance with either the SI or the inch-pound unit of measurement system shall be permitted.

    (a) True
    (b) False

ARTICLE 100 DEFINITIONS

Introduction to Article 100—Definitions

Have you ever had a conversation with someone, only to discover that what you said and what he or she heard were completely different? This often happens when people in a conversation have different definitions for the words being used, and that's why the definitions of key terms are located right at the beginning of the *NEC* (Article 100), or at the beginning of each article. If we can all agree on important definitions, then we speak the same language and avoid misunderstandings. Because the *Code* exists to protect people and property, it's very important to know the definitions presented in Article 100.

Here are a few tips for learning the many definitions in the *NEC*:

- **Break the task down.** Study a few words at a time, rather than trying to learn them all at one sitting.
- **Review the graphics in the textbook.** These will help you see how terms are applied.
- **Relate the definitions to your work.** As you read a word, think about how it applies to the work you're doing. This will provide a natural reinforcement to the learning process.

Accessible (as it applies to wiring methods). Not permanently closed in by the building structure or finish and capable of being removed or exposed without damaging the building structure or finish. ▶Figure 100–1

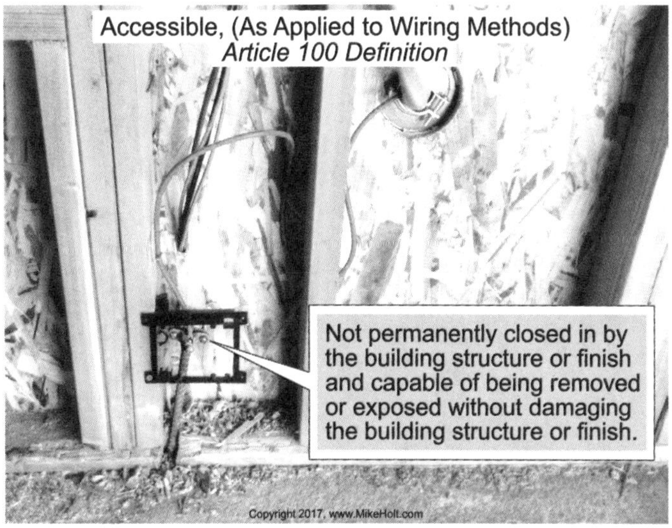

Accessible, Readily (Readily Accessible). Capable of being reached quickly for operation, renewal or inspections without requiring those to whom ready access is requisite to take actions such as the use tools (other than keys), to climb over or under, remove obstacles, or resort to portable ladders, and so forth. ▶Figure 100–2

Accessible, (As Applied to Wiring Methods)
Article 100 Definition

Not permanently closed in by the building structure or finish and capable of being removed or exposed without damaging the building structure or finish.

Copyright 2017, www.MikeHolt.com

▶Figure 100–1

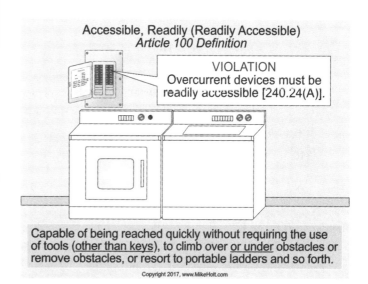

Accessible, Readily (Readily Accessible)
Article 100 Definition

VIOLATION
Overcurrent devices must be readily accessible [240.24(A)].

Capable of being reached quickly without requiring the use of tools (other than keys), to climb over or under obstacles or remove obstacles, or resort to portable ladders and so forth.

Copyright 2017, www.MikeHolt.com

▶Figure 100–2

Note: Use of keys is a common practice under controlled or supervised conditions.

Adjustable Speed Drive. A piece of equipment that provides a way to adjust the speed of an electric motor.

Author's Comment:

- Adjustable-speed drives are often referred to as "variable-speed drives" or "variable-frequency drives (VFDs)."

Note: A variable frequency drive is one type of electronic adjustable speed drive that controls the speed of an alternating-current motor by changing the frequency and voltage of the motor's power supply.

Adjustable Speed Drive System. A combination of an adjustable speed drive, its associated motor(s), and any other equipment associated with the two.

Ampacity. The maximum current, in amperes, a conductor can carry continuously, under the conditions of use without exceeding its temperature rating.

Author's Comment:

- See 310.10 and 310.15 for details and examples. ▶Figure 100–3

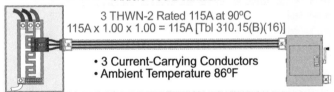

Ampacity
Article 100 Definition

3 THWN-2 Rated 115A at 90°C
115A x 1.00 x 1.00 = 115A [Tbl 310.15(B)(16)]
- 3 Current-Carrying Conductors
- Ambient Temperature 86°F

3 THWN-2 Rated 115A at 90°C
115A x 0.87x 0.80 = 80A [310.15(B)(3)]
- Ambient Temperature 110°F
- 5 Current-Carrying Conductors

The maximum current, in amperes, a conductor can carry continuously, under the conditions of use [310.15] without exceeding its temperature rating.
Copyright 2017, www.MikeHolt.com

▶Figure 100–3

Appliance [Article 422]. Electrical equipment, other than industrial equipment, built in standardized sizes. Examples of appliances are ranges, ovens, cooktops, refrigerators, drinking water coolers, or beverage dispensers.

Approved. Acceptable to the authority having jurisdiction, usually the electrical inspector. ▶Figure 100–4

Approved
Article 100 Definition

Okay

Acceptable to the authority having jurisdiction (AHJ).
Copyright 2017, www.MikeHolt.com

▶Figure 100–4

Author's Comment:

- Product listing doesn't mean the product is approved, but it can be a basis for approval. See 90.4, 90.7, 110.2, and the definitions in this article for "Authority Having Jurisdiction," "Identified," "Labeled," and "Listed."

Arc-Fault Circuit Interrupter (AFCI). An arc-fault circuit interrupter is a device intended to de-energize the circuit when it detects the current waveform characteristics unique to an arcing fault. ▶Figure 100–5 and ▶Figure 100–6

Arc-Fault Circuit Interrupter (AFCI)
Article 100 Definition

AFCI Circuit Breaker   AFCI Receptacle

A device intended to provide protection from the effects of arc faults by recognizing characteristics unique to arcing, and by functioning to de-energize the circuit when an arc fault is detected.
Copyright 2017, www.MikeHolt.com

▶Figure 100–5

Arc-Fault Circuit Interrupter (AFCI)
Article 100 Definition

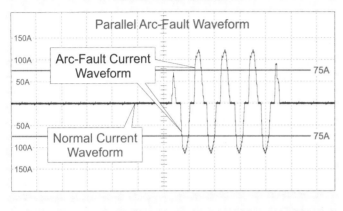

▶Figure 100–6

Attachment Plug (Plug Cap), (Plug) [Article 406]. A wiring device at the end of a flexible cord intended to be inserted into a receptacle in order to make an electrical connection. ▶Figure 100–7

Attachment Plug (Plug Cap), (Plug)
Article 100 Definition

A device that makes an electrical connection between a flexible cord and a receptacle.

▶Figure 100–7

Authority Having Jurisdiction (AHJ). The organization, office, or individual responsible for approving equipment, materials, an installation, or a procedure. See 90.4 and 90.7 for more information.

Note: The authority having jurisdiction may be a federal, state, or local government department or an individual, such as a fire chief, fire marshal, chief of a fire prevention bureau or labor department or health department, a building official or electrical inspector, or others having statutory authority. In some circumstances, the property owner or his/her agent assumes the role, and at government installations, the commanding officer, or departmental official may be the authority having jurisdiction.

Author's Comment:

- Typically, the authority having jurisdiction is the electrical inspector who has legal statutory authority. In the absence of federal, state, or local regulations, the operator of the facility or his or her agent, such as an architect or engineer of the facility, can assume the role.

- Some believe the authority having jurisdiction should have a strong background in the electrical field, such as having studied electrical engineering or having obtained an electrical contractor's license, and in a few states this is a legal requirement. Memberships, certifications, and active participation in electrical organizations, such as the International Association of Electrical Inspectors (IAEI), speak to an individual's qualifications. Visit www.IAEI.org for more information about that organization.

Automatic. Functioning without the necessity of human intervention.

Bathroom. A bathroom is an area that includes a basin as well as one or more of the following: a toilet, urinal, tub, shower, bidet, or similar plumbing fixture. ▶Figure 100–8

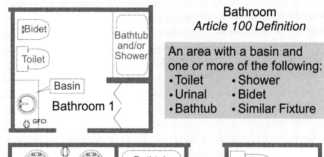
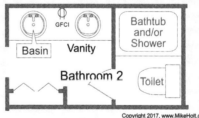

▶Figure 100–8

Author's Comment:

- 15A and 20A, 125V receptacles located in bathrooms must be GFCI protected [210.8(A)(1) and 210.8(B)(1)].

Battery System. An interconnection of one or more storage batteries and their chargers. It can also include converters, inverters, and other associated equipment. ▶Figure 100–9

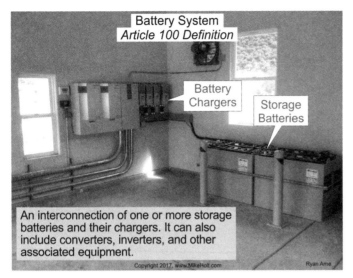

An interconnection of one or more storage batteries and their chargers. It can also include converters, inverters, and other associated equipment.

▶Figure 100–9

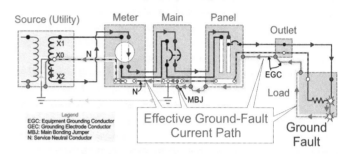

The purpose of bonding is to connect two or more conductive objects together to ensure the electrical continuity of the ground-fault current path.

▶Figure 100–11

Bonded (Bonding). Connected to establish electrical continuity and conductivity. ▶Figure 100–10

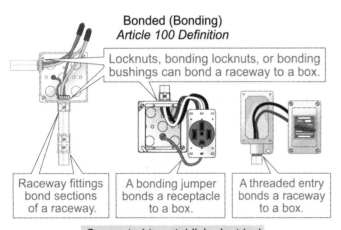

▶Figure 100–10

Author's Comment:

- The purpose of bonding is to connect two or more conductive objects together to ensure the electrical continuity of the ground-fault current path, provide the capacity and ability to conduct safely any fault current likely to be imposed, and to minimize voltage between conductive components. ▶Figure 100–11 and ▶Figure 100–12

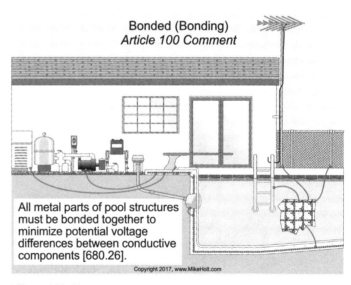

All metal parts of pool structures must be bonded together to minimize potential voltage differences between conductive components [680.26].

▶Figure 100–12

Bonding Conductor or Jumper. A conductor that ensures electrical conductivity between metal parts of the electrical installation. ▶Figure 100–13

Bonding Jumper, Main. A conductor, screw, or strap that connects the circuit equipment grounding conductor to the neutral conductor at service equipment in accordance with 250.24(B) [250.24(A)(4), 250.28, and 408.3(C)]. ▶Figure 100–14

Bonding Conductor or Jumper
Article 100 Definition

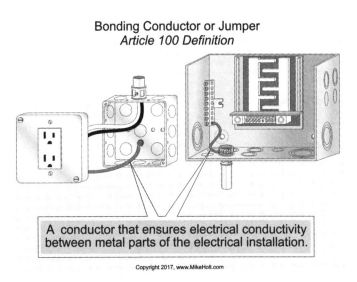

A conductor that ensures electrical conductivity between metal parts of the electrical installation.

Copyright 2017, www.MikeHolt.com

▶Figure 100–13

Bonding Jumper, Main
Article 100 Definition

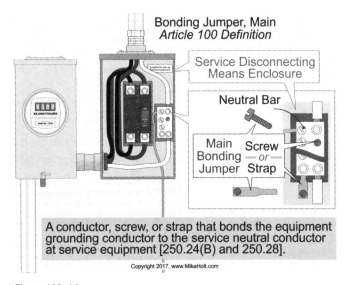

Service Disconnecting Means Enclosure

Neutral Bar

Main Bonding Jumper — Screw or Strap

A conductor, screw, or strap that bonds the equipment grounding conductor to the service neutral conductor at service equipment [250.24(B) and 250.28].

Copyright 2017, www.MikeHolt.com

▶Figure 100–14

Bonding Jumper, System
Separately Derived System, Transformer
Article 100 Definition

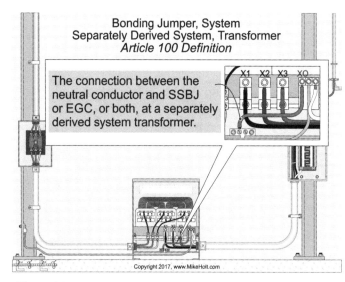

The connection between the neutral conductor and SSBJ or EGC, or both, at a separately derived system transformer.

Copyright 2017, www.MikeHolt.com

▶Figure 100–15

Bonding Jumper, System
Separately Derived System, Generator
Article 100 Definition

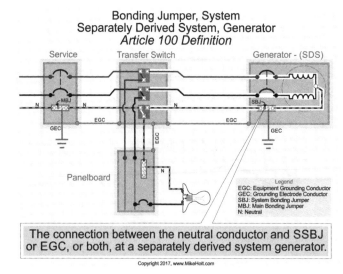

Legend
EGC: Equipment Grounding Conductor
GEC: Grounding Electrode Conductor
SBJ: System Bonding Jumper
MBJ: Main Bonding Jumper
N: Neutral

The connection between the neutral conductor and SSBJ or EGC, or both, at a separately derived system generator.

Copyright 2017, www.MikeHolt.com

▶Figure 100–16

Bonding Jumper, System. The connection between the neutral conductor and the supply-side bonding jumper or equipment grounding conductor, or both, at a separately derived system transformer or separately derived system generator. ▶Figure 100–15 and ▶Figure 100–16

Branch Circuit [Article 210]. The conductors between the final over-current protection device and the receptacle outlets, lighting outlets, or other outlets as defined in this article. ▶Figure 100–17

Branch Circuit, Individual. A branch circuit that only supplies one load.

Branch Circuit, Multiwire. A branch circuit that consists of two or more ungrounded circuit conductors with a common neutral conductor. There must be a voltage between the ungrounded conductors and an equal difference of voltage from each ungrounded conductor to the common neutral conductor. ▶Figure 100–18

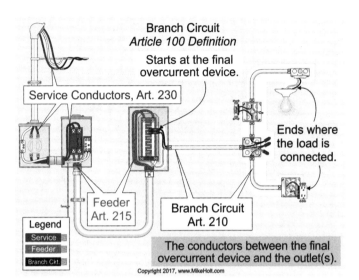

Branch Circuit
Article 100 Definition

Starts at the final overcurrent device.

Service Conductors, Art. 230

Ends where the load is connected.

Feeder Art. 215

Branch Circuit Art. 210

Legend
Service
Feeder
Branch Ckt.

The conductors between the final overcurrent device and the outlet(s).

Copyright 2017, www.MikeHolt.com

▶Figure 100–17

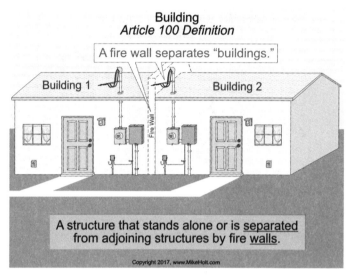

Building
Article 100 Definition

A fire wall separates "buildings."

Building 1

Building 2

A structure that stands alone or is <u>separated</u> from adjoining structures by fire <u>walls</u>.

Copyright 2017, www.MikeHolt.com

▶Figure 100–19

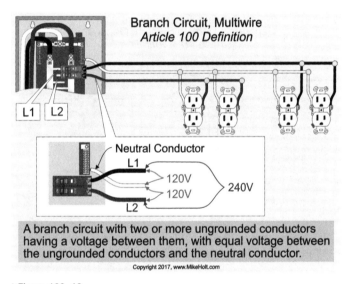

Branch Circuit, Multiwire
Article 100 Definition

L1   L2

Neutral Conductor
L1
120V
240V
120V
L2

A branch circuit with two or more ungrounded conductors having a voltage between them, with equal voltage between the ungrounded conductors and the neutral conductor.

Copyright 2017, www.MikeHolt.com

▶Figure 100–18

Author's Comment:

- Multiwire branch circuits offer the advantage of fewer conductors within a raceway, smaller raceway sizing, and a reduction of material and labor costs. In addition, multiwire branch circuits can reduce circuit voltage drop by as much as 50 percent. However, because of the dangers associated with multiwire branch circuits, the *NEC* contains additional requirements to ensure a safe installation. See 210.4, 300.13(B), and 408.41 in this textbook for details.

Building. A structure that stands alone or is <u>separated</u> from adjoining structures by fire <u>walls</u>. ▶**Figure 100–19**

Author's Comment:

- A cable routing assembly is typically a "U" shaped trough, with or without covers, designed to hold cables, and it isn't a raceway.

Cabinet [Article 312]. An enclosure for either surface mounting or flush mounting provided with a frame in which a door can be hung. ▶**Figure 100–20**

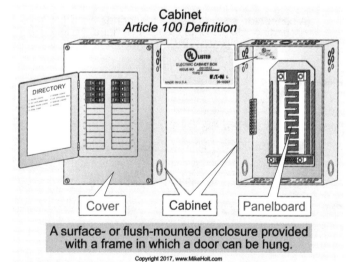

Cabinet
Article 100 Definition

DIRECTORY

Cover   Cabinet   Panelboard

A surface- or flush-mounted enclosure provided with a frame in which a door can be hung.

Copyright 2017, www.MikeHolt.com

▶Figure 100–20

Author's Comment:

- Cabinets are used to enclose panelboards. See the definition of "Panelboard" in this article.

Cable Routing Assembly. A channel or channels, with their fittings, that support and route communications wires and cables, optical fiber cables, data cables, Class 2 and Class 3, and Type PLTC cables, and power-limited fire alarm cables in plenum, riser, and general-purpose applications. ▶Figure 100–21

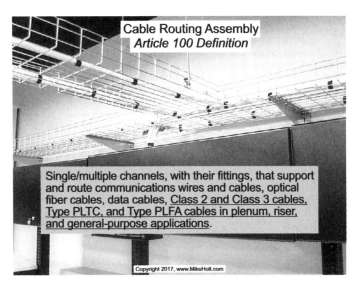

Cable Routing Assembly
Article 100 Definition

Single/multiple channels, with their fittings, that support and route communications wires and cables, optical fiber cables, data cables, Class 2 and Class 3 cables, Type PLTC, and Type PLFA cables in plenum, riser, and general-purpose applications.

Copyright 2017, www.MikeHolt.com

▶Figure 100–21

Charge Controller. Equipment that controls dc voltage or dc current, or both, and is used to charge a battery or other energy storage device. ▶Figure 100–22

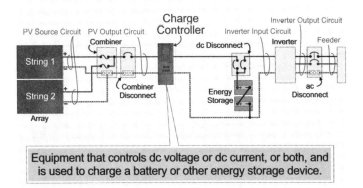

Charge Controller
Article 100 Definition

Equipment that controls dc voltage or dc current, or both, and is used to charge a battery or other energy storage device.

Copyright 2017, www.MikeHolt.com

▶Figure 100–22

Circuit Breaker. A device designed to be opened and closed manually, and which opens automatically on a predetermined overcurrent without damage to itself. Circuit breakers are available in different configurations, such as inverse time, adjustable trip (electronically controlled), and instantaneous trip/motor-circuit protectors. ▶Figure 100–23

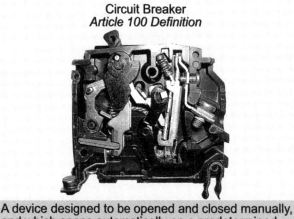

Circuit Breaker
Article 100 Definition

A device designed to be opened and closed manually, and which opens automatically on a predetermined overcurrent without damage to itself.

Copyright 2017, www.MikeHolt.com

▶Figure 100–23

Circuit Breaker, Inverse Time. Inverse time breakers operate on the principle that as the current increases, the time it takes for the devices to open decreases. This type of breaker provides overcurrent protection (overload, short circuit, and ground fault). This is the most common type of circuit breaker that you'll buy over-the-counter.

Circuit Breaker, Adjustable Trip. Adjustable trip breakers permit the thermal trip setting to be adjusted. The adjustment is often necessary to coordinate the operation of the circuit breakers with other overcurrent protection devices.

Author's Comment:

- Coordination means that the devices with the lowest ratings, closest to the fault, operate and isolate the fault and minimize disruption so the rest of the system can remain energized and functional. This sounds simple, but large systems (especially emergency systems) may require an expensive engineering study. If you're responsible for bidding a project, be aware of this requirement.

Circuit Breaker, Instantaneous Trip. Instantaneous trip breakers operate on the principle of electromagnetism only and are used for motors. Sometimes these devices are called motor-circuit protectors. This type of overcurrent protection device doesn't provide overload protection. It only provides short-circuit and ground-fault protection; overload protection must be provided separately.

Author's Comment:

■ Instantaneous trip circuit breakers have no intentional time delay and are sensitive to current inrush, and to vibration and shock. Consequently, they shouldn't be used where these factors are known to exist.

Clothes Closet. A nonhabitable room or space intended primarily for the storage of garments and apparel. ▶Figure 100–24

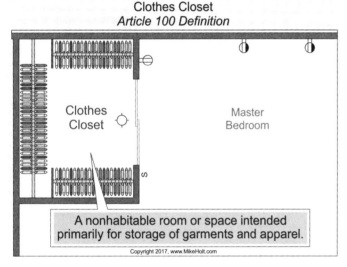

▶Figure 100–24

Author's Comment:

■ The definition of "Clothes Closet" provides clarification in the application of overcurrent protection devices [240.24(D)] and luminaires [410.16] in clothes closets.

Combustible Dust. Dust particles that are 500 microns or smaller and present a fire or explosion hazard when dispersed and ignited in air.

Author's Comment:

■ The size of the material may be a significant factor in distinguishing dust (Class II) from fibers and flyings (Class III).

Communications Equipment. Electronic telecommunications equipment used for the transmission of audio, video, and data, including support equipment such as computers, as well as the conductors that are used solely for the operation of the equipment.

Note: Communications equipment includes computers, routers, and servers essential to the transmission of audio, video, and data. ▶Figure 100–25

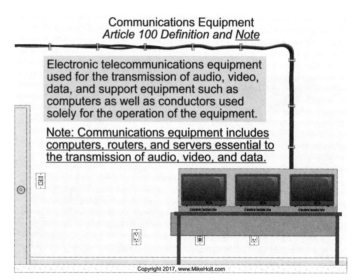

▶Figure 100–25

Communications Raceway. An enclosed nonmetallic channel designed for holding communications wires and cables, optical fiber cables, data cables associated with information technology and communications equipment, Class 2, Class 3, and Type PLTC cables, and power-limited fire alarm cables in plenum spaces, risers, and general-purpose applications. ▶Figure 100–26

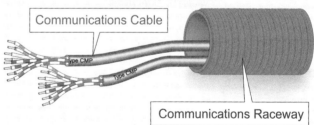

▶Figure 100–26

Composite Optical Fiber Cable. A cable containing optical fibers and current-carrying electrical conductors.

Author's Comment:

- Article 770 permits the use of composite cables only where the optical fibers and current-carrying electrical conductors are functionally associated [770.133(A)].

Concealed. Rendered inaccessible by the structure or finish of the building.

Note: Conductors in a concealed raceway are considered concealed, even though they may be made accessible by withdrawing them from the raceway. ▶Figure 100–27

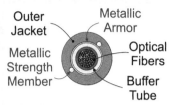

Conductive Optical Fiber Cable
Article 100 Definition

Outer Jacket — Metallic Armor — Optical Fibers — Buffer Tube — Metallic Strength Member

An optical fiber cable containing conductive members such as metallic strength members, metallic vapor barriers, and metallic armor or sheath.

Copyright 2017, www.MikeHolt.com

▶Figure 100–28

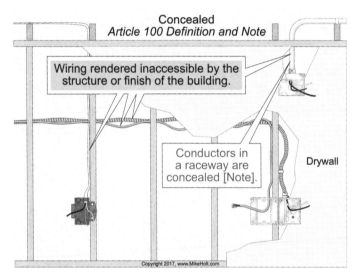

Concealed
Article 100 Definition and Note

Wiring rendered inaccessible by the structure or finish of the building.

Conductors in a raceway are concealed [Note].

Drywall

Copyright 2017, www.MikeHolt.com

▶Figure 100–27

Author's Comment:

- Wiring behind panels designed to allow access, such as removable ceiling tile, is considered exposed.

Conductive Optical Fiber Cable. An optical fiber cable containing conductive members such as metallic strength members, metallic vapor barriers, or metallic armor or sheath. ▶Figure 100–28

Conduit Body. A fitting that's installed in a conduit or tubing system and provides access to conductors through a removable cover. ▶Figure 100–29

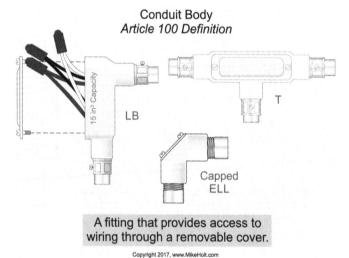

Conduit Body
Article 100 Definition

15 in³ Capacity

LB

T

Capped ELL

A fitting that provides access to wiring through a removable cover.

Copyright 2017, www.MikeHolt.com

▶Figure 100–29

Connector, Pressure (Solderless). A device that establishes a conductive connection between conductors or between a conductor and a terminal by the means of mechanical pressure. ▶Figure 100–30

Continuous Load. A load where the maximum current is expected to exist for 3 hours or more continuously, such as store or parking lot lighting.

Control Circuit. The circuit of a control apparatus or system that carries the electric signals directing the performance of the controller but doesn't carry the main power current. ▶Figure 100–31

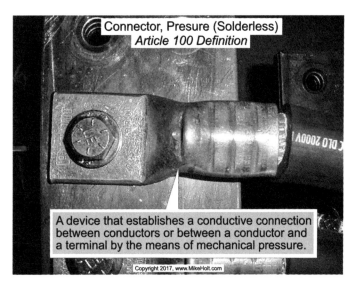

A device that establishes a conductive connection between conductors or between a conductor and a terminal by the means of mechanical pressure.

Connector, Presure (Solderless)
Article 100 Definition

▶Figure 100–30

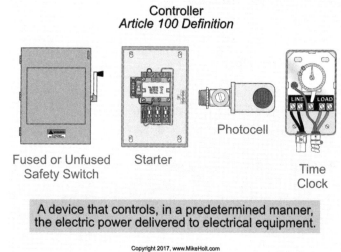

Controller
Article 100 Definition

Fused or Unfused Safety Switch

Starter

Photocell

Time Clock

A device that controls, in a predetermined manner, the electric power delivered to electrical equipment.

▶Figure 100–32

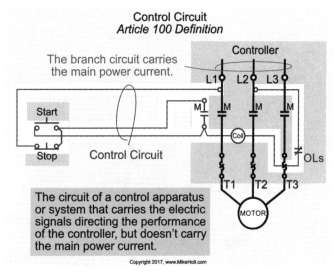

Control Circuit
Article 100 Definition

The branch circuit carries the main power current.

Controller

The circuit of a control apparatus or system that carries the electric signals directing the performance of the controller, but doesn't carry the main power current.

▶Figure 100–31

Controller. A device that controls the electric power delivered to electrical equipment in some predetermined manner. This includes time clocks, lighting contactors, photocells, and equipment with similar functions. ▶Figure 100–32

Author's Comment:

■ For the definition of "Controller" as it relates to motors, see 430.2.

Coordination, _Selective_ (Selective _Coordination_). Localization of an overcurrent condition to restrict outages to the circuit or equipment affected, accomplished by the choice of overcurrent protective devices. Selective coordination includes all currents, from overloads to short circuits. ▶Figure 100–33

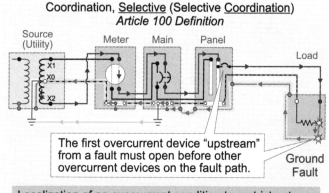

Coordination, Selective (Selective Coordination)
Article 100 Definition

Source (Utility)

Meter   Main   Panel   Load

The first overcurrent device "upstream" from a fault must open before other overcurrent devices on the fault path.

Ground Fault

Localization of an overcurrent condition to restrict outages to the circuit or equipment affected, accomplished by the choice of overcurrent devices. Selective coordination includes all currents from overloads to short circuits.

▶Figure 100–33

Author's Comment:

- Selective coordination means the overcurrent protection scheme confines the interruption to a particular area rather than to the whole system. For example, if someone plugs in a space heater and raises the total demand on a 20A circuit to 25A, or if a short circuit or ground fault occurs with selective coordination, the only breaker or fuse that will open is the one protecting just that branch circuit. Without selective coordination, an entire building can go dark!

Demand Factor. The ratio of the maximum demand to the total connected load.

Author's Comment:

- This definition is primarily used in the application of the requirements of Article 220—Branch-Circuit, Feeder, and Service Calculations.

Device. A component of an electrical installation, other than a conductor, intended to carry or control electric energy as its principal function. ▶Figure 100–34

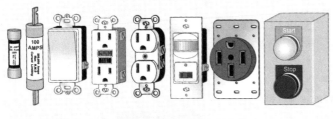

Device
Article 100 Definition

A component of an electrical installation, other than a conductor, intended to carry or control electric energy as its principal function.

Copyright 2017, www.MikeHolt.com

▶Figure 100–34

Author's Comment:

- Devices include receptacles, switches, illuminated switches, circuit breakers, fuses, time clocks, controllers, and so forth, but not locknuts or other mechanical fittings. A device may consume very small amounts of energy, such as an illuminated switch, but still be classified as a device based on its principal function.

Disconnecting Means. A device that opens all of the ungrounded circuit conductors from their power source. This includes devices such as switches, attachment plugs and receptacles, and circuit breakers. ▶Figure 100–35

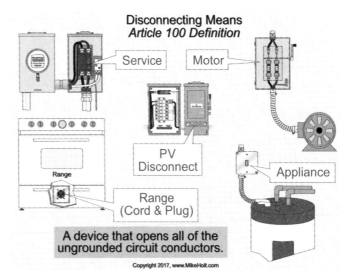

Disconnecting Means
Article 100 Definition

Service   Motor

PV
Disconnect

Range

Range
(Cord & Plug)

Appliance

A device that opens all of the
ungrounded circuit conductors.

Copyright 2017, www.MikeHolt.com

▶Figure 100–35

Dust-Ignitionproof [as applied to Hazardous (Classified) Locations]. Equipment enclosed in a manner that excludes dust and doesn't permit arcs, sparks, or heat inside the enclosure to ignite accumulations or suspensions of a specified dust on, or in, the vicinity of the enclosure.

Dusttight. Enclosures constructed so that dust won't enter under specific test conditions. ▶Figure 100–36

Note 1: Enclosure Types 3, 3S, 3SX, 4, 4X, 5, 6, 6P, 12, 12K, and 13, per NEMA 250, *Enclosures for Electrical Equipment*, are considered dusttight and suitable for use in unclassified locations and in Class II, Division 2, and Class III hazardous (classified) locations.

Duty, Continuous. Operation at a substantially constant load for an indefinite length of time.

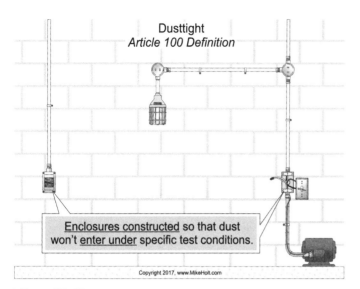

Dusttight
Article 100 Definition

Enclosures constructed so that dust won't enter under specific test conditions.

Copyright 2017, www.MikeHolt.com

▶Figure 100–36

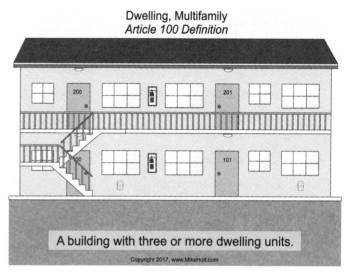

Dwelling, Multifamily
Article 100 Definition

A building with three or more dwelling units.

Copyright 2017, www.MikeHolt.com

▶Figure 100–38

Duty, Varying. Operation at loads, and for intervals of time, which may both be subject to wide variation.

Dwelling, One-Family. A building that consists solely of one dwelling unit.

Dwelling, Two-Family. A building that consists solely of two dwelling units. ▶Figure 100–37

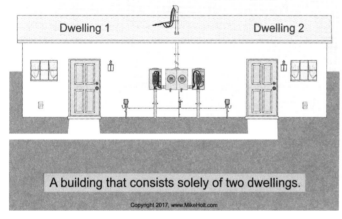

Dwelling, Two-Family
Article 100 Definition

Dwelling 1   Dwelling 2

A building that consists solely of two dwellings.

Copyright 2017, www.MikeHolt.com

▶Figure 100–37

Dwelling, Multifamily. A building that contains three or more dwelling units. ▶Figure 100–38

Dwelling Unit. A space that provides independent living facilities, with space for eating, living, and sleeping; as well as permanent facilities for cooking and sanitation. ▶Figure 100–39

Dwelling Unit
Article 100 Definition

Bedroom 1 | Closet | Dining Room | Kitchen
Hallway
Bath
Bedroom 2 | Laundry | Living Room

A single unit that provides permanent provisions for living, sleeping, cooking, and sanitation.

Copyright 2017, www.MikeHolt.com

▶Figure 100–39

Effective Ground-Fault Current Path. An intentionally constructed low-impedance conductive path designed to carry fault current from the point of a ground fault to the source for the purpose of opening the circuit overcurrent protective device. ▶Figure 100–40

Author's Comment:

■ In the preceding Figure, "EGC" represents the equipment grounding conductor [250.118], "MBJ" represents the main bonding jumper, "N" represents the service neutral conductor (grounded service conductor), and "GEC" represents the grounding electrode conductor.

Effective Ground-Fault Current Path
Article 100 Definition

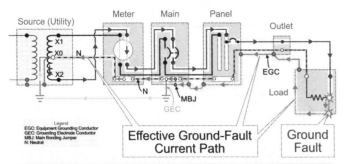

An intentionally constructed, low-impedance, electrically conductive path designed to carry fault current from the point of a ground fault to the supply source.

Copyright 2017, www.MikeHolt.com

▶Figure 100–40

- The current path shown between the supply source grounding electrode and the grounding electrode at the service main shows that some current will flow through the earth but the earth isn't part of the effective ground-fault current path.

- The effective ground-fault current path is intended to help remove dangerous voltage from a ground fault by opening the circuit overcurrent protection device.

Electric-Discharge Lighting. Systems of illumination utilizing fluorescent lamps, high-intensity discharge (HID) lamps, or neon tubing. ▶Figure 100–41

Electric-Discharge Lighting
Article 100 Definition

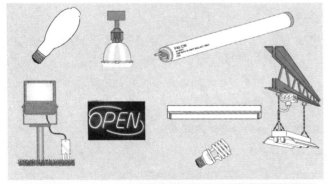

Systems of illumination utilizing fluorescent lamps, high-intensity discharge (HID) lamps, or neon tubing.

Copyright 2017, www.MikeHolt.com

▶Figure 100–41

Electric Sign [Article 600]. A fixed, stationary, or portable self-contained, electrically <u>operated and/or electrically</u> illuminated piece of equipment with words or symbols designed to convey information or attract attention. ▶Figure 100–42

Electric Sign
Article 100 Definition

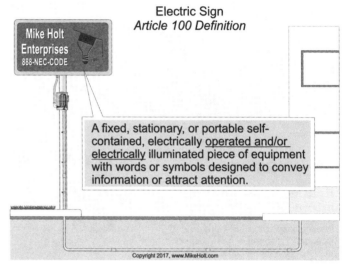

A fixed, stationary, or portable self-contained, electrically <u>operated and/or electrically</u> illuminated piece of equipment with words or symbols designed to convey information or attract attention.

Copyright 2017, www.MikeHolt.com

▶Figure 100–42

Enclosed. Surrounded by a case, housing, fence, or wall(s) that prevents accidental contact with energized parts.

Energized. Electrically connected to a source of voltage.

Equipment. A general term including fittings, devices, appliances, luminaires, machinery, and the like as part of, or in connection with, an electrical installation. ▶Figure 100–43

Equipment
Article 100 Definition

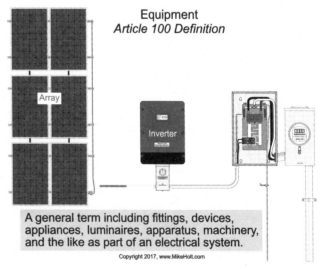

A general term including fittings, devices, appliances, luminaires, apparatus, machinery, and the like as part of an electrical system.

Copyright 2017, www.MikeHolt.com

▶Figure 100–43

Explosionproof Equipment. Equipment capable of withstanding an explosion that may occur within it, and of preventing the ignition of gas or vapor surrounding the enclosure by sparks, flashes, or an explosion within, and that operates at such an external temperature that surrounding flammable atmosphere won't be ignited by its heat. ▶Figure 100–44

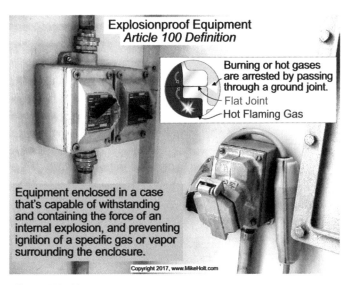

Explosionproof Equipment
Article 100 Definition

Burning or hot gases are arrested by passing through a ground joint.
Flat Joint
Hot Flaming Gas

Equipment enclosed in a case that's capable of withstanding and containing the force of an internal explosion, and preventing ignition of a specific gas or vapor surrounding the enclosure.

Copyright 2017, www.MikeHolt.com

▶Figure 100–44

Exposed (as applied to live parts). Capable of being accidentally touched or approached to an unsafe distance.

Note: This term applies to parts that aren't suitably guarded, isolated, or insulated for the condition.

Exposed (as applied to wiring methods). On or attached to the surface of a building, or behind panels designed to allow access. ▶Figure 100–45

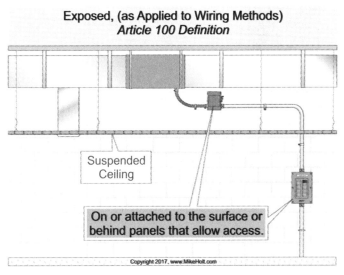

Exposed, (as Applied to Wiring Methods)
Article 100 Definition

Suspended Ceiling

On or attached to the surface or behind panels that allow access.

Copyright 2017, www.MikeHolt.com

▶Figure 100–45

Feeder [Article 215]. The conductors between the service equipment, a separately derived system, or other power supply and the final branch-circuit overcurrent protection device. ▶Figure 100–46

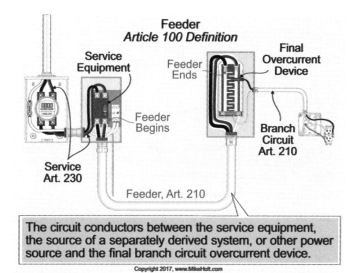

Feeder
Article 100 Definition

Service Equipment
Feeder Ends
Final Overcurrent Device

Feeder Begins

Service Art. 230

Branch Circuit Art. 210

Feeder, Art. 210

The circuit conductors between the service equipment, the source of a separately derived system, or other power source and the final branch circuit overcurrent device.

Copyright 2017, www.MikeHolt.com

▶Figure 100–46

Author's Comment:

■ An "other power source" includes a solar PV system or conductors from a generator.

Field Evaluation Body (FEB). An organization or part of an organization that performs field evaluations of electrical or other equipment.

Field Labeled (as applied to evaluated products). Equipment or materials which have a label, symbol, or other identifying mark of an FEB indicating the equipment or materials were evaluated and found to comply with requirements as described in an accompanying field evaluation report.

Fitting. An accessory, such as a locknut, intended to perform a mechanical function. ▶Figure 100–47

Garage. A building or portion of a building where self-propelled vehicles can be kept.

Ground. The earth. ▶Figure 100–48

Ground Fault. An unintentional electrical connection between an ungrounded conductor and the metal parts of enclosures, raceways, or equipment. ▶Figure 100–49

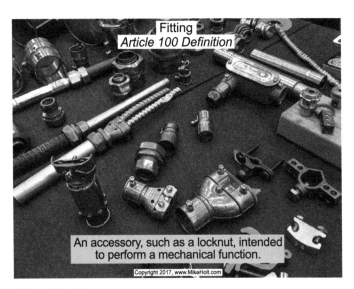

▶Figure 100–47

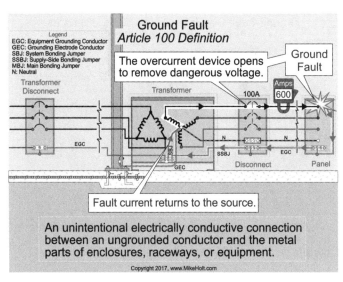

An unintentional electrically conductive connection between an ungrounded conductor and the metal parts of enclosures, raceways, or equipment.

▶Figure 100–49

▶Figure 100–48

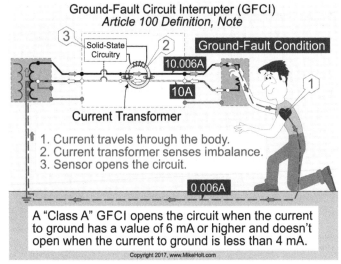

A "Class A" GFCI opens the circuit when the current to ground has a value of 6 mA or higher and doesn't open when the current to ground is less than 4 mA.

▶Figure 100–50

Ground-Fault Circuit Interrupter (GFCI). A device intended to protect people by de-energizing a circuit when a current imbalance has been detected that exceeds the value established for a "Class A" device.

Note: Class A ground-fault circuit interrupter opens the circuit when the imbalance current has a value of 6 mA or higher and doesn't trip when the current to ground is less than 4 mA. ▶Figure 100–50

Author's Comment:

■ A GFCI operates on the principle of monitoring the unbalanced current between the current-carrying circuit conductors. On a 120V circuit, the GFCI will monitor the unbalanced current between the ungrounded and neutral conductors; on 240V GFCIs, this monitoring is between all circuit conductors. GFCI-protective devices are commercially available in receptacles, circuit breakers, cord sets, and other types of devices. ▶Figure 100–51

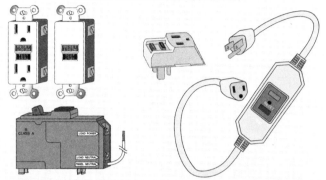

Ground-Fault Circuit Interrupter (GFCI) Devices
Article 100 Definition Comment

A GFCI is designed to protect persons against electric shock. It operates on the principle of monitoring the unbalanced current between the ungrounded and neutral conductors.

Copyright 2017, www.MikeHolt.com

▶Figure 100–51

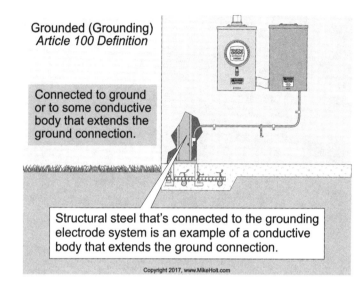

Grounded (Grounding)
Article 100 Definition

Connected to ground or to some conductive body that extends the ground connection.

Structural steel that's connected to the grounding electrode system is an example of a conductive body that extends the ground connection.

Copyright 2017, www.MikeHolt.com

▶Figure 100–52

Ground-Fault Protection of Equipment. A system intended to provide protection of equipment from damaging ground-fault currents by opening all ungrounded conductors of the faulted circuit. This protection is provided at current levels less than those required to protect conductors from damage through the operation of a supply circuit overcurrent device [215.10, 230.95, and 240.13].

Author's Comment:

- This type of protective device isn't intended to protect people and trips at a higher level than required for "Class A" GFCIs. This type of device is typically referred to as ground-fault protection for equipment, or GFPE, but should never be called a GFCI.

Grounded (Grounding). Connected to ground or to a conductive body that extends the ground connection. ▶Figure 100–52

Author's Comment:

- An example of a "body that extends the ground (earth) connection" is the termination to structural steel that's connected to the earth either directly or by the termination to another grounding electrode in accordance with 250.52.

Grounded System, Solidly. A power-supply system connected to ground (earth) without inserting any resistor or impedance device between the system and ground. ▶Figure 100–53

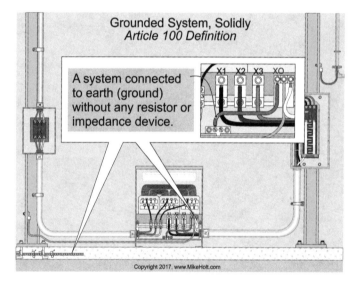

Grounded System, Solidly
Article 100 Definition

A system connected to earth (ground) without any resistor or impedance device.

Copyright 2017, www.MikeHolt.com

▶Figure 100–53

Grounded Conductor [Article 200]. The system or circuit conductor that's intentionally grounded (connected to the earth). ▶Figure 100–54

Grounding Conductor, Equipment (EGC). The conductive path(s) that provides a ground-fault current path and connects metal parts of equipment to the system neutral conductor, to the grounding electrode conductor, or both [250.110 through 250.126]. ▶Figure 100–55

Note 1: The circuit equipment grounding conductor also performs bonding.

Author's Comment:

- To quickly remove dangerous touch voltage on metal parts from a ground fault, the equipment grounding conductor must

Grounded Conductor
Article 100 Definition

Wye 3-phase, 4-wire System 1-phase, 3-wire System Delta 3-phase, 4-wire System

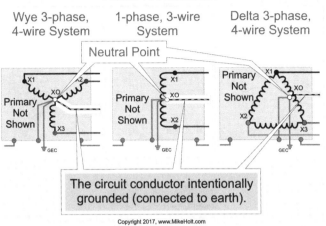

The circuit conductor intentionally grounded (connected to earth).

Copyright 2017, www.MikeHolt.com

▶Figure 100–54

Grounding Conductor, Equipment (EGC)
Article 100 Definition

Legend
EGC: Equipment Grounding Conductor
GEC: Grounding Electrode Conductor
SBJ: System Bonding Jumper
SSBJ: Supply-Side Bonding Jumper
MBJ: Main Bonding Jumper
N: Neutral

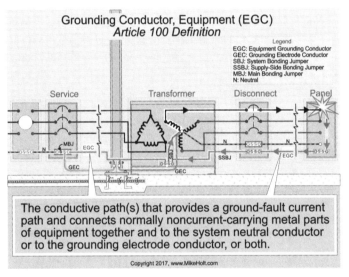

The conductive path(s) that provides a ground-fault current path and connects normally noncurrent-carrying metal parts of equipment together and to the system neutral conductor or to the grounding electrode conductor, or both.

Copyright 2017, www.MikeHolt.com

▶Figure 100–55

Opening an Overcurrent Device

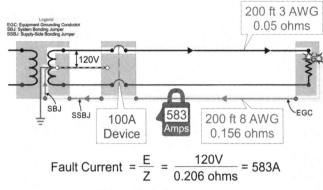

$$\text{Fault Current} = \frac{E}{Z} = \frac{120V}{0.206 \text{ ohms}} = 583A$$

The 100A overcurrent device quickly opens and removes dangerous voltage from metal parts.

Copyright 2017, www.MikeHolt.com

▶Figure 100–56

Types of Equipment Grounding Conductors (EGC)
250.118

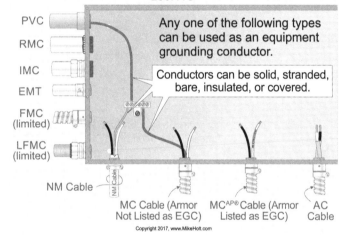

Any one of the following types can be used as an equipment grounding conductor.

Conductors can be solid, stranded, bare, insulated, or covered.

Copyright 2017, www.MikeHolt.com

▶Figure 100–57

be connected to the system neutral conductor at the source, and have low enough impedance so fault current will quickly rise to a level that will open the circuit's overcurrent protection device [250.2 and 250.4(A)(3)]. ▶Figure 100–56

Note 2: An equipment grounding conductor can be any one or a combination of the types listed in 250.118. ▶Figure 100–57

Author's Comment:

■ Equipment grounding conductors include:
   ♦ A bare or insulated conductor
   ♦ Rigid Metal Conduit

♦ Intermediate Metal Conduit
♦ Electrical Metallic Tubing
♦ Listed Flexible Metal Conduit as limited by 250.118(5)
♦ Listed Liquidtight Flexible Metal Conduit as limited by 250.118(6)
♦ Armored Cable
♦ The copper metal sheath of Mineral-Insulated Cable
♦ Metal-Clad Cable as limited by 250.118(10)
♦ Metal cable trays as limited by 250.118(11) and 392.60
♦ Electrically continuous metal raceways listed for grounding
♦ Surface Metal Raceways listed for grounding

Grounding Electrode. A conducting object used to make a direct electrical connection to the earth [250.50 through 250.70]. ▶Figure 100–58

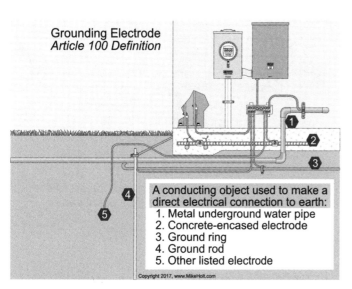

Grounding Electrode
Article 100 Definition

A conducting object used to make a direct electrical connection to earth:
1. Metal underground water pipe
2. Concrete-encased electrode
3. Ground ring
4. Ground rod
5. Other listed electrode

Copyright 2017, www.MikeHolt.com

▶Figure 100–58

Grounding Electrode Conductor (GEC). The conductor used to connect the system neutral conductor or the equipment to the grounding electrode system. ▶Figure 100–59

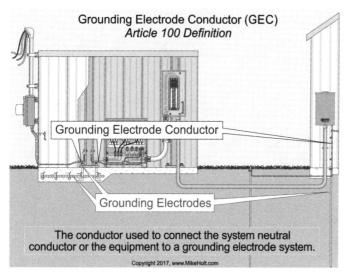

Grounding Electrode Conductor (GEC)
Article 100 Definition

Grounding Electrode Conductor

Grounding Electrodes

The conductor used to connect the system neutral conductor or the equipment to a grounding electrode system.

Copyright 2017, www.MikeHolt.com

▶Figure 100–59

Guest Room. An accommodation that combines living, sleeping, sanitary, and storage facilities. ▶Figure 100–60

Guest Suite. An accommodation with two or more contiguous rooms comprising a compartment, with or without doors between such rooms, that provides living, sleeping, sanitary, and storage facilities.

Guest Room
Article 100 Definition

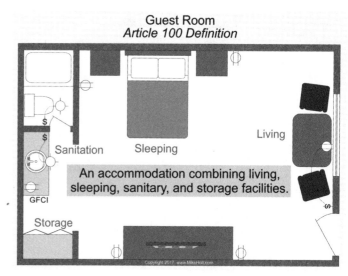

Sanitation   Sleeping   Living

An accommodation combining living, sleeping, sanitary, and storage facilities.

GFCI

Storage

Copyright 2017, www.MikeHolt.com

▶Figure 100–60

Handhole Enclosure. An enclosure for underground system use sized to allow personnel to reach into it for the purpose of installing or maintaining equipment or wiring. It may have an open or closed bottom. ▶Figure 100–61

Handhole Enclosure
Article 100 Definition

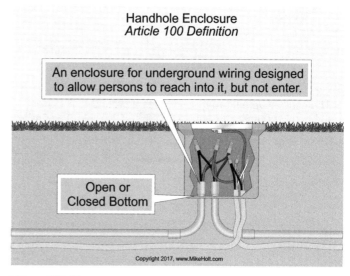

An enclosure for underground wiring designed to allow persons to reach into it, but not enter.

Open or Closed Bottom

Copyright 2017, www.MikeHolt.com

▶Figure 100–61

Author's Comment:

■ See 314.30 for the installation requirements for handhole enclosures.

Hermetic Refrigerant Motor-Compressor. A compressor and motor enclosed in the same housing, operating in the refrigerant.

Hoistway. A vertical opening or space in which an elevator is designed to operate. ▶Figure 100–62

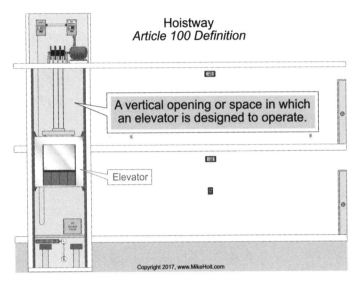

Hoistway
Article 100 Definition

A vertical opening or space in which an elevator is designed to operate.

Elevator

Copyright 2017, www.MikeHolt.com

▶Figure 100–62

Hybrid System. A system comprised of multiple electric power sources, such as photovoltaic, wind, micro-hydro generators, engine-driven generators, and others, but not the electric utility power system. ▶Figure 100–63

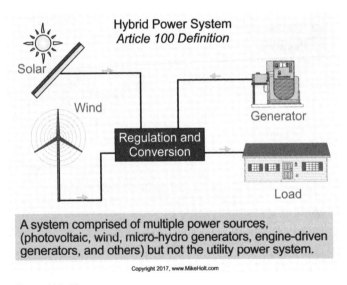

Hybrid Power System
Article 100 Definition

Solar

Wind

Generator

Regulation and Conversion

Load

A system comprised of multiple power sources, (photovoltaic, wind, micro-hydro generators, engine-driven generators, and others) but not the utility power system.

Copyright 2017, www.MikeHolt.com

▶Figure 100–63

Identified Equipment. Recognized as suitable for a specific purpose, function, or environment by listing, labeling, or other means approved by the authority having jurisdiction. ▶Figure 100–64

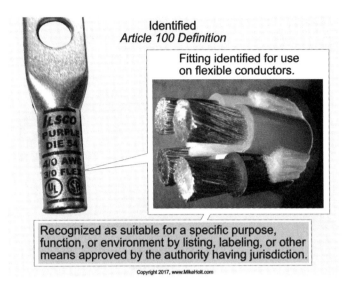

Identified
Article 100 Definition

Fitting identified for use on flexible conductors.

Recognized as suitable for a specific purpose, function, or environment by listing, labeling, or other means approved by the authority having jurisdiction.

Copyright 2017, www.MikeHolt.com

▶Figure 100–64

Author's Comment:

■ See 90.4, 90.7, 110.3(A)(1), and the definitions for "Approved," "Labeled," and "Listed" in this article.

Information Technology Equipment (ITE). Equipment used for creation and manipulation of data, voice, and video, but not communications equipment. ▶Figure 100–65

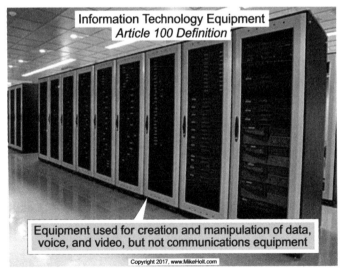

Information Technology Equipment
Article 100 Definition

Equipment used for creation and manipulation of data, voice, and video, but not communications equipment

Copyright 2017, www.MikeHolt.com

▶Figure 100–65

Innerduct. A nonmetallic raceway placed within a larger raceway. ▶Figure 100–66

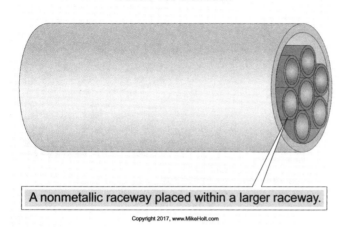

Figure 100–66

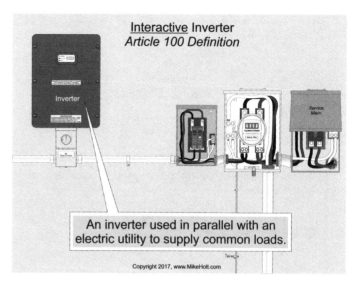

Figure 100–68

In Sight From (Within Sight). Visible and not more than 50 ft away from the equipment. ▶Figure 100–67

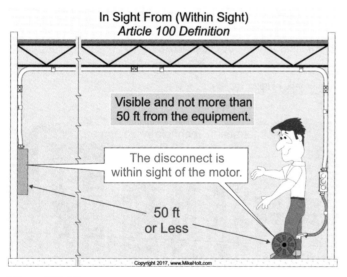

▶Figure 100–67

Interactive Inverter. An inverter is used in parallel with an electric utility to supply common loads. ▶Figure 100–68

Interrupting Rating. The highest short-circuit current at rated voltage the device is identified to interrupt under standard test conditions.

Author's Comment:

■ For more information, see 110.9 in this textbook.

Intersystem Bonding Termination. A device that provides a means to connect intersystem bonding conductors for communications systems (twisted wire, antennas, and coaxial cable) to the grounding electrode system, in accordance with 250.94. ▶Figure 100–69

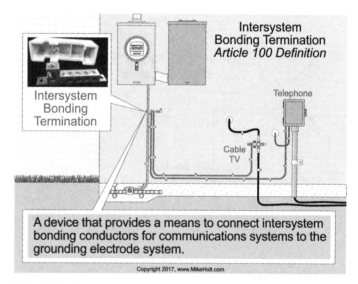

▶Figure 100–69

Isolated. Not readily accessible to persons unless special means for access are used.

Kitchen. An area with a sink and permanent provisions for food preparation and cooking. ▶Figure 100–70

▶Figure 100–70

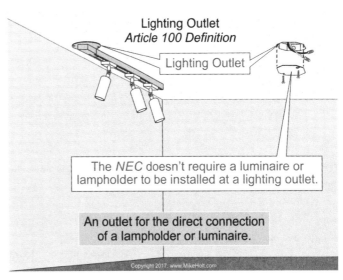

▶Figure 100–72

Labeled. Equipment or materials that have a label, symbol, or other identifying mark in the form of a sticker, decal, printed label, or with the identifying mark molded or stamped into the product by a testing laboratory acceptable to the authority having jurisdiction. ▶Figure 100–71

Lighting Track (Track Lighting). This is a manufactured assembly designed to support and energize luminaires that can be readily repositioned on the track, and whose length may be altered by the addition or subtraction of sections of track. ▶Figure 100–73

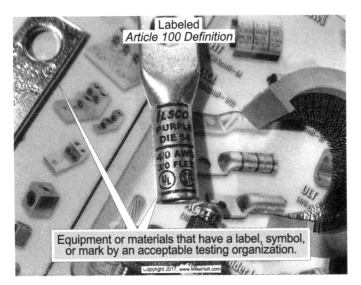

▶Figure 100–71

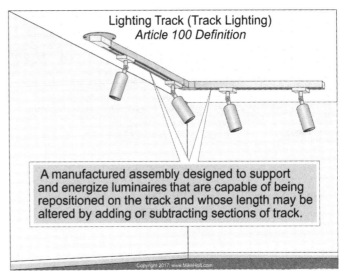

▶Figure 100–73

Author's Comment:

■ Labeling and listing of equipment typically provides the basis for equipment approval by the authority having jurisdiction [90.4, 90.7, 110.2, and 110.3].

Lighting Outlet. An outlet for the connection of a lampholder or luminaire. ▶Figure 100–72

Listed. Equipment or materials included in a list published by a testing laboratory acceptable to the authority having jurisdiction. The listing organization must periodically inspect the production of listed equipment or material to ensure the equipment or material meets appropriate designated standards and is suitable for a specified purpose.

Author's Comment:

- The *NEC* doesn't require all electrical equipment to be listed, but some *Code* requirements do specifically require product listing. Organizations such as OSHA increasingly require that listed equipment be used when such equipment is available [90.7, 110.2, and 110.3].

Location, Damp. Locations protected from weather and not subject to saturation with water or other liquids.

Note: This includes locations partially protected under canopies, marquees, roofed open porches, and interior locations subject to moderate degrees of moisture, such as some basements, barns, and cold-storage warehouses. ▶Figure 100–74

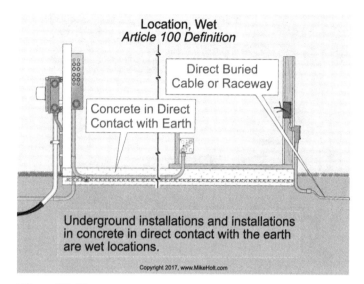

▶Figure 100–75

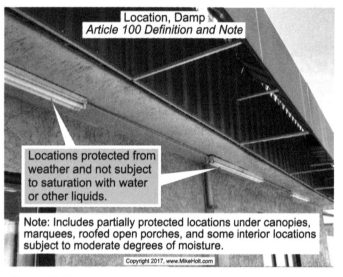

▶Figure 100–74

Location, Dry. An area not normally subjected to dampness or wetness, but which may temporarily be subjected to dampness or wetness, such as a building under construction.

Location, Wet. An installation underground, in concrete slabs in direct contact with the earth, as well as locations subject to saturation with water, and unprotected locations exposed to weather. ▶Figure 100–75 and ▶Figure 100–76

Author's Comment:

- The interior of a raceway installed in wet locations is considered a wet location, and the conductors used must be suitable for wet locations [300.5(B) and 300.9].

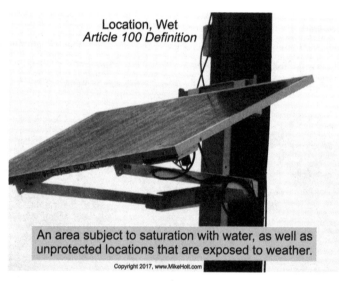

▶Figure 100–76

Luminaire [Article 410]. A complete lighting unit consisting of a light source with the parts designed to position the light source and connect it to the power supply and distribute the light. A lampholder by itself isn't a luminaire. ▶Figure 100–77

Multioutlet Assembly [Article 380]. A surface, flush, or freestanding raceway designed to hold conductors and receptacles. ▶Figure 100–78

Neutral Conductor. The conductor connected to the neutral point of a system that's intended to carry current under normal conditions. ▶Figure 100–79

Luminaire
Article 100 Definition

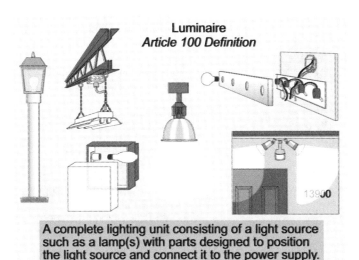

A complete lighting unit consisting of a light source such as a lamp(s) with parts designed to position the light source and connect it to the power supply.

Copyright 2017, www.MikeHolt.com

▶Figure 100–77

Multioutlet Assembly
Article 100 Definition

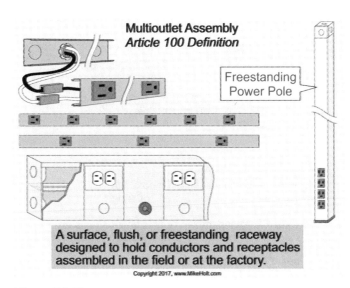

Freestanding Power Pole

A surface, flush, or freestanding raceway designed to hold conductors and receptacles assembled in the field or at the factory.

Copyright 2017, www.MikeHolt.com

▶Figure 100–78

Neutral Conductor
Article 100 Definition

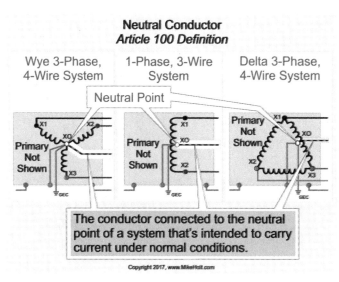

Wye 3-Phase, 4-Wire System 1-Phase, 3-Wire System Delta 3-Phase, 4-Wire System

Neutral Point

The conductor connected to the neutral point of a system that's intended to carry current under normal conditions.

Copyright 2017, www.MikeHolt.com

▶Figure 100–79

Neutral Point
Article 100 Definition

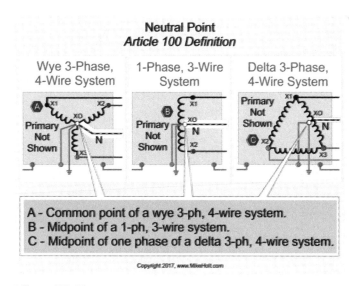

Wye 3-Phase, 4-Wire System 1-Phase, 3-Wire System Delta 3-Phase, 4-Wire System

A - Common point of a wye 3-ph, 4-wire system.
B - Midpoint of a 1-ph, 3-wire system.
C - Midpoint of one phase of a delta 3-ph, 4-wire system.

Copyright 2017, www.MikeHolt.com

▶Figure 100–80

Author's Comment:

■ The neutral conductor of a solidly grounded system is required to be grounded (connected to the earth), therefore this conductor is also called a "grounded conductor."

Neutral Point. The common point of a 4-wire, three-phase, wye-connected system; the midpoint of a 3-wire, single-phase system; or the midpoint of the single-phase portion of a three-phase, delta-connected system. ▶Figure 100–80

Nonautomatic. Requiring human intervention to perform a function.

Nonconductive Optical Fiber Cable. A factory assembly of one or more optical fibers containing no electrically conductive materials. ▶Figure 100–81

Nonlinear Load. A load where the current waveform doesn't follow the applied sinusoidal voltage waveform. ▶Figure 100–82

Note: Single-phase nonlinear loads include electronic equipment, such as copy machines, laser printers, and electric-discharge lighting. Three-phase nonlinear loads include uninterruptible power supplies, induction motors, and electronic switching devices, such as adjustable speed drives (variable frequency drives). ▶Figure 100–83

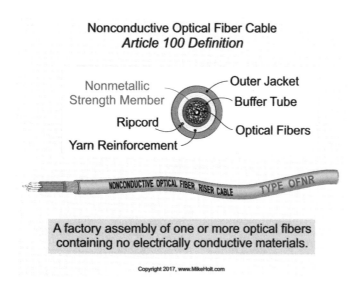

Nonconductive Optical Fiber Cable
Article 100 Definition

A factory assembly of one or more optical fibers containing no electrically conductive materials.

▶Figure 100–81

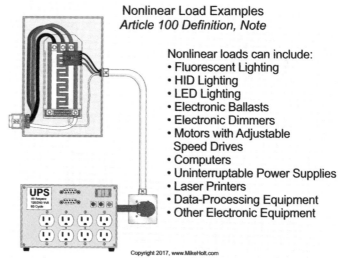

Nonlinear Load Examples
Article 100 Definition, Note

Nonlinear loads can include:
• Fluorescent Lighting
• HID Lighting
• LED Lighting
• Electronic Ballasts
• Electronic Dimmers
• Motors with Adjustable Speed Drives
• Computers
• Uninterruptable Power Supplies
• Laser Printers
• Data-Processing Equipment
• Other Electronic Equipment

▶Figure 100–83

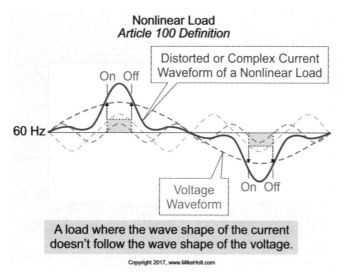

Nonlinear Load
Article 100 Definition

A load where the wave shape of the current doesn't follow the wave shape of the voltage.

▶Figure 100–82

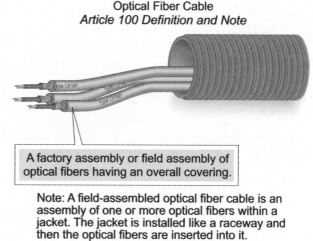

Optical Fiber Cable
Article 100 Definition and Note

A factory assembly or field assembly of optical fibers having an overall covering.

Note: A field-assembled optical fiber cable is an assembly of one or more optical fibers within a jacket. The jacket is installed like a raceway and then the optical fibers are inserted into it.

▶Figure 100–84

Author's Comment:

■ The subject of nonlinear loads is beyond the scope of this textbook. For more information on this topic, visit www.MikeHolt.com, click on the "Technical" link, then on the "Power Quality" link.

Oil Immersion [as applied to Hazardous (Classified) Locations]. Electrical equipment immersed in a protective liquid.

Optical Fiber Cable. A factory assembly or field assembly of optical fibers having an overall covering. ▶Figure 100–84

Note: A field-assembled optical fiber cable is an assembly of one or more optical fibers within a jacket. The jacket is installed like a raceway, and then the optical fibers are inserted into it.

Outlet. A point in the wiring system where electric current is taken to supply a load (utilization equipment). This includes receptacle outlets and lighting outlets, as well as outlets for ceiling paddle fans and smoke alarms. ▶Figure 100–85

Outline Lighting [Article 600]. An arrangement of incandescent lamps, electric-discharge lighting, or other electrically powered light sources to outline or call attention to certain features such as the shape of a building or the decoration of a window. ▶Figure 100–86

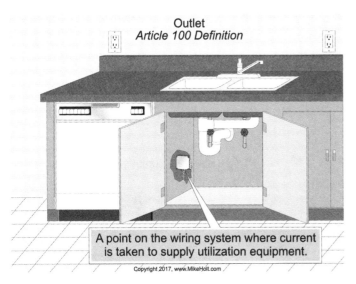

Outlet
Article 100 Definition

A point on the wiring system where current is taken to supply utilization equipment.

Copyright 2017, www.MikeHolt.com

▶Figure 100–85

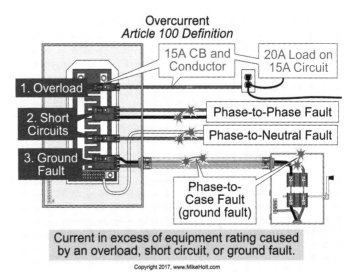

Overcurrent
Article 100 Definition

15A CB and Conductor

20A Load on 15A Circuit

1. Overload

2. Short Circuits

3. Ground Fault

Phase-to-Phase Fault

Phase-to-Neutral Fault

Phase-to-Case Fault (ground fault)

Current in excess of equipment rating caused by an overload, short circuit, or ground fault.

Copyright 2017, www.MikeHolt.com

▶Figure 100–87

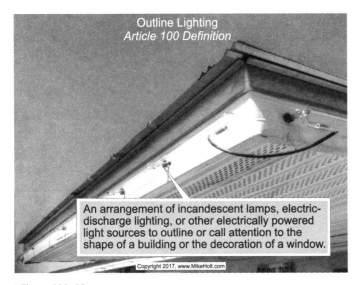

Outline Lighting
Article 100 Definition

An arrangement of incandescent lamps, electric-discharge lighting, or other electrically powered light sources to outline or call attention to the shape of a building or the decoration of a window.

Copyright 2017, www.MikeHolt.com

▶Figure 100–86

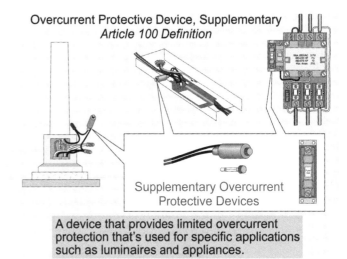

Overcurrent Protective Device, Supplementary
Article 100 Definition

Supplementary Overcurrent Protective Devices

A device that provides limited overcurrent protection that's used for specific applications such as luminaires and appliances.

Copyright 2017, www.MikeHolt.com

▶Figure 100–88

Overcurrent. Current, in amperes, greater than the rated current of the equipment or conductors resulting from an overload, short circuit, or ground fault. ▶Figure 100–87

Overcurrent Protective Device, Supplementary. A device intended to provide limited overcurrent protection for specific applications and utilization equipment, such as luminaires and appliances. This limited overcurrent protection is in addition to the required overcurrent protection provided in the branch circuit by the branch-circuit overcurrent protection device. ▶Figure 100–88

Overload. The operation of equipment above its current rating, or current in excess of conductor ampacity. When an overload condition persists for a sufficient length of time, it can result in equipment failure or in a fire from damaging or dangerous overheating. A fault, such as a short circuit or ground fault, isn't an overload.

Panelboard [Article 408]. A distribution point containing overcurrent protection devices and designed to be installed in a cabinet. ▶Figure 100–89

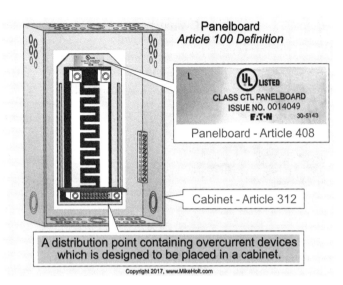

Panelboard
Article 100 Definition

Panelboard - Article 408

Cabinet - Article 312

A distribution point containing overcurrent devices which is designed to be placed in a cabinet.

Copyright 2017, www.MikeHolt.com

▶Figure 100–89

Author's Comment:

■ See the definition of "Cabinet" in this article.

■ The slang term in the electrical field for a panelboard is "the guts." This is the interior of the panelboard assembly and is covered by Article 408, while the cabinet is covered by Article 312.

Photovoltaic (PV) System. The combination of all components and subsystems that convert solar energy into electric energy for utilization loads. ▶Figure 100–90

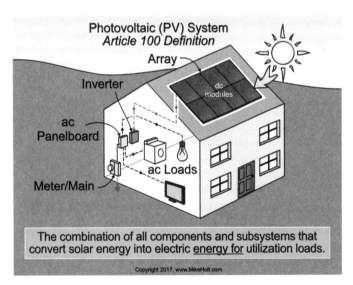

Photovoltaic (PV) System
Article 100 Definition

Array

Inverter

dc modules

ac Panelboard

ac Loads

Meter/Main

The combination of all components and subsystems that convert solar energy into electric energy for utilization loads.

Copyright 2017, www.MikeHolt.com

▶Figure 100–90

Premises Wiring. The interior and exterior wiring, including power, lighting, control, and signal circuits, and all associated hardware, fittings, and wiring devices. This includes both permanently and temporarily installed wiring from the service point to the outlets, or where there's no service point, wiring from and including the electric power source, such as a generator, transformer, or PV system to the outlets. ▶Figure 100–91

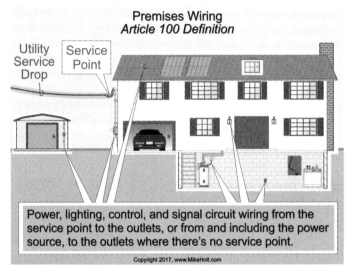

Premises Wiring
Article 100 Definition

Utility Service Drop

Service Point

Power, lighting, control, and signal circuit wiring from the service point to the outlets, or from and including the power source, to the outlets where there's no service point.

Copyright 2017, www.MikeHolt.com

▶Figure 100–91

Premises wiring doesn't include the internal wiring of electrical equipment and appliances, such as luminaires, dishwashers, water heaters, motors, controllers, motor control centers, air-conditioning equipment, and so on [90.7 and 300.1(B)]. ▶Figure 100–92

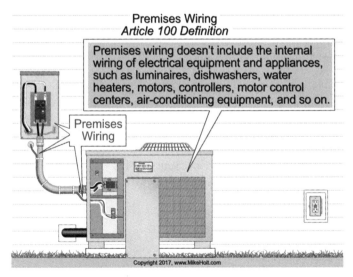

Premises Wiring
Article 100 Definition

Premises wiring doesn't include the internal wiring of electrical equipment and appliances, such as luminaires, dishwashers, water heaters, motors, controllers, motor control centers, air-conditioning equipment, and so on.

Premises Wiring

Copyright 2017, www.MikeHolt.com

▶Figure 100–92

Note: Electric power sources include, but aren't limited to, interconnected or stand-alone batteries, PV systems, other distributed generation systems, or generators.

Purged and Pressurized [as applied to Hazardous (Classified) Locations].

(1) Purging (Class I). Supplying an enclosure with a protective gas at a sufficient positive pressure to reduce the concentration of any flammable gas or vapor.

(2) Pressurization (Class I or II). Supplying an enclosure with a protective gas with or without continuous flow at sufficient pressure to prevent the entrance of a flammable gas or vapor, a combustible dust, or an ignitible fiber.

Qualified Person. A person who has the skill and knowledge related to the construction and operation of electrical equipment and its installation. This person must have received safety training to recognize and avoid the hazards involved with electrical systems. ▶Figure 100–93

▶Figure 100–93

Note: NFPA 70E, *Standard for Electrical Safety in the Workplace*, provides information on safety training requirements expected of a "qualified person."

Author's Comment:

■ Examples of this safety training include, but aren't limited to, training in the use of special precautionary techniques, personal protective equipment (PPE), insulating and shielding materials, and in the use of insulated tools and test equipment when working on or near exposed conductors or circuit parts that can become energized.

■ In many parts of the United States, electricians, electrical contractors, electrical inspectors, and electrical engineers must complete from 6 to 24 hours of *NEC* review each year as a requirement to maintain licensing. This in itself doesn't make one qualified to deal with the specific hazards involved with electrical systems.

Raceway. An enclosed channel designed for the installation of conductors, cables, or busbars.

Author's Comment:

■ A cable tray system isn't a raceway; it's a support system for cables and raceways [392.2].

Rainproof. Constructed, protected, or treated to prevent rain from interfering with the successful operation of the apparatus under specified test conditions.

Raintight. A raintight enclosure is constructed or protected so that exposure to a beating rain won't result in the entrance of water under specified test conditions.

Receptacle [Article 406]. A contact device installed at an outlet for the connection of an attachment plug, or for the direct connection of equipment designed to mate with the contact device (SQL receptacle). ▶Figure 100–94

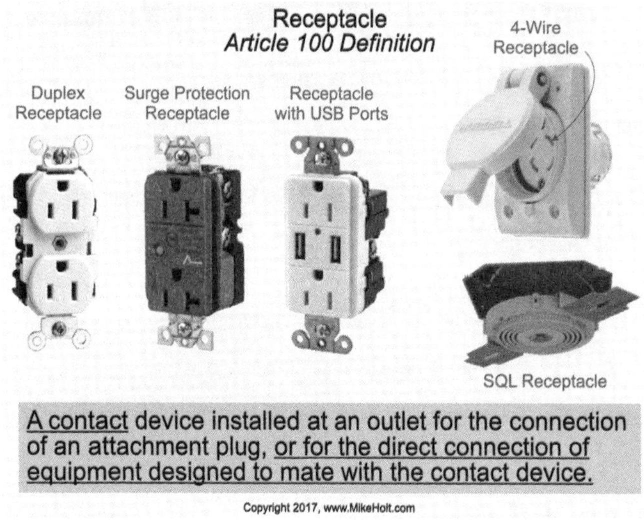

▶Figure 100–94

Author's Comment:

- Outlet boxes are permitted to support listed locking support and mounting receptacles (SQL receptacles) used in combination with compatible attachment fittings [314.27(E)]. For additional information about listed locking, support and mounting receptacles, visit http://www.safetyquicklight.com/.

- See 314.27(E) for the specific *NEC* application for the direct connection of equipment designed to mate with the contact device.

A single receptacle contains one contact device on a yoke; a multiple receptacle has more than one contact device on the same yoke. ▶Figure 100–95

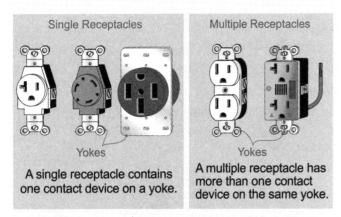

Receptacle
Article 100 Definition

▶Figure 100–95

Receptacle Outlet. An opening in an outlet box where receptacles have been installed.

Remote-Control Circuit [Article 725]. An electric circuit that controls another circuit by a relay or equivalent device installed in accordance with Article 725. ▶Figure 100–96

Retrofit Kit. An assembly of parts for the field conversion of utilization equipment.

Sealable Equipment. Equipment enclosed with a means of sealing or locking so live parts can't be made accessible without opening the enclosure.

Note: The equipment may or may not be operable without opening the enclosure.

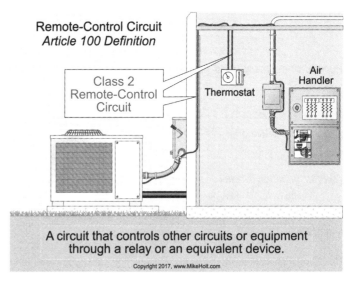

Remote-Control Circuit
Article 100 Definition

▶Figure 100–96

Separately Derived System. An electrical source, other than a service, having no direct connection(s) to circuit conductors of any other electrical source other than those established by grounding and bonding connections. ▶Figure 100–97 and ▶Figure 100–98

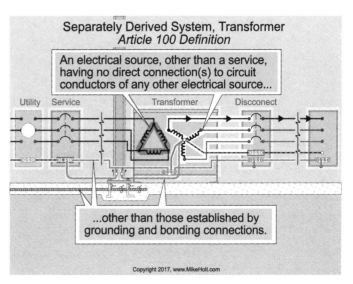

Separately Derived System, Transformer
Article 100 Definition

▶Figure 100–97

Author's Comment:

- An alternate alternating-current power source such as an on-site generator isn't a separately derived system if the neutral conductor is solidly interconnected to a service-supplied system neutral conductor. An example is a generator provided with a transfer switch that includes a neutral conductor that's not switched. ▶Figure 100–99

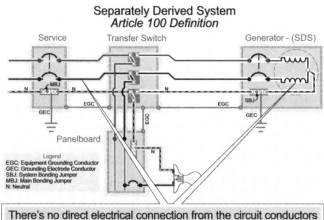

Separately Derived System
Article 100 Definition

There's no direct electrical connection from the circuit conductors of one system to the circuit conductors of the other system other than through the bonding and grounding connections.

▶Figure 100–98

Service
Article 100 Definition

The conductors and equipment that deliver electric energy from the utility to the wiring system of the premises.

▶Figure 100–100

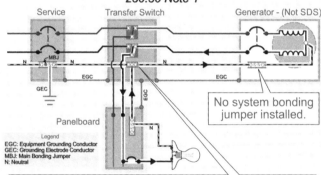

Generator, Not a Separately Derived System (SDS)
250.30 Note 1

No system bonding jumper installed.

A generator whose transfer switch doesn't switch the neutral isn't a separately derived system because there's a direct electrical connection between the generator and supply conductors via the unswitched neutral conductor.

▶Figure 100–99

- Separately derived systems are actually much more complicated than the above definition suggests, and understanding them requires additional study. For more information, see 250.30.

Service [Article 230]. The conductors from the electric utility power supply that deliver electric energy to the wiring system of the premises. ▶Figure 100–100

Author's Comment:

- Conductors from a UPS system, solar PV system, generator, or transformer aren't service conductors. See the definitions of "Feeder" and "Service Conductors" in this article.

Service Conductors. The conductors from the service point to the service disconnect. ▶Figure 100–101

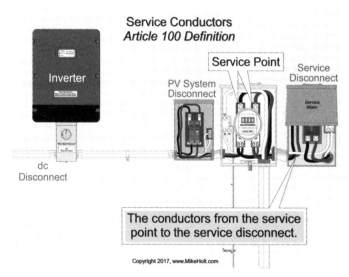

Service Conductors
Article 100 Definition

The conductors from the service point to the service disconnect.

▶Figure 100–101

Author's Comment:

- These conductors fall within the requirements of Article 230, since they're owned by the customer.

Service Conductors, Overhead. Overhead conductors between the service point and the first point of connection to the service-entrance conductors at the building. ▶Figure 100–102

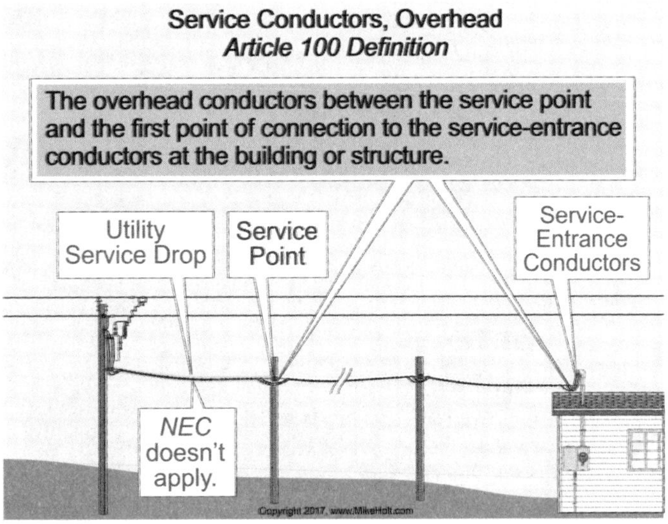

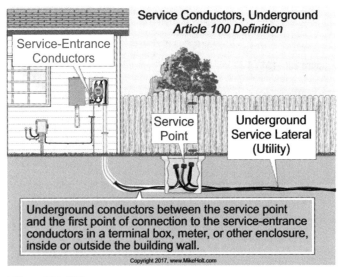

Service Conductors, Overhead
Article 100 Definition

The overhead conductors between the service point and the first point of connection to the service-entrance conductors at the building or structure.

Utility Service Drop

Service Point

Service-Entrance Conductors

NEC doesn't apply.

▶Figure 100–102

Author's Comment:

- Service conductors fall within the requirements of Article 230, since they aren't under the exclusive control of the electric utility.

- Service conductors can include overhead service conductors, overhead service entrance-conductors, and underground service conductors. Service conductors don't include service lateral conductors, which fall within the scope of the electric utility, not the *NEC*.

Service Conductors, Underground. Underground conductors between the service point and the first point of connection to the service-entrance conductors in a terminal box, meter, or other enclosure, inside or outside the building wall. ▶Figure 100–103

Service Conductors, Underground
Article 100 Definition

Service-Entrance Conductors

Service Point

Underground Service Lateral (Utility)

Underground conductors between the service point and the first point of connection to the service-entrance conductors in a terminal box, meter, or other enclosure, inside or outside the building wall.

▶Figure 100–103

Author's Comment:

- Service conductors fall within the requirements of Article 230, since they aren't under the exclusive control of the electric utility.

Note: Where there's no terminal box, meter, or other enclosure, the point of connection is the point of entrance of the service conductors into the building.

Service Drop. Overhead conductors between the electric utility supply and the service point. ▶Figure 100–104

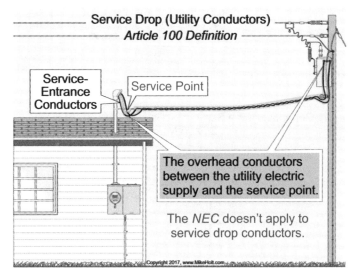

Service Drop (Utility Conductors)
Article 100 Definition

Service-Entrance Conductors

Service Point

The overhead conductors between the utility electric supply and the service point.

The *NEC* doesn't apply to service drop conductors.

▶Figure 100–104

Author's Comment:

- Service drop conductors don't fall within the requirements of Article 230, since they're under the exclusive control of the electric utility.

Service-Entrance Conductors, Overhead System. The conductors between the terminals of service equipment and service drop or overhead service conductors. ▶Figure 100–105

Author's Comment:

- Overhead service-entrance conductors fall within the requirements of Article 230, since they aren't under the exclusive control of the electric utility.

Service-Entrance Conductors, Underground System. The conductors between the terminals of service equipment and underground service conductors.

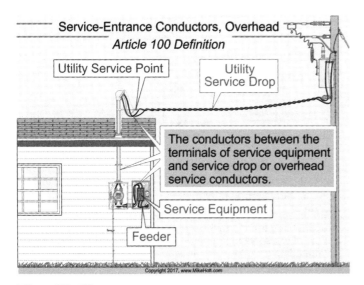

▶Figure 100–105

Author's Comment:

- Underground service-entrance conductors fall within the requirements of Article 230, since they aren't under the exclusive control of the electric utility.

Service Equipment [Article 230]. Disconnects such as circuit breaker(s) or switch(es) connected to the load end of service conductors, intended to control and cut off the service supply to the buildings or structure. ▶Figure 100–106

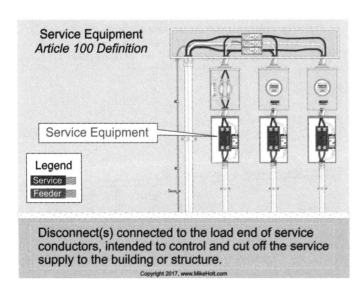

▶Figure 100–106

Author's Comment:

- It's important to know where a service begins and where it ends in order to properly apply the *NEC* requirements. Sometimes the service ends before the metering equipment. ▶Figure 100–107

- Service equipment is often referred to as the "service disconnect" or "service disconnecting means."

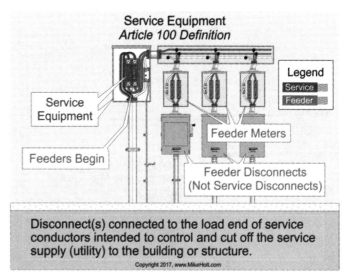

▶Figure 100–107

Service Lateral. Underground electric utility conductors from the electric utility supply to the service point. ▶Figure 100–108

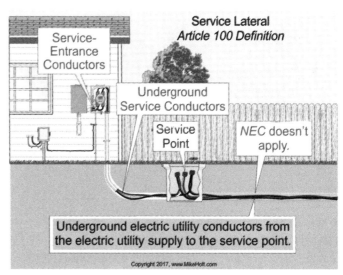

▶Figure 100–108

Author's Comment:

■ These conductors don't fall within the requirements of Article 230, since they're under the exclusive control of the electric utility.

Service Point [Article 230]. The point where the electric utility conductors make contact with premises wiring. ▶Figure 100–109

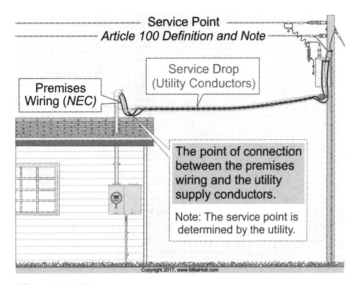

▶Figure 100–109

Note: The service point is the point where the serving electric utility ends and the premises wiring begins.

Author's Comment:

■ For utility-owned transformers, the service point will be at the electric utility transformer secondary terminals, at the service drop, or the meter socket enclosure, depending on where the electric utility conductors terminate. ▶Figure 100–110

■ For customer-owned transformers, the service point will be at the termination of the electric utility conductors, often at the electric utility pole. ▶Figure 100–111

Short-Circuit Current Rating. The prospective symmetrical fault current at a nominal voltage to which electrical equipment can be connected without sustaining damage exceeding defined acceptance criteria.

Signaling Circuit [Article 725]. A circuit that energizes signaling equipment. ▶Figure 100–112

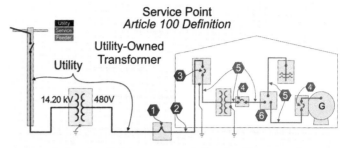

1. Service Point
2. Service Conductors
3. Service Equipment
4. Feeder Disconnect
5. Feeder Conductors
6. Transfer Switch

For utility-owned transformers, the service point will be at the utility transformer secondary terminals or junction box, at the service drop, or at the meter socket enclosure, depending on where the utility conductors terminate.

Copyright 2017, www.MikeHolt.com

▶Figure 100–110

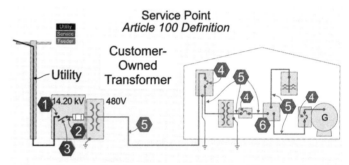

1. Service Point
2. Service Conductors
3. Service Equipment
4. Feeder Disconnect
5. Feeder Conductors
6. Transfer Switch

For customer-owned transformers, the service point will be at the termination of the utility conductors, often at the utility pole.

Copyright 2017, www.MikeHolt.com

▶Figure 100–111

Special Permission. Written consent from the authority having jurisdiction.

Author's Comment:

■ See the definition of "Authority Having Jurisdiction."

Stand-Alone System. A system that supplies power independently of an electrical production and distribution network. ▶Figure 100–113

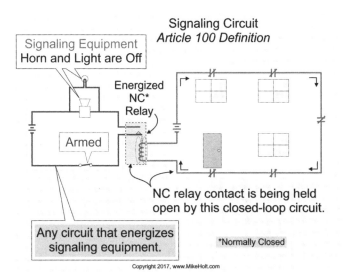

Signaling Circuit
Article 100 Definition

▶Figure 100–112

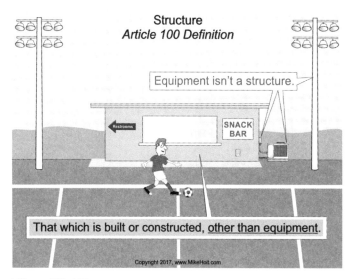

Structure
Article 100 Definition

▶Figure 100–114

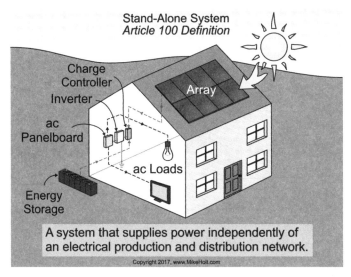

Stand-Alone System
Article 100 Definition

▶Figure 100–113

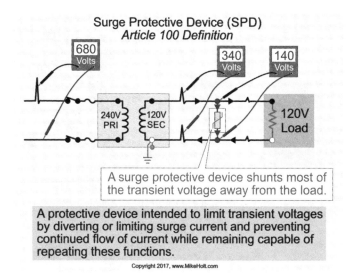

Surge Protective Device (SPD)
Article 100 Definition

▶Figure 100–115

Structure. That which is built or constructed, <u>other than equipment</u>.
▶Figure 100–114

Surge Protective Device (SPD) [Article 285]. A protective device intended to limit transient voltages by diverting or limiting surge current and preventing the continued flow of current while remaining capable of repeating these functions. ▶Figure 100–115

Type 1. A permanently connected surge protective device listed for installation at or ahead of service equipment. ▶Figure 100–116

Type 2. A permanently connected surge protective device listed for installation on the load side of the service disconnect. ▶Figure 100–117

Type 3. A surge protective device listed for installation on branch circuits. ▶Figure 100–118

Author's Comment:

- Type 3 surge protective devices can be installed anywhere on the load side of branch-circuit overcurrent protection up to the equipment served, provided there's a minimum of 30 ft of conductor length between the connection and the service or separately derived system [285.25].

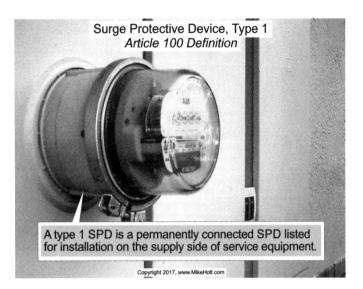

A type 1 SPD is a permanently connected SPD listed for installation on the supply side of service equipment.

Surge Protective Device, Type 1
Article 100 Definition

Copyright 2017, www.MikeHolt.com

▶Figure 100–116

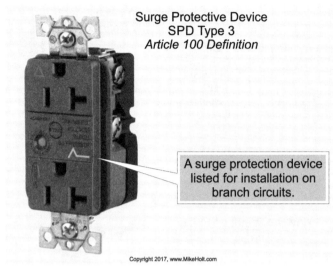

Surge Protective Device
SPD Type 3
Article 100 Definition

A surge protection device listed for installation on branch circuits.

Copyright 2017, www.MikeHolt.com

▶Figure 100–118

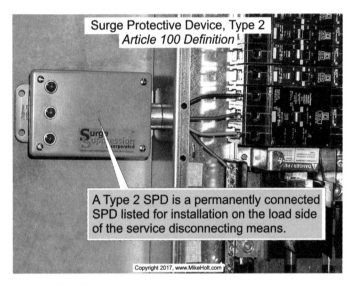

Surge Protective Device, Type 2
Article 100 Definition

A Type 2 SPD is a permanently connected SPD listed for installation on the load side of the service disconnecting means.

Copyright 2017, www.MikeHolt.com

▶Figure 100–117

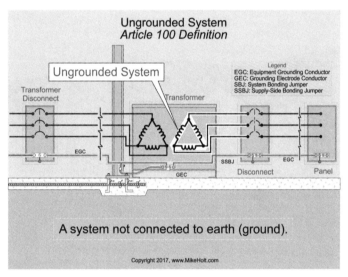

Ungrounded System
Article 100 Definition

Ungrounded System

Legend
EGC: Equipment Grounding Conductor
GEC: Grounding Electrode Conductor
SBJ: System Bonding Jumper
SSBJ: Supply-Side Bonding Jumper

Transformer Disconnect

Transformer

EGC

SSBJ

GEC

EGC

Disconnect

Panel

A system not connected to earth (ground).

Copyright 2017, www.MikeHolt.com

▶Figure 100–119

Type 4. A component surge protective device; this includes those installed in receptacles and relocatable power taps (plug strips).

Note: For further information, see UL 1449, *Standard for Surge Protective Devices.*

Switch, General-Use Snap. A switch constructed to be installed in a device box or a box cover.

Ungrounded System. An electrical power system that's not connected to the ground (earth) or a conductive body that extends the ground (earth) connection. ▶Figure 100–119

Utilization Equipment. Equipment that utilizes electricity for electronic, electromechanical, chemical, heating, lighting, or similar purposes.

Voltage (of a circuit). The greatest effective root-mean-square (RMS) difference of voltage between any two conductors of the circuit. ▶Figure 100–120

Voltage, Nominal. A value assigned for conveniently designating voltage classes, such as 120/240V, 120/208V, or 277/480V [220.5(A)]. ▶Figure 100–121

Note 1: The actual voltage at which a circuit operates can vary from the nominal within a range that permits satisfactory operation of equipment.

Voltage (of a Circuit)
Article 100 Definition

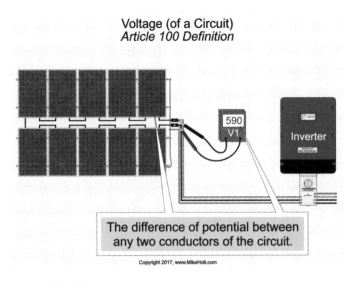

The difference of potential between any two conductors of the circuit.

Copyright 2017, www.MikeHolt.com

▶Figure 100–120

Voltage, Nominal
Article 100 Definition and Note 1

A value assigned for conveniently designating a voltage class, such as 120/208V, 120/240V, or 277/480V.

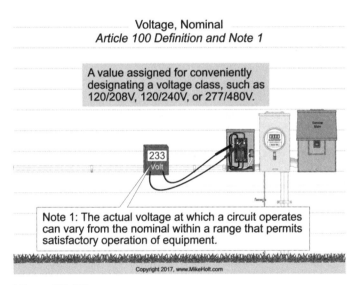

Note 1: The actual voltage at which a circuit operates can vary from the nominal within a range that permits satisfactory operation of equipment.

Copyright 2017, www.MikeHolt.com

▶Figure 100–121

Author's Comment:

- Common voltage ratings of electrical equipment are 115V, 200V, 208V, 230V, and 460V. The electrical power supplied might be at the 240V, nominal voltage, but the voltage at the equipment will be less. Therefore, electrical equipment is rated at a value less than the nominal system voltage.

Note 3: Some battery units are rated 48V dc nominal, even if they have a charging float voltage up to 58V dc.

Voltage to Ground. The greatest difference of voltage (RMS) between an ungrounded conductor and the neutral point of the circuit that's grounded. ▶Figure 100–122

Voltage to Ground
Article 100 Definition

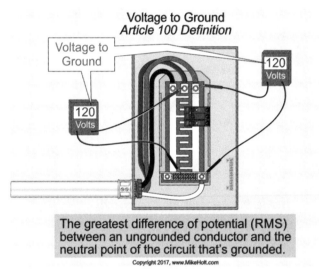

The greatest difference of potential (RMS) between an ungrounded conductor and the neutral point of the circuit that's grounded.

Copyright 2017, www.MikeHolt.com

▶Figure 100–122

Watertight. Constructed so that moisture won't enter the enclosure under specific test conditions.

Weatherproof. Constructed or protected so that exposure to the weather won't interfere with successful operation.

ARTICLE

100 PRACTICE QUESTIONS

Please use the 2017 *Code* book to answer the following questions.

1. Capable of being removed or exposed without damaging the building structure or finish, or not permanently closed in by the structure or finish of the building is known as "_____."

   (a) accessible (as applied to equipment)
   (b) accessible (as applied to wiring methods)
   (c) accessible, readily
   (d) all of these

2. Capable of being reached quickly for operation, renewal, or inspections without resorting to portable ladders or the use of tools (other than keys) is known as "_____."

   (a) accessible (as applied to equipment)
   (b) accessible (as applied to wiring methods)
   (c) accessible, readily
   (d) all of these

3. "_____" means acceptable to the authority having jurisdiction.

   (a) Identified
   (b) Listed
   (c) Approved
   (d) Labeled

4. In many circumstances, the authority having jurisdiction can be a property owner or his/her designated agent.

   (a) True
   (b) False

5. A circuit breaker is a device designed to _____ the circuit automatically on a predetermined overcurrent without damage to itself when properly applied within its rating.

   (a) energize
   (b) reset
   (c) connect
   (d) open

6. Wires are considered _____ if rendered inaccessible by the structure or finish of the building.

   (a) inaccessible
   (b) concealed
   (c) hidden
   (d) enclosed

7. A device intended for the protection of personnel that functions to de-energize a circuit or portion thereof within an established period of time when the current to ground exceeds the values established for a Class A device, is a(n) "_____."

   (a) dual-element fuse
   (b) inverse time breaker
   (c) ground-fault circuit interrupter
   (d) safety switch

8. A Class A GFCI protection device is designed to trip when the current to ground is _____ or higher.

   (a) 4 mA
   (b) 5 mA
   (c) 6 mA
   (d) 7 mA

9. A conducting object through which a direct connection to earth is established is a "____."

   (a) bonding conductor
   (b) grounding conductor
   (c) grounding electrode
   (d) grounded conductor

10. A conductor used to connect the system grounded conductor, or the equipment to a grounding electrode or to a point on the grounding electrode system, is called the "____ conductor."

    (a) main grounding
    (b) common main
    (c) equipment grounding
    (d) grounding electrode

11. Equipment or materials included in a list published by a testing laboratory acceptable to the authority having jurisdiction are said to be "____."

    (a) booked
    (b) a digest
    (c) a manifest
    (d) listed

12. A ____ location is protected from weather and not subject to saturation with water or other liquids.

    (a) dry
    (b) damp
    (c) wet
    (d) moist

13. A ____ location may be temporarily subject to dampness and wetness.

    (a) dry
    (b) damp
    (c) moist
    (d) wet

14. Conduit installed underground or encased in concrete slabs that are in direct contact with the earth is considered a ____ location.

    (a) dry
    (b) damp
    (c) wet
    (d) moist

15. A(n) "____" is a point on the wiring system at which current is taken to supply utilization equipment.

    (a) box
    (b) receptacle
    (c) outlet
    (d) device

16. A "raceway" is an enclosed channel designed expressly for the holding of wires, cables, or busbars, with additional functions as permitted in the *Code*.

    (a) True
    (b) False

17. A contact device installed at an outlet for the connection of an attachment plug, or for the direct connection of electrical utilization equipment designed to mate with the corresponding contact device, is known as a(n) "____."

    (a) attachment point
    (b) tap
    (c) receptacle
    (d) wall plug

18. A single receptacle is a single contact device with no other contact device on the same ____.

    (a) circuit
    (b) yoke
    (c) run
    (d) equipment

ARTICLE 110

REQUIREMENTS FOR ELECTRICAL INSTALLATIONS

Introduction to Article 110—Requirements for Electrical Installations

Article 110 sets the stage for how you'll implement the rest of the *NEC*. This article contains a few of the most important and yet neglected parts of the *Code*. For example:

- How should conductors be terminated?
- What kinds of warnings, markings, and identification does a given installation require?
- What's the right working clearance for a given installation?
- What do the temperature limitations at terminals mean?
- What are the *NEC* requirements for dealing with flash protection?

It's critical that you master Article 110; as you read this article, you're building your foundation for correctly applying the *NEC*. In fact, this article itself is a foundation for much of the *Code*. The purpose for the *National Electrical Code* is to provide a safe installation, but Article 110 is perhaps focused a little more on providing an installation that's safe for the installer and maintenance electrician, so time spent in this article is time well spent.

Part I. General Requirements

110.1 Scope

Article 110 covers the general requirements for the examination and approval, installation and use, access to and spaces about electrical equipment; as well as general requirements for enclosures intended for personnel entry (manholes, vaults, and tunnels).

Note: See Annex J for information regarding ADA accessibility design.

Author's Comment:

- Requirements for people with disabilities include things like mounting heights for switches and receptacles, and requirements for the distance that objects such as wall sconces protrude from a wall.

110.2 Approval of Conductors and Equipment

The authority having jurisdiction must approve all electrical conductors and equipment. ▶Figure 110–1

Author's Comment:

- For a better understanding of product approval, review 90.4, 90.7, 110.3, and the definitions for "Approved," "Identified," "Labeled," and "Listed" in Article 100.

▶Figure 110–1

110.3 Examination, Identification, Installation, Use, and Product Listing (Certification) of Equipment

(A) Guidelines for Approval. The authority having jurisdiction must approve equipment. In doing so, consideration must be given to the following:

(1) Suitability for installation and use in accordance with the *NEC*

Note 1: Equipment may be new, reconditioned, refurbished, or remanufactured.

Note 2: Suitability of equipment use may be identified by a description marked on, or provided with, a product to identify the suitability of the product for a specific purpose, environment, or application. Special conditions of use or other limitations may be marked on the equipment, in the product instructions, or appropriate listing and labeling information. Suitability of equipment may be evidenced by listing or labeling.

(2) Mechanical strength and durability

(3) Wire-bending and connection space

(4) Electrical insulation

(5) Heating effects under all conditions of use

(6) Arcing effects

(7) Classification by type, size, voltage, current capacity, and specific use

(8) Other factors contributing to the practical safeguarding of persons using or in contact with the equipment

(B) Installation and Use. Equipment must be installed and used in accordance with any instructions included in the listing or labeling requirements. ▶Figure 110–2

▶Figure 110–2

(C) Product Listing (Certification). Product certification (testing, evaluation, and listing) must be performed by a recognized qualified testing laboratory in accordance with standards that achieve effective safety to comply with the *NEC*.

Note: OSHA recognizes qualified electrical testing laboratories that provide product certification that meets OSHA electrical standards.

110.4 Voltages

The voltage rating of electrical equipment isn't permitted to be less than the nominal voltage of a circuit to which it's connected. ▶Figure 110–3

110.5 Conductor Material

Conductors are to be copper or aluminum unless otherwise provided in this *Code*; and when the conductor material isn't specified in a rule, the sizes given in the *NEC* are based on a copper conductor. ▶Figure 110–4

Voltage Rating of Electrical Equipment
110.4

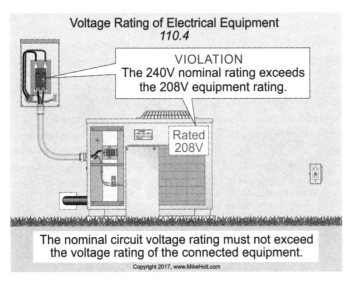

VIOLATION
The 240V nominal rating exceeds the 208V equipment rating.

Rated 208V

The nominal circuit voltage rating must not exceed the voltage rating of the connected equipment.

Copyright 2017, www.MikeHolt.com

▶Figure 110–3

Conductor Material
110.5

THHN CU 600V

THWN AL 600V

Conductors are to be copper or aluminum unless otherwise provided in this *Code*; and when the conductor material isn't specified in a rule, the sizes given in the *NEC* are based on a copper conductor.

Copyright 2017, www.MikeHolt.com

▶Figure 110–4

110.6 Conductor Sizes

Conductor sizes are expressed in American Wire Gage (AWG), typically from 18 AWG up to 4/0 AWG. Conductor sizes larger than 4/0 AWG are expressed in kcmil (thousand circular mils). ▶Figure 110–5

Conductor Sizes, AWG or Cmils
110.6

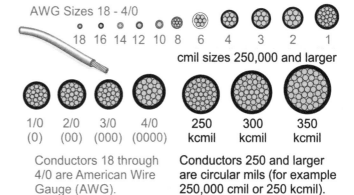

AWG Sizes 18 - 4/0

18 16 14 12 10 8 6 4 3 2 1

cmil sizes 250,000 and larger

1/0 (0)   2/0 (00)   3/0 (000)   4/0 (0000)   250 kcmil   300 kcmil   350 kcmil

Conductors 18 through 4/0 are American Wire Gauge (AWG).

Conductors 250 and larger are circular mils (for example 250,000 cmil or 250 kcmil).

Copyright 2017, www.MikeHolt.com

▶Figure 110–5

110.7 Wiring Integrity

Completed installations must be free from short circuits, ground faults, or any connections to ground unless required or permitted by the *Code*.
▶Figure 110–6

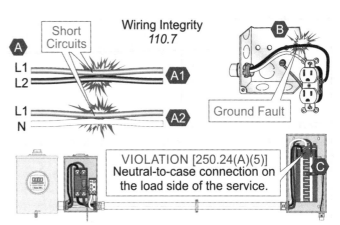

Short Circuits

Wiring Integrity
110.7

A

L1
L2   A1

L1
N   A2

B

Ground Fault

VIOLATION [250.24(A)(5)]
Neutral-to-case connection on the load side of the service.

C

All wiring must be installed so as to be free from short circuits, ground faults, and any connection to ground unless required or permitted by the *NEC*.

Copyright 2017, www.MikeHolt.com

▶Figure 110–6

110.11 Deteriorating Agents

Electrical equipment and conductors must be suitable for the environment and conditions of use. Consideration must also be given to the presence of corrosive gases, fumes, vapors, liquids, or other substances that can have a deteriorating effect on the conductors or equipment. ▶Figure 110–7

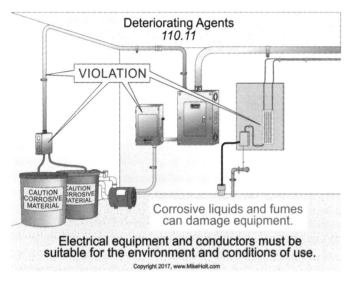

▶Figure 110–7

Author's Comment:

- Conductors aren't permitted to be exposed to ultraviolet rays from the sun unless identified for the purpose [310.10(D)].

Note 1: Raceways, cable trays, cablebus, cable armor, boxes, cable sheathing, cabinets, elbows, couplings, fittings, supports, and support hardware must be of materials that are suitable for the environment in which they're to be installed, in accordance with 300.6. ▶Figure 110–8

Note 2: Some cleaning and lubricating compounds contain chemicals that can cause deterioration of the plastic used for insulating and structural applications in equipment.

Equipment not identified for outdoor use and equipment identified only for indoor use must be protected against damage from the weather during construction.

Note 3: See Table 110.28 for NEMA enclosure-type designations.

Note 4: See the *International Building Code (IBC)* and the *International Residential Code (IRC)* for minimum flood provisions. ▶Figure 110–9

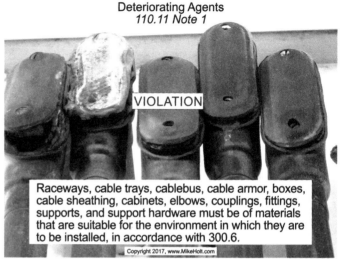

Raceways, cable trays, cablebus, cable armor, boxes, cable sheathing, cabinets, elbows, couplings, fittings, supports, and support hardware must be of materials that are suitable for the environment in which they are to be installed, in accordance with 300.6.

▶Figure 110–8

See the *International Building Code (IBC)* and the *International Residential Code (IRC)* for minimum flood provisions.

▶Figure 110–9

110.12 Mechanical Execution of Work

Electrical equipment must be installed in a neat and workmanlike manner. ▶Figure 110–10

(A) Unused Openings. Unused openings, other than those intended for the operation of equipment or for mounting purposes, or those that are part of the design for listed products, must be closed by fittings that provide protection substantially equivalent to the wall of the equipment. ▶Figure 110–11

Note: Accepted industry practices are described in ANSI/NECA 1, *Standard for Good Workmanship in Electrical Construction.*

▶Figure 110–10

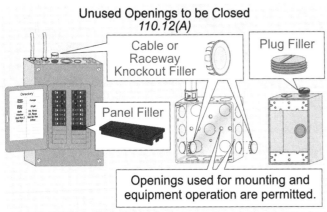

Unused openings, other than those for equipment operation or mounting purposes, must be effectively closed with a fitting that provides equivalent protection.

▶Figure 110–11

Author's Comment:

■ The National Electrical Contractors Association (NECA) created a series of National Electrical Installation Standards (NEIS)® that established the industry's first quality guidelines for electrical installations. These standards define a benchmark or baseline of quality and workmanship for installing electrical products and systems. They explain what installing electrical products and systems in a "neat and workmanlike manner" means. For more information about these standards, visit www.NECA-NEIS.org.

(B) Integrity of Electrical Equipment. Internal parts of electrical equipment aren't permitted to be damaged or contaminated by foreign material, such as paint, plaster, cleaners, and so forth. ▶Figure 110–12

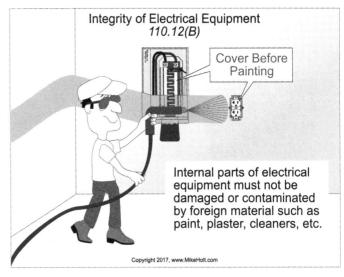

▶Figure 110–12

Author's Comment:

■ Precautions must be taken to provide protection from contamination of the internal parts of panelboards and receptacles during building construction. Make sure that electrical equipment is properly masked and protected before painting or other phases of the project that can cause damage take place. ▶Figure 110–13

▶Figure 110–13

Electrical equipment containing damaged parts, such as broken, bent, cut, or deteriorated by corrosion, chemical action, or overheating aren't permitted to be installed. ▶Figure 110–14

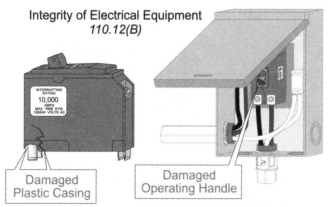

Integrity of Electrical Equipment
110.12(B)

Damaged Plastic Casing

Damaged Operating Handle

Defective or damaged electrical components that may adversely affect the safe operation or strength of the equipment must not be installed.

Copyright 2017, www.MikeHolt.com

▶Figure 110–14

Author's Comment:

■ Damaged parts include cracked insulators, arc shields not in place, overheated fuse clips, and damaged or missing switch handles or circuit-breaker handles.

110.13 Mounting and Cooling of Equipment

(A) Mounting. Electrical equipment must be firmly secured to the surface on which it's mounted. ▶Figure 110–15

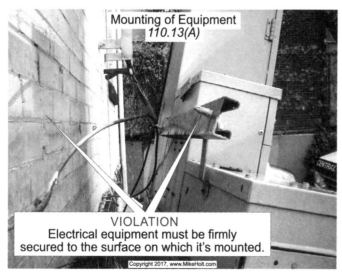

Mounting of Equipment
110.13(A)

VIOLATION
Electrical equipment must be firmly secured to the surface on which it's mounted.

Copyright 2017, www.MikeHolt.com

▶Figure 110–15

110.14 Conductor Termination and Splicing

 Scan this QR code to watch Mike explain this topic; it's a sample video clip from Mike's *Understanding the NEC Volume 1* DVDs.

Conductor terminal and splicing devices must be identified for the conductor material and they must be properly installed and used. ▶Figure 110–16

Conductor Termination and Splicing
110.14

Conductor terminal and splicing devices must be identified for the conductor material and they must be properly installed and used.

Copyright 2017, www.MikeHolt.com

▶Figure 110–16

Author's Comment:

■ Switches and receptacles marked "CO/ALR" are designed to ensure a good connection through the use of a larger contact area and compatible materials. The terminal screws are plated with the element called "Indium." Indium is an extremely soft metal that forms a gas-sealed connection with the aluminum conductor.

Connectors and terminals for conductors more finely stranded than Class B and Class C, as shown in Table 10 of Chapter 9, must be identified for the use of finely stranded conductors. ▶Figure 110–17

Author's Comment:

■ According to UL Standard 486 A-B, a terminal/lug/connector must be listed and marked for use with other than Class B stranded conductors. With no marking or factory literature/instructions to the contrary, terminals may only be used with Class B stranded conductors.

■ See the definition of "Identified" in Article 100.

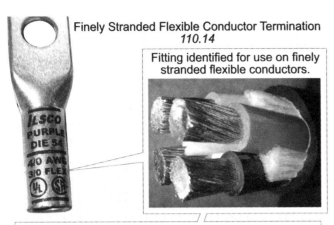

Finely Stranded Flexible Conductor Termination
110.14

Fitting identified for use on finely stranded flexible conductors.

Connectors and terminations for conductors more finely stranded than Class B and Class C [Chapter 9, Table 10] stranding must be identified for the conductor class.

Copyright 2017, www.MikeHolt.com

▶Figure 110–17

- Conductor terminations must comply with the manufacturer's instructions as required by 110.3(B). For example, if the instructions for the device state "Suitable for 18-12 AWG Stranded," then only stranded conductors can be used with the terminating device. If the instructions state "Suitable for 18-12 AWG Solid," then only solid conductors are permitted, and if the instructions state "Suitable for 18-12 AWG," then either solid or stranded conductors can be used with the terminating device.

Copper and Aluminum Mixed. Copper and aluminum conductors must not make contact with each other in a device unless the device is listed and identified for this purpose. ▶Figure 110–18

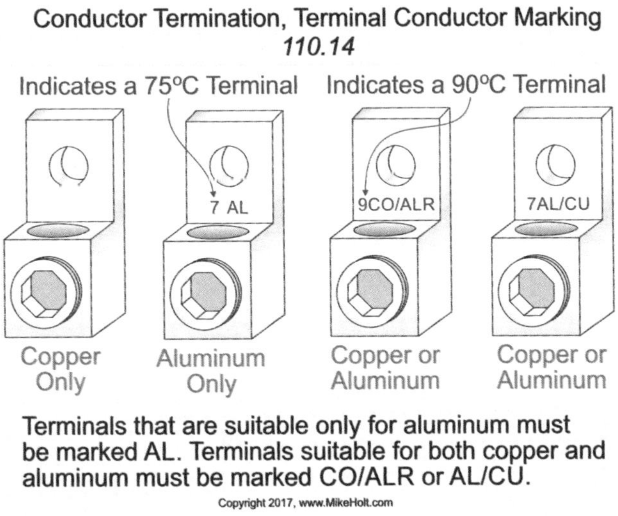

Conductor Termination, Terminal Conductor Marking
110.14

Indicates a 75°C Terminal   Indicates a 90°C Terminal

7 AL   9CO/ALR   7AL/CU

| Copper Only | Aluminum Only | Copper or Aluminum | Copper or Aluminum |

Terminals that are suitable only for aluminum must be marked AL. Terminals suitable for both copper and aluminum must be marked CO/ALR or AL/CU.

Copyright 2017, www.MikeHolt.com

▶Figure 110–18

Author's Comment:

- Few terminations are listed for the mixing of aluminum and copper conductors, but if they are, that will be marked on the product package or terminal device. The reason copper and aluminum shouldn't be in contact with each other is because corrosion develops between the two different metals due to galvanic action, resulting in increased contact resistance at the splicing device. This increased resistance can cause the splice to overheat and cause a fire.

(A) Terminations. Conductor terminals must ensure a good connection without damaging the conductors.

Terminals for more than one conductor and terminals used for aluminum conductors must be identified for this purpose, either within the equipment instructions or on the terminal itself. ▶Figure 110–19

Conductor Termination, One Wire Per Terminal
110.14(A)

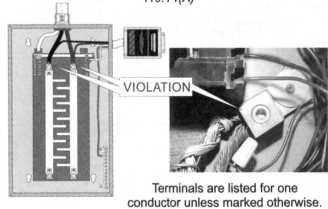

VIOLATION

Terminals are listed for one conductor unless marked otherwise.

Copyright 2017, www.MikeHolt.com

▶Figure 110–19

Author's Comment:

- Split-bolt connectors are commonly listed for only two conductors, although some are listed for three conductors. However, it's a common industry practice to terminate as many conductors as possible within a split-bolt connector, even though this violates the *NEC*. ▶Figure 110–20

(B) Conductor Splices. Conductors must be spliced by a splicing device identified for the purpose or by exothermic welding. ▶Figure 110–21

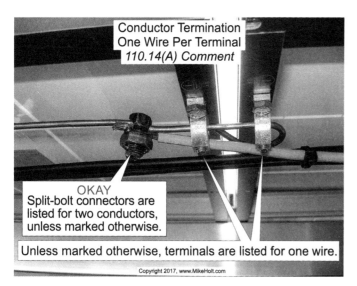

Conductor Termination
One Wire Per Terminal
110.14(A) Comment

OKAY
Split-bolt connectors are listed for two conductors, unless marked otherwise.

Unless marked otherwise, terminals are listed for one wire.

Copyright 2017, www.MikeHolt.com

▶Figure 110–20

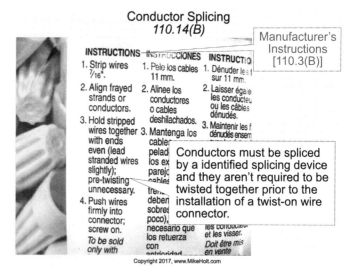

Conductor Splicing
110.14(B)

Manufacturer's Instructions [110.3(B)]

Conductors must be spliced by a identified splicing device and they aren't required to be twisted together prior to the installation of a twist-on wire connector.

Copyright 2017, www.MikeHolt.com

▶Figure 110–22

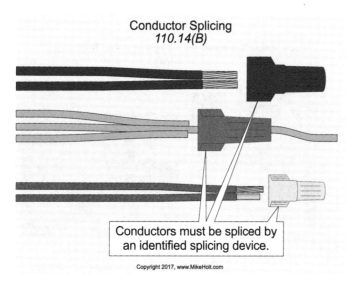

Conductor Splicing
110.14(B)

Conductors must be spliced by an identified splicing device.

Copyright 2017, www.MikeHolt.com

▶Figure 110–21

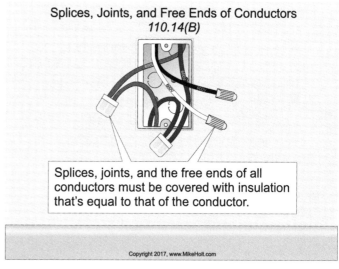

Splices, Joints, and Free Ends of Conductors
110.14(B)

Splices, joints, and the free ends of all conductors must be covered with insulation that's equal to that of the conductor.

Copyright 2017, www.MikeHolt.com

▶Figure 110–23

Author's Comment:

- Conductors aren't required to be twisted together prior to the installation of a twist-on wire connector, unless specifically required in the installation instructions. ▶Figure 110–22

- Unused circuit conductors aren't required to be removed. However, to prevent an electrical hazard, the free ends of the conductors must be insulated to prevent the exposed end of the conductor from touching energized parts. This requirement can be met by the use of an insulated twist-on or push-on wire connector. ▶Figure 110–23

- See the definition of "Energized" in Article 100.

Underground Splices, Single Conductors. Single direct burial conductors of types UF or USE can be spliced underground without a junction box, but the conductors must be spliced with a device listed for direct burial [300.5(E) and 300.15(G)]. ▶Figure 110–24

Underground Splices, Multiconductor Cable. Multiconductor UF or USE cable can have the individual conductors spliced underground without a junction box as long as a listed splice kit that encapsulates the conductors as well as the cable jacket is used.

(C) Temperature Limitations (Conductor Size). Conductors are to be sized using their ampacity from the insulation temperature rating column of Table 310.15(B)(16) that corresponds to the lowest temperature rating of any terminal, device, or conductor of the circuit.

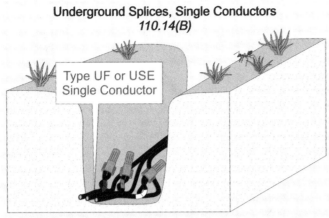

Underground Splices, Single Conductors
110.14(B)

Type UF or USE
Single Conductor

Single Type UF or USE conductors can be spliced
underground with a device that's listed for direct burial.
Copyright 2017, www.MikeHolt.com

▶Figure 110–24

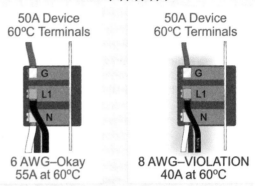

Conductor Sizing, Equipment Rated 100A or Less
110.14(C)(1)(a)(1)

50A Device
60°C Terminals

50A Device
60°C Terminals

6 AWG–Okay
55A at 60°C

8 AWG–VIOLATION
40A at 60°C

Unless listed and marked otherwise, conductors must
be sized using the 60°C column of Table 310.15(B)(16).
Copyright 2017, www.MikeHolt.com

▶Figure 110–26

Conductors with insulation temperature ratings higher than the termination's temperature rating can be used for ampacity adjustment, correction, or both. ▶Figure 110–25

(3) Conductors terminating on terminals rated 75°C are to be sized in accordance with the ampacities listed in the 75°C temperature column of Table 310.15(B)(16). ▶Figure 110–27

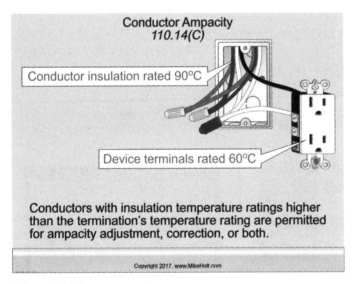

Conductor Ampacity
110.14(C)

Conductor insulation rated 90°C

Device terminals rated 60°C

Conductors with insulation temperature ratings higher
than the termination's temperature rating are permitted
for ampacity adjustment, correction, or both.
Copyright 2017, www.MikeHolt.com

▶Figure 110–25

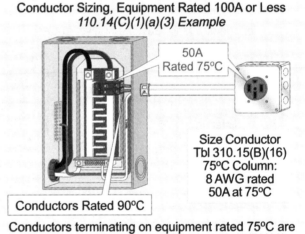

Conductor Sizing, Equipment Rated 100A or Less
110.14(C)(1)(a)(3) Example

50A
Rated 75°C

Size Conductor
Tbl 310.15(B)(16)
75°C Column:
8 AWG rated
50A at 75°C

Conductors Rated 90°C

Conductors terminating on equipment rated 75°C are
sized to the 75°C ampacity of Table 310.15(B)(16).
Copyright 2017, www.MikeHolt.com

▶Figure 110–27

(1) Equipment Temperature Rating Provisions. Unless the equipment is listed and marked otherwise, conductor sizing for equipment terminations must be based on Table 310.15(B)(16) in accordance with (a) or (b):

(a) Equipment Rated 100A or Less.

(1) Conductors must be sized using the 60°C temperature column of Table 310.15(B)(16). ▶Figure 110–26

(4) For motors marked with design letters B, C, or D, conductors having an insulation rating of 75°C or higher can be used, provided the ampacity of such conductors doesn't exceed the 75°C ampacity. ▶Figure 110–28

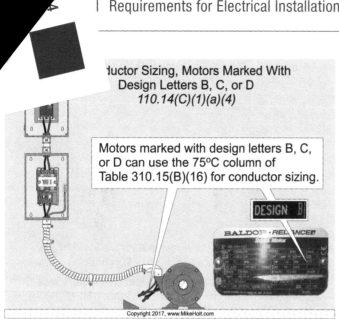

Conductor Sizing, Motors Marked With
Design Letters B, C, or D
110.14(C)(1)(a)(4)

Motors marked with design letters B, C, or D can use the 75°C column of Table 310.15(B)(16) for conductor sizing.

DESIGN B

▶Figure 110–28

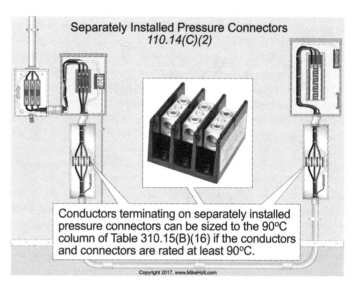

Separately Installed Pressure Connectors
110.14(C)(2)

Conductors terminating on separately installed pressure connectors can be sized to the 90°C column of Table 310.15(B)(16) if the conductors and connectors are rated at least 90°C.

▶Figure 110–30

(b) Equipment Rated Over 100A.

(1) Conductors with an insulation temperature rating of 75°C must be sized to the 75°C temperature column of Table 310.15(B)(16). ▶Figure 110–29

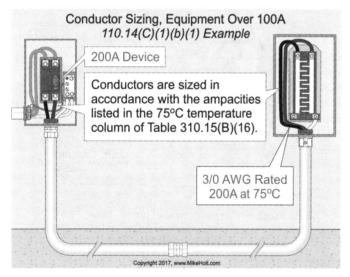

Conductor Sizing, Equipment Over 100A
110.14(C)(1)(b)(1) Example

200A Device

Conductors are sized in accordance with the ampacities listed in the 75°C temperature column of Table 310.15(B)(16).

3/0 AWG Rated 200A at 75°C

▶Figure 110–29

(2) Conductors with an insulation temperature rating of 90°C can be sized to the 75°C column of Table 310.15(B)(16).

(2) Separate Connector Provisions. Conductors can be sized to the 90°C column of Table 310.15(B)(16) if the conductors and pressure connectors are rated at least 90°C. ▶Figure 110–30

Note: Equipment markings or listing information may restrict the sizing and temperature ratings of connected conductors.

(D) Torque. Where tightening torque values are indicated on equipment or installation instructions, a calibrated torque tool must be used to achieve the indicated torque value, unless the equipment manufacturer provides an alternative method of achieving the required torque. ▶Figure 110–31

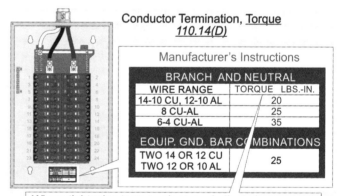

Conductor Termination, Torque
110.14(D)

Manufacturer's Instructions

BRANCH AND NEUTRAL	
WIRE RANGE	TORQUE LBS.-IN.
14-10 CU, 12-10 AL	20
8 CU-AL	25
6-4 CU-AL	35

EQUIP. GND. BAR COMBINATIONS	
TWO 14 OR 12 CU	25
TWO 12 OR 10 AL	

Where tightening torque values are indicated on equipment or installation instructions, a calibrated torque tool must be used to achieve the indicated torque value, unless the equipment manufacturer provides an alternative method of achieving the required torque.

▶Figure 110–31

Author's Comment:

- Conductors must terminate in devices that have been properly tightened in accordance with the manufacturer's torque specifications included with equipment instructions. Failure to torque terminals properly can result in excessive heating of terminals or splicing devices due to a loose connection. A loose connection can also lead to arcing which increases the heating effect and may also lead to a short circuit or ground fault. Any of these can result in a fire or other failure, including an arc-flash event. In addition, this is a violation of 110.3(B), which requires all equipment to be installed in accordance with listing or labeling instructions.

110.15 High-Leg Conductor Identification

On a 4-wire, delta-connected, three-phase system, where the midpoint of one phase winding of the secondary is grounded (a high-leg system), the conductor with 208V to ground must be durably and permanently marked by an outer finish orange in color, or other effective means. Such identification must be placed at each point on the system where a connection is made if the neutral conductor is present [230.56]. ▶Figure 110–32

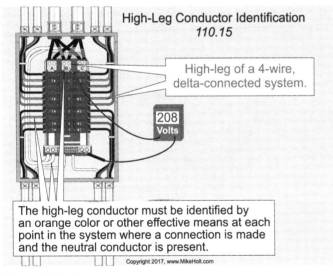

High-Leg Conductor Identification
110.15

High-leg of a 4-wire, delta-connected system.

208 Volts

The high-leg conductor must be identified by an orange color or other effective means at each point in the system where a connection is made and the neutral conductor is present.

Copyright 2017, www.MikeHolt.com

▶Figure 110–32

Author's Comment:

- The high-leg conductor is also called the "wild leg," "stinger leg," or "bastard leg."
- Other important *NEC* rules relating to the high leg are as follows:
  - **Panelboards.** Since 1975, panelboards supplied by a 4-wire, delta-connected, three-phase system must have the high-leg conductor terminate to the "B" phase of a panelboard [408.3(E)]. Section 408.3(F)(1) requires panelboards to be field-marked with "Caution Phase B Has 208V to Ground."
  - **Disconnects.** The *NEC* doesn't specify the termination location for the high-leg conductor in switch equipment (Switches—Article 404), but the generally accepted practice is to terminate this conductor to the "B" phase.
  - **Utility Meter Equipment.** The ANSI standard for meter equipment requires the high-leg conductor (208V to neutral) to terminate on the "C" (right) phase of the meter socket enclosure. This is because the demand meter needs 120V, and it obtains that voltage from the "B" phase.
- Also hope the electric utility lineman isn't color blind and doesn't inadvertently cross the "orange" high-leg conductor (208V) with the red (120V) service conductor at the weatherhead. It's happened before…

⚠ **WARNING:** *When replacing equipment in existing facilities that contain a high-leg conductor, care must be taken to ensure the high-leg conductor is replaced in its original location. Prior to 1975, the high-leg conductor was required to terminate on the "C" phase of panelboards and switchboards. Failure to re-terminate the high leg in accordance with the existing installation can result in 120V circuits being inadvertently connected to the 208V high leg, with disastrous results.*

110.16 Arc-Flash Hazard Warning

(A) Arc-Flash Hazard Warning Label. Switchboards, switchgear, panelboards, industrial control panels, meter socket enclosures, and motor control centers in other than dwelling units must be marked to warn qualified persons of the danger associated with an arc flash from short circuits or ground faults. The arc-flash hazard warning marking must be permanently affixed, have sufficient durability to withstand the environment involved [110.21(B)], and be clearly visible to qualified persons before they examine, adjust, service, or perform maintenance on the equipment. ▶Figure 110–33

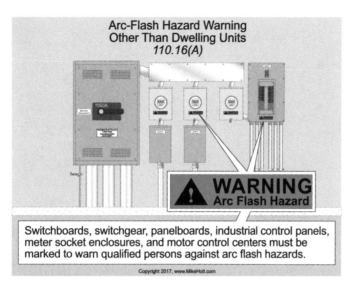

▶Figure 110–33

Author's Comment:

- See the definition of "Qualified Person" in Article 100.

- This rule is intended to warn qualified persons who work on energized electrical systems that an arc-flash hazard exists so they'll select proper personal protective equipment (PPE) in accordance with industry accepted safe work practice standards. ▶Figure 110–34

▶Figure 110–34

(B) Service Equipment Available Fault Current Label. Service equipment rated 1,200A or more must have a field or factory installed label containing the following details and have sufficient durability to withstand the environment: ▶Figure 110–35

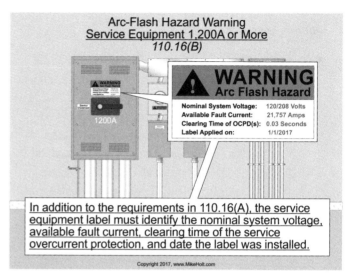

▶Figure 110–35

(1) Nominal system voltage

(2) Available fault current at the service overcurrent protection device

(3) Clearing time of the service overcurrent protection device based on the available fault current at the service equipment

(4) Date the service equipment available fault current label was installed

Ex: Service equipment labeling isn't required if an arc-flash label in accordance with NFPA 70E, Standard for Electrical Safety in the Workplace *[see Note 3] is applied.* ▶Figure 110–36

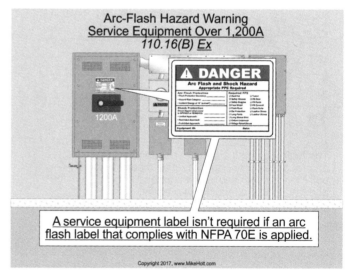

▶Figure 110–36

Note 1: NFPA 70E, *Standard for Electrical Safety in the Workplace*, provides guidance in determining the severity of potential exposure, planning safe work practices, arc-flash labeling, and selecting personal protective equipment. ▶Figure 110–37

Arc-Flash Hazard Warning, Service Equipment
110.16(B) Note 1

NFPA 70E, *Standard for Electrical Safety in the Workplace*, provides guidance in determining the severity of potential exposure, planning safe work practices, arc-flash labeling, and selecting personal protective equipment.

Copyright 2017, www.MikeHolt.com

▶Figure 110–37

Note No. 3: NFPA 70E, *Standard for Electrical Safety in the Workplace* provides specific criteria for developing arc-flash labels, such as nominal system voltage, incident energy levels, arc-flash boundaries, and selecting personal protective equipment.

110.21 Markings

(A) Equipment Markings.

(1) General. The manufacturer's name, trademark, or other descriptive marking must be placed on all electrical equipment and, where required by the *Code*, markings such as voltage, current, wattage, or other ratings must be provided. Marking must have sufficient durability to withstand the environment involved.

(2) Reconditioned Equipment. Reconditioned equipment must be marked with the name, trademark, or other descriptive marking by the organization responsible for reconditioning the electrical equipment, along with the date of the reconditioning.

Reconditioned equipment must be identified as "reconditioned" and approval of the reconditioned equipment isn't based solely on the equipment's original listing.

Ex: Reconditioning markings aren't required in industrial occupancies, where conditions of maintenance and supervision ensure that only qualified persons service the equipment.

Note: Normal servicing of equipment isn't considered to be reconditioning equipment.

(B) Field-Applied Hazard Markings. Where caution, warning, or danger signs or labels are required, the labels must meet the following:

(1) The markings <u>must warn</u> of the <u>hazards</u> using effective words, colors, symbols, <u>or a combination of</u> words, <u>colors, and symbols</u>. ▶Figure 110–38

Field-Applied Hazard Markings
110.21(B)(1)

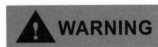

The markings <u>must warn</u> of the <u>hazards</u> using effective words, colors, symbols, or a combination of words, <u>colors, and symbols</u>.

Copyright 2017, www.MikeHolt.com

▶Figure 110–38

Note: ANSI Z535.4, *Product Safety Signs and Labels*, provides guidelines for the design and durability of signs and labels.

(2) The label can't be handwritten, and it must be permanently affixed to the equipment. ▶Figure 110–39

Field-Applied Hazard Markings
Signs or Labels Required by the *Code*
110.21(B)(2)

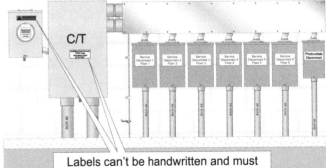

Labels can't be handwritten and must be permanently affixed to the equipment.

Markings must withstand the environment [110.21(B)(3)].

Copyright 2017, www.MikeHolt.com

▶Figure 110–39

Ex to (2): Labels that contain information that's likely to change can be handwritten, if it's legible.

Author's Comment:

- A permanently affixed sign includes a sticker, but not a piece of paper taped to the equipment.

(3) The marking must be of sufficient durability to withstand the environment involved.

110.22 Identification of Disconnecting Means

(A) General. Each disconnect must be legibly marked to indicate its purpose unless located and arranged so the purpose is evident. The marking must be of sufficient durability to withstand the environment involved. ▶Figure 110–40

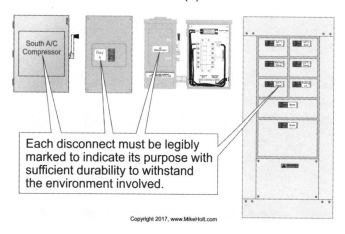

Identification of Disconnecting Means
110.22(A)

Each disconnect must be legibly marked to indicate its purpose with sufficient durability to withstand the environment involved.

Copyright 2017, www.MikeHolt.com

▶Figure 110–40

(C) Tested Series Combination Systems. Tested series-rated installations must be legibly field-marked in accordance with 240.86(B) with a readily visible permanently affixed caution label having sufficient durability to withstand the environment involved and comply with 110.21(B) to indicate that the equipment has been applied with a series combination rating:

CAUTION—SERIES COMBINATION SYSTEM
RATED ____ AMPERES. IDENTIFIED REPLACEMENT
COMPONENTS REQUIRED

110.25 Lockable Disconnecting Means

If the *Code* requires a disconnect to be lockable in the open position, the provisions for locking must remain in place whether the lock is installed or not. ▶Figure 110–41

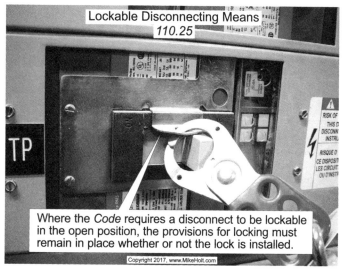

Lockable Disconnecting Means
110.25

Where the *Code* requires a disconnect to be lockable in the open position, the provisions for locking must remain in place whether or not the lock is installed.

Copyright 2017, www.MikeHolt.com

▶Figure 110–41

Part II. 1,000V, Nominal, or Less

110.26 Spaces About Electrical Equipment

For the purpose of safe operation and maintenance of equipment, access and working space must be provided about all electrical equipment. ▶Figure 110–42

Spaces About Electrical Equipment
110.26

AREA IN FRONT OF THIS ELECTRICAL PANEL MUST BE KEPT CLEAR FOR 36 INCHES OSHA-NEC REGULATIONS

For the purposes of safe operation and maintenance of equipment, access and working space must be provided about all electrical equipment.

Copyright 2017, www.MikeHolt.com

▶Figure 110–42

(A) Working Space. Equipment that may need examination, adjustment, servicing, or maintenance while energized must have working space provided in accordance with 110.26(A)(1), (2), (3), and (4):

Author's Comment:

- The phrase "while energized" is the root of many debates. As always, check with the AHJ to see what equipment he or she believes needs a clear working space.

Note: NFPA 70E, *Standard for Electrical Safety in the Workplace*, provides guidance in determining the severity of potential exposure, planning safe work practices, arc-flash labeling, and selecting personal protective equipment.

(1) Depth of Working Space. The working space, which is measured from the enclosure front, isn't permitted to be less than the distances contained in Table 110.26(A)(1). ▶Figure 110–43

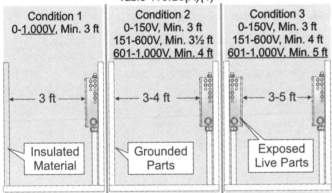

Depth of Working Space, Conditions
Table 110.26(A)(1)

| Condition 1 0-1,000V, Min. 3 ft | Condition 2 0-150V, Min. 3 ft 151-600V, Min. 3½ ft 601-1,000V, Min. 4 ft | Condition 3 0-150V, Min. 3 ft 151-600V, Min. 4 ft 601-1,000V, Min. 5 ft |

3 ft — Insulated Material
3-4 ft — Grounded Parts
3-5 ft — Exposed Live Parts

The working space from the enclosure must not be less than the distances shown in Table 110.26(A)(1).
Copyright 2017, www.MikeHolt.com

▶Figure 110–43

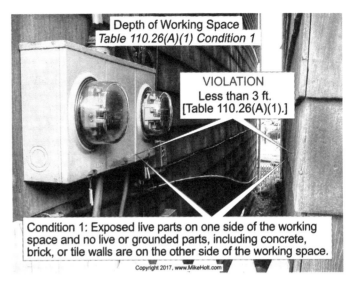

Depth of Working Space
Table 110.26(A)(1) Condition 1

VIOLATION
Less than 3 ft.
[Table 110.26(A)(1).]

Condition 1: Exposed live parts on one side of the working space and no live or grounded parts, including concrete, brick, or tile walls are on the other side of the working space.
Copyright 2017, www.MikeHolt.com

▶Figure 110–44

Depth of Working Space
Table 110.26(A)(1) Condition 2

120V to Ground - 3 ft
277V to Ground - 3½ ft
1,000V to Ground - 4 ft

Exposed live parts on one side of the working space and grounded parts on the other. Concrete, brick, tile and similar surfaces are considered grounded.
Copyright 2017, www.MikeHolt.com

▶Figure 110–45

Table 110.26(A)(1) Working Space			
Voltage–to–Ground	Condition 1	Condition 2	Condition 3
0–150V	3 ft	3 ft	3 ft
151– 600V	3 ft	3½ft	4 ft
601– 1,000V	3 ft	4 ft	5 ft

▶Figure 110–44, ▶Figure 110–45, *and* ▶Figure 110–46

▶Figure 110–46

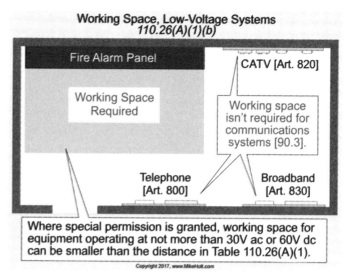

▶Figure 110–48

(a) Rear and Sides. Working space isn't required for the back or sides of assemblies where all connections and all renewable or adjustable parts are accessible from the front. ▶**Figure 110–47**

▶Figure 110–47

(b) Low Voltage. If special permission is granted in accordance with 90.4, working space for equipment that operates at not more than 30V ac or 60V dc can be less than the distance in Table 110.26(A)(1). ▶Figure 110–48

Author's Comment:

■ See the definition of "Special Permission" in Article 100.

(c) Existing Buildings. If electrical equipment is being replaced, Condition 2 working space is permitted between dead-front switchboards, switchgear, panelboards, or motor control centers located across the aisle from each other where conditions of maintenance and supervision ensure that written procedures have been adopted to prohibit equipment on both sides of the aisle from being open at the same time, and only authorized, qualified persons will service the installation.

Author's Comment:

■ The working space requirements of 110.26 don't apply to equipment included in Chapter 8—Communications Circuits [90.3].

(2) Width of Working Space. The width of the working space must be a minimum of 30 in., but in no case less than the width of the equipment. ▶Figure 110–49 and ▶Figure 110–50

Author's Comment:

■ The width of the working space can be measured from left-to-right, from right-to-left, or simply centered on the equipment, and can overlap the working space for other electrical equipment. ▶Figure 110–51

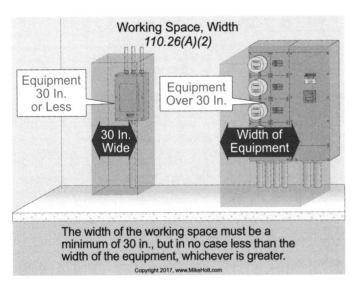

▶Figure 110–49

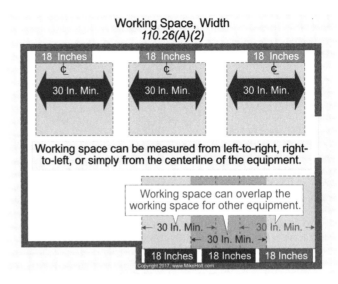

▶Figure 110–51

▶Figure 110–50

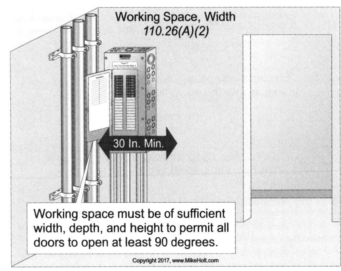

▶Figure 110–52

The working space must be of sufficient width, depth, and height to permit all equipment doors to open 90 degrees. ▶Figure 110–52

(3) Height of Working Space (Headroom). The height of the working space in front of equipment isn't permitted to be less than 6½ ft, measured from the grade, floor, platform, or the equipment height, whichever is greater. ▶Figure 110–53

Equipment such as raceways, cables, wireways, cabinets, panels, and so on, can be located above or below electrical equipment, but must not extend more than 6 in. into the equipment's working space. ▶Figure 110–54

Ex 1: The minimum headroom requirement doesn't apply to service equipment or panelboards rated 200A or less located in an existing dwelling unit.

Author's Comment:

■ See the definition of "Dwelling Unit" in Article 100.

Working Space, Height
110.26(A)(3)

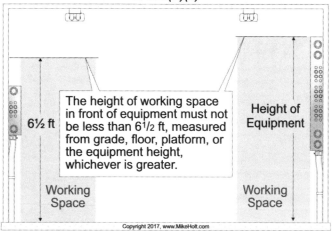

The height of working space in front of equipment must not be less than 6½ ft, measured from grade, floor, platform, or the equipment height, whichever is greater.

6½ ft

Height of Equipment

Working Space

Working Space

▶Figure 110–53

Working Space, Height
110.26(A)(3)

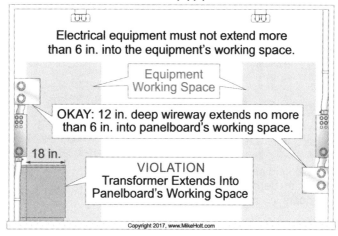

Electrical equipment must not extend more than 6 in. into the equipment's working space.

Equipment Working Space

OKAY: 12 in. deep wireway extends no more than 6 in. into panelboard's working space.

18 in.

VIOLATION
Transformer Extends Into Panelboard's Working Space

▶Figure 110–54

Ex 2: Meters are permitted to extend beyond the other equipment.

Ex 3: For battery systems, see 480.10(D) for top clearance requirements.

(4) Limited Access. Where equipment is likely to require examination, adjustment, servicing, or maintenance while energized is located in a space with limited access, all of the following conditions apply:

(a)(1) Above Suspended Ceiling. Equipment installed above a suspended ceiling must have an access opening not smaller than 22 in. × 22 in.

(a)(2) Crawl Space. Equipment installed in a crawl space must have an accessible opening not smaller than 22 in. × 30 in.

(b) The width of the working space must be a minimum of 30 in., but in no case less than the width of the equipment.

(c) The working space must permit equipment doors to open 90 degrees.

(d) The working space in front of the equipment must comply with the depth requirements of Table 110.26(A)(1), and horizontal ceiling structural members are permitted in this space.

(B) Clear Working Space. The working space required by this section must be clear at all times; therefore, this space isn't permitted for storage. ▶Figure 110–55

Clear Working Space, No Storage
110.26(B)

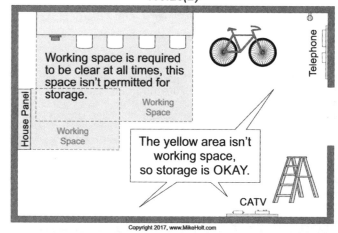

Working space is required to be clear at all times, this space isn't permitted for storage.

House Panel

Working Space

Working Space

The yellow area isn't working space, so storage is OKAY.

Telephone

CATV

▶Figure 110–55

When normally enclosed live parts are exposed for inspection or servicing, the working space, if in a passageway or open space, must be suitably guarded.

Author's Comment:

■ When working in a passageway, the working space should be guarded from occupants using it. When working on electrical equipment in a passageway one must be mindful of a fire alarm evacuation with numerous occupants congregated and moving through the area.

CAUTION: *It's very dangerous to service energized parts in the first place, and it's unacceptable to be subjected to additional dangers by working around bicycles, boxes, crates, appliances, and other impediments.*

Author's Comment:

- Signaling and communications equipment aren't permitted to be installed in a manner that encroaches on the working space of the electrical equipment. ▶Figure 110–56

Clear Working Space
110.26(B) Comment

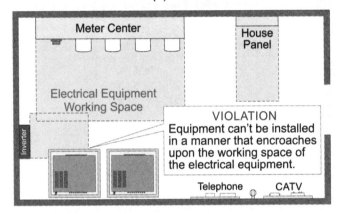

Copyright 2017, www.MikeHolt.com

▶Figure 110–56

(C) Entrance to and Egress from Working Space.

(1) Minimum Required. At least one entrance of sufficient area must provide access to and egress from the working space.

Author's Comment:

- Check to see what the authority having jurisdiction considers "Sufficient Area." Building codes contain minimum dimensions for doors and openings for personnel travel.

(2) Large Equipment. An entrance to and egress from each end of the working space of electrical equipment rated 1,200A or more that's over 6 ft wide is required. The opening must be a minimum of 24 in. wide and 6½ ft high. ▶Figure 110–57

A single entrance to and egress from the required working space is permitted where either of the following conditions is met:

(a) Unobstructed Egress. Only one entrance is required where the location permits a continuous and unobstructed way of egress travel. ▶Figure 110–58

Entrance to and Egress from Working Space
Large Equipment
110.26(C)(2)

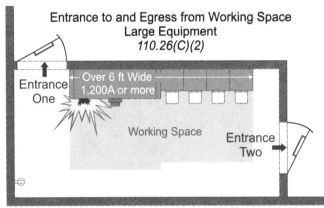

For equipment rated 1,200A or more and over 6 ft wide, an entrance to and egress from (2 ft wide x 6½ ft high) is required at each end of the working space.

Copyright 2017, www.MikeHolt.com

▶Figure 110–57

Entrance to and Egress from Working Space
Large Equipment, Unobstructed Egress
110.26(C)(2)(a)

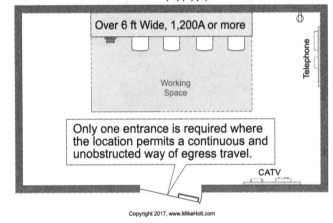

Copyright 2017, www.MikeHolt.com

▶Figure 110–58

(b) Double Workspace. Only one entrance is required where the required working space depth is doubled, and the equipment is located so the edge of the entrance is no closer than the required working space distance. ▶Figure 110–59

(3) Personnel Doors. If equipment with overcurrent or switching devices rated 800A or more is installed, personnel door(s) for entrance to and egress from the working space located less than 25 ft from the nearest edge of the working space must have the door(s) open in the direction of egress and be equipped with listed panic hardware. ▶Figure 110–60

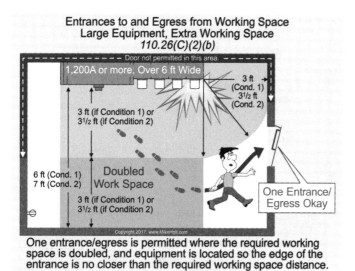

Entrances to and Egress from Working Space
Large Equipment, Extra Working Space
110.26(C)(2)(b)

One entrance/egress is permitted where the required working space is doubled, and equipment is located so the edge of the entrance is no closer than the required working space distance.

▶Figure 110–59

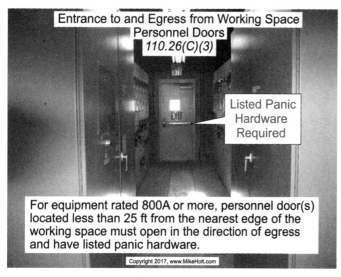

Entrance to and Egress from Working Space
Personnel Doors
110.26(C)(3)

Listed Panic Hardware Required

For equipment rated 800A or more, personnel door(s) located less than 25 ft from the nearest edge of the working space must open in the direction of egress and have listed panic hardware.

▶Figure 110–60

Author's Comment:

■ History has shown that electricians who suffer burns on their hands in electrical arc-flash or arc-blast events often can't open doors equipped with knobs that must be turned.

■ Since this requirement is in the *NEC*, the electrical contractor is responsible for ensuring that panic hardware is installed where required. Some are offended at being held liable for nonelectrical responsibilities, but this rule is designed to save the lives of electricians. For this and other reasons, many construction professionals routinely hold "pre-construction" or "pre-con" meetings to review potential opportunities for miscommunication—before the work begins.

(D) Illumination. Service equipment, switchboards, switchgear, and panelboards, as well as motor control centers located indoors must have illumination located indoors controlled by manual means; automatic control without manual control isn't permitted. ▶Figure 110–61

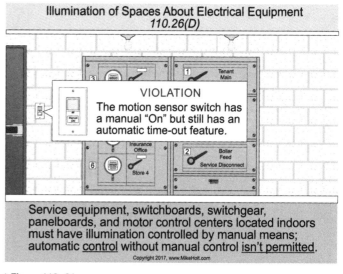

Illumination of Spaces About Electrical Equipment
110.26(D)

VIOLATION
The motion sensor switch has a manual "On" but still has an automatic time-out feature.

Service equipment, switchboards, switchgear, panelboards, and motor control centers located indoors must have illumination controlled by manual means; automatic control without manual control isn't permitted.

▶Figure 110–61

Author's Comment:

■ The *Code* doesn't provide the minimum foot-candles required to provide proper illumination. Proper illumination of electrical equipment rooms is essential for the safety of those qualified to work on such equipment.

(E) Dedicated Equipment Space. Switchboards, switchgear, panelboards, and motor control centers must have dedicated equipment space and be protected from damage as follows:

(1) Indoors.

(a) Dedicated Electrical Space. The footprint space (width and depth of the equipment) extending from the floor to a height of 6 ft above the equipment or to the structural ceiling, whichever is lower, must be dedicated for the electrical installation. ▶Figure 110–62

No piping, ducts, or other equipment foreign to the electrical installation can be installed in this dedicated footprint space. ▶Figure 110–63

Ex: Suspended ceilings with removable panels can be within the dedicated footprint space [110.26(E)(1)(d)].

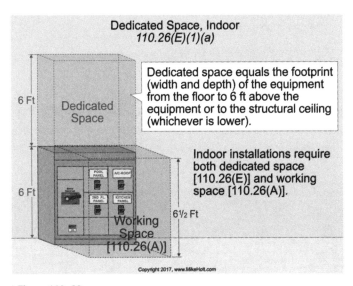

▶Figure 110–62

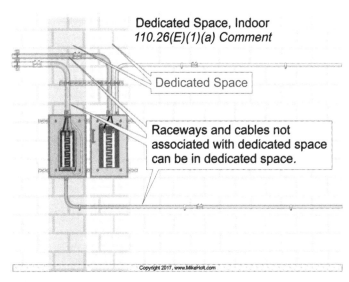

▶Figure 110–64

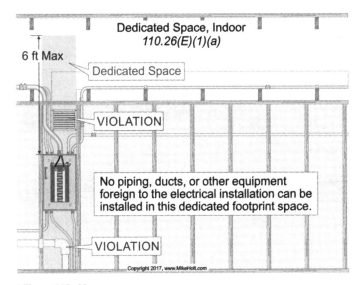

▶Figure 110–63

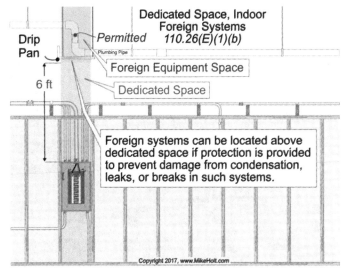

▶Figure 110–65

Author's Comment:

- Electrical raceways and cables not associated with the dedicated space can be within the dedicated space. These aren't considered "equipment foreign to the electrical installation." ▶Figure 110–64

(b) Foreign Systems. Foreign systems can be located above the dedicated space if protection is installed to prevent damage to the electrical equipment from condensation, leaks, or breaks in the foreign systems. Such protection can be as simple as a drip-pan. ▶Figure 110–65

(c) Sprinkler Protection. Sprinkler protection piping isn't permitted in the dedicated space, but the *NEC* doesn't prohibit sprinklers from spraying water on electrical equipment.

(d) Suspended Ceilings. A dropped, suspended, or similar ceiling isn't considered a structural ceiling. ▶Figure 110–66

(2) Outdoor. Outdoor installations must comply with the following:

(a) Installation Requirements. Switchboards, switchgear, panelboards, and motor control centers installed outdoors must be:

(1) Installed in <u>identified</u> enclosures

(2) Protected from accidental contact by unauthorized personnel, or by vehicular traffic ▶Figure 110–67

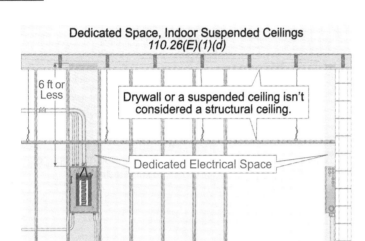

▶Figure 110–66

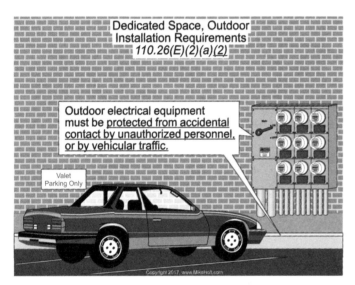

▶Figure 110–67

(3) Protected by accidental spillage or leakage from piping systems

(b) Work Space. Switchboards, switchgear, panelboards, and motor control centers installed outdoors must have sufficient working space clearance in accordance with 110.26(A). No architectural appurtenance or other equipment is permitted in the work space.

(c) Dedicated Equipment Space Outdoor. The footprint space (width and depth of the equipment) extending from grade to a height of 6 ft above the equipment must be dedicated for the electrical installation. No piping, ducts, or other equipment foreign to the electrical installation can be installed in this dedicated footprint space.

Author's Comment:

- See the definition of "Accessible (as applied to equipment)" in Article 100.

(F) Locked Electrical Equipment Rooms or Enclosures. Electrical equipment rooms or enclosures containing electrical apparatus controlled by a lock(s) are considered accessible to qualified persons. ▶Figure 110–68

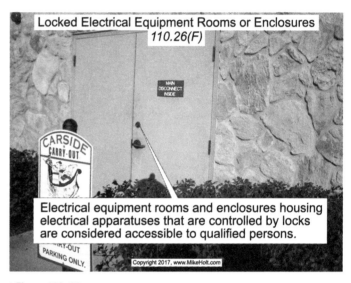

▶Figure 110–68

110.27 Guarding

(A) Guarding Live Parts. Live parts of electrical equipment operating at 50V to 1,000V between ungrounded conductors must be guarded against accidental contact. This can be done by:

(1) Locating them in a separate room, vault, or enclosure.

(2) Guarding with a permanent partition or screen. ▶Figure 110–69

(3) Locating them on a balcony or platform to exclude unqualified persons.

(4) Elevating them above the floor or working surface, in accordance with the following:

(a) 8 ft for 50V through 300V between ungrounded conductors.

(b) 8 ft 6 in. for 301V through 600V between ungrounded conductors.

(c) 8 ft 7 in. for 601V through 1,000V between ungrounded conductors.

(B) Prevent Physical Damage. Electrical equipment must not be installed where subject to physical damage, unless enclosures or guards are arranged and they're of sufficient strength to prevent damage. ▶Figure 110–70

Guarding Live Parts from Accidental Contact
110.27(A)(2)

A suitable permanent, substantial partition or a screen arranged so only qualified persons have access can be used to guard against accidental contact.

▶Figure 110–69

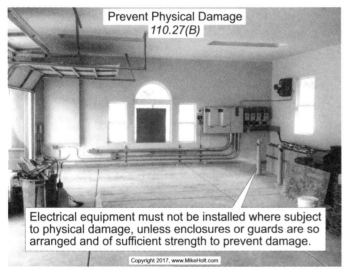

Prevent Physical Damage
110.27(B)

Electrical equipment must not be installed where subject to physical damage, unless enclosures or guards are so arranged and of sufficient strength to prevent damage.

▶Figure 110–70

(C) Warning Signs. Entrances to rooms and other guarded locations containing exposed live parts must be marked with conspicuous signs forbidding unqualified persons from entering.

110.28 Enclosure Types

Enclosures must be marked with an enclosure-type number and be suitable for the location in accordance with Table 110.28. The enclosures aren't intended to protect against condensation, icing, corrosion, or contamination that might occur within the enclosure or that enters via the raceway or unsealed openings. ▶Figure 110–71

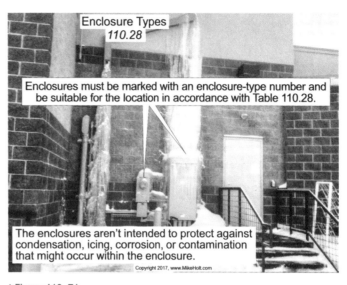

Enclosure Types
110.28

Enclosures must be marked with an enclosure-type number and be suitable for the location in accordance with Table 110.28.

The enclosures aren't intended to protect against condensation, icing, corrosion, or contamination that might occur within the enclosure.

▶Figure 110–71

Note: Raintight enclosures include Types 3, 3S, 3SX, 3X, 4, 4X, 6, and 6P; rainproof enclosures are Types 3R, and 3RX; watertight enclosures are Types 4, 4X, 6, and 6P; driptight enclosures are Types 2, 5, 12, 12K, and 13; and dusttight enclosures are Types 3, 3S, 3SX, 3X, 5, 12, 12K, and 13.

ARTICLE 110 PRACTICE QUESTIONS

Please use the 2017 *Code* book to answer the following questions.

1. In judging equipment for approval, considerations such as _____ shall be evaluated.

   (a) mechanical strength
   (b) wire-bending space
   (c) arcing effects
   (d) all of these

2. Listed or labeled equipment shall be installed and used in accordance with any instructions included in the listing or labeling.

   (a) True
   (b) False

3. Conductors normally used to carry current shall be _____ unless otherwise provided in this *NEC*.

   (a) bare
   (b) stranded
   (c) of copper or aluminum
   (d) none of these

4. Conductor sizes are expressed in American Wire Gage (AWG) or in _____.

   (a) inches
   (b) circular mils
   (c) square inches
   (d) cubic inches

5. Wiring shall be installed so that the completed system will be free from _____, other than as required or permitted elsewhere in the *NEC*.

   (a) short circuits
   (b) ground faults
   (c) connections to the earth
   (d) all of these

6. Unless identified for use in the operating environment, no conductors or equipment shall be _____ having a deteriorating effect on the conductors or equipment.

   (a) located in damp or wet locations
   (b) exposed to fumes, vapors, liquids, or gases
   (c) exposed to excessive temperatures
   (d) all of these

7. Some cleaning and lubricating compounds can cause severe deterioration of many plastic materials used for insulating and structural applications in equipment.

   (a) True
   (b) False

8. When protecting equipment against damage from the weather during construction, minimum _____ provisions provided in NFPA *5000 Building Construction and Safety Code*, the *International Building Code (IBC)*, and the *International Residential Code for One- and Two-Family Dwellings (IRC)* can be referenced for additional information.

   (a) safety
   (b) flood
   (c) weather
   (d) none of these

9. The *NEC* requires that electrical equipment be _____.

   (a) installed in a neat and workmanlike manner
   (b) installed under the supervision of a licensed person
   (c) completed before being inspected
   (d) all of these

10. Unused openings other than those intended for the operation of equipment, intended for mounting purposes, or permitted as part of the design for listed equipment shall be _____.

    (a) filled with cable clamps or connectors only
    (b) taped over with electrical tape
    (c) repaired only by welding or brazing in a metal slug
    (d) closed to afford protection substantially equivalent to the wall of the equipment

11. Accepted industry workmanship practices are described in ANSI/NECA 1-2015, *Standard for Good Workmanship in Electrical Construction*, and other ANSI-approved installation standards.

    (a) True
    (b) False

12. Internal parts of electrical equipment, including _____, shall not be damaged or contaminated by foreign materials such as paint, plaster, cleaners, abrasives, or corrosive residues.

    (a) busbars
    (b) wiring terminals
    (c) insulators
    (d) all of these

13. Wooden plugs driven into holes in _____ or similar materials shall not be used for securing electrical equipment.

    (a) masonry
    (b) concrete
    (c) plaster
    (d) all of these

14. Conductor terminal and splicing devices shall be _____ for the conductor material and they shall be properly installed and used.

    (a) listed
    (b) approved
    (c) identified
    (d) all of these

15. Connectors and terminals for conductors more finely stranded than Class B and Class C, as shown in Table 10 of Chapter 9, shall be _____ for the specific conductor class or classes.

    (a) listed
    (b) approved
    (c) identified
    (d) all of these

16. Connection of conductors to terminal parts shall ensure a thoroughly good connection without damaging the conductors and shall be made by means of _____.

    (a) solder lugs
    (b) pressure connectors
    (c) splices to flexible leads
    (d) any of these

17. Connection by means of wire-binding screws, studs, and nuts having upturned lugs or the equivalent shall be permitted for _____ AWG or smaller conductors.

    (a) 12
    (b) 10
    (c) 8
    (d) 6

18. Soldered splices shall first be spliced or joined so as to be mechanically and electrically secure without solder and then be soldered.

    (a) True
    (b) False

19. The temperature rating associated with the ampacity of a _____ shall be selected and coordinated so as not to exceed the lowest temperature rating of any connected termination, conductor, or device.

    (a) terminal
    (b) conductor
    (c) device
    (d) all of these

20. Conductor ampacity shall be determined using the _____ column of Table 310.15(B)(16) for circuits rated 100A or less or marked for 14 AWG through 1 AWG conductors.

    (a) 30°C
    (b) 60°C
    (c) 75°C
    (d) 90°C

21. For circuits rated 100A or less, when the equipment terminals are listed for use with 75°C conductors, the _____ column of Table 310.15(B)(16) shall be used to determine the ampacity of THHN conductors.

    (a) 30°C
    (b) 60°C
    (c) 75°C
    (d) 90°C

22. Conductors shall have their ampacity determined using the _____ column of Table 310.15(B)(16) for circuits rated over 100A, or marked for conductors larger than 1 AWG, unless the equipment terminals are listed for use with higher temperature-rated conductors.

    (a) 30°C
    (b) 60°C
    (c) 75°C
    (d) 90°C

23. Separately installed pressure connectors shall be used with conductors at the _____ not exceeding the ampacity at the listed and identified temperature rating of the connector.

    (a) voltages
    (b) temperatures
    (c) listings
    (d) ampacities

24. Where a tightening torque is indicated as a numeric value on equipment or in installation instructions provided by the manufacturer, a(n) _____ torque tool shall be used to achieve the indicated torque value, unless the equipment manufacturer has provided installation instructions for an alternative method of achieving the required torque.

    (a) calibrated
    (b) identified
    (c) adjustable
    (d) listed

25. On a 4-wire, delta-connected system where the midpoint of one phase winding is grounded, only the conductor or busbar having the higher phase voltage-to-ground shall be durably and permanently marked by an outer finish that is _____ in color.

    (a) black
    (b) red
    (c) blue
    (d) orange

26. Electrical equipment such as switchboards, switchgear, panelboards, industrial control panels, meter socket enclosures, and motor control centers, that are in other than dwelling units, and are likely to require _____ while energized, shall be field or factory marked to warn qualified persons of potential electric arc-flash hazards.

    (a) examination
    (b) adjustment
    (c) servicing or maintenance
    (d) any of these

27. In other than dwelling units, in addition to requirements for field or factory marking of equipment to warn qualified persons of potential electric arc-flash hazards, a permanent label shall be field or factory applied to service equipment rated _____ or more.

    (a) 600A
    (b) 1,000A
    (c) 1,200A
    (d) 1,600A

28. Service equipment labeling in other than dwelling units shall not be required if an arc-flash label is applied in accordance with _____ industry practice.

    (a) routine
    (b) acceptable
    (c) documented
    (d) none of these

29. NFPA 70E, *Standard for Electrical Safety in the Workplace*, provides guidance, such as determining severity of potential exposure, planning safe work practices, arc-flash labeling, and selecting _____.

    (a) personal protective equipment
    (b) coordinated overcurrent protective devices
    (c) a and b
    (d) none of these

30. Acceptable industry practices for equipment labeling are described in NFPA 70E, *Standard for Electrical Safety in the Workplace*. This standard provides specific criteria for developing arc-flash labels for equipment that provides _____, and so forth.

    (a) nominal system voltage and incident energy levels
    (b) arc-flash boundaries
    (c) minimum required levels of personal protective equipment
    (d) all of these

31. Where required by the *NEC*, markings or labels on all electrical equipment shall contain voltage, current, wattage, or other ratings and the marking or label shall be of sufficient durability to withstand _____.

    (a) the voltages encountered
    (b) painting and other finishes applied
    (c) the environment involved
    (d) any lack of planning by the installer

32. Reconditioned equipment shall be marked with the name, trademark, or other descriptive marking by which the _____ responsible for reconditioning the electrical equipment can be identified, along with the date of the reconditioning.

    (a) name of the individual
    (b) approving authority
    (c) organization
    (d) listing agency

33. Industry standards are available for application of reconditioned and refurbished equipment. _____ servicing of equipment that remains within a facility should not be considered reconditioning or refurbishing.

    (a) Normal
    (b) Incidental
    (c) Emergency
    (d) none of these

34. Where caution, warning, or danger signs or labels are required by this *Code*, the label marking shall warn of the hazards using effective _____.

    (a) words
    (b) colors
    (c) symbols
    (d) any combination of words, colors, or symbols

35. Each disconnecting means shall be legibly marked to indicate its purpose unless located and arranged so _____.

    (a) that it can be locked out and tagged
    (b) it is not readily accessible
    (c) the purpose is evident
    (d) that it operates at less than 300 volts-to-ground

36. The *NEC* requires tested series-rated installations of circuit breakers or fuses to be legibly marked in the field to indicate the equipment has been applied with a series combination rating.

    (a) True
    (b) False

37. Access and _____ shall be provided and maintained about all electrical equipment to permit ready and safe operation and maintenance of such equipment.

    (a) ventilation
    (b) cleanliness
    (c) circulation
    (d) working space

38. NFPA 70E, *Standard for Electrical Safety in the Workplace*, provides guidance for working space about electrical equipment, such as determining severity of potential exposure, planning safe work practices, arc-flash labeling, and selecting personal protective equipment.

    (a) True
    (b) False

39. Working space distances for enclosed live parts shall be measured from the _____ of equipment or apparatus, if the live parts are enclosed.

    (a) enclosure
    (b) opening
    (c) a or b
    (d) none of these

40. A minimum working space depth of _____ft to live parts of equipment operating at 277 volts-to-ground is required where there are exposed live parts on one side and no live or grounded parts on the other side.

    (a) 2
    (b) 3
    (c) 4
    (d) 6

41. The minimum working space on a circuit for equipment operating at 120 volts-to-ground, with exposed live parts on one side and no live or grounded parts on the other side of the working space, is _____ft.

    (a) 1
    (b) 3
    (c) 4
    (d) 6

42. Concrete, brick, or tile walls are considered _____, as applied to working space requirements.

    (a) inconsequential
    (b) in the way
    (c) grounded
    (d) none of these

43. The required working space for access to live parts of equipment operating at 300 volts-to-ground, where there are exposed live parts on one side and grounded parts on the other side, is _____ft.

    (a) 3
    (b) 3½
    (c) 4
    (d) 4½

44. The minimum working space on a circuit for equipment operating at 750 volts-to-ground, with exposed live parts on one side and grounded parts on the other side of the working space, is _____ft.

    (a) 1
    (b) 3
    (c) 4
    (d) 6

45. The required working space for access to live parts of equipment operating at 300 volts-to-ground, where there are exposed live parts on both sides of the workspace is _____ft.

    (a) 3
    (b) 3½
    (c) 4
    (d) 4½

46. The working space in front of the electric equipment shall not be less than _____ in. wide, or the width of the equipment, whichever is greater.

    (a) 15
    (b) 30
    (c) 40
    (d) 60

47. Equipment associated with the electrical installation can be located above or below other electrical equipment within their working space when the associated equipment does not extend more than _____ in. from the front of the electrical equipment.

    (a) 3
    (b) 6
    (c) 12
    (d) 30

48. The minimum height of working spaces about electrical equipment, switchboards, panelboards, or motor control centers operating at 1,000V, nominal, or less and likely to require examination, adjustment, servicing, or maintenance while energized shall be 6½ ft or the height of the equipment, whichever is greater, except for service equipment or panelboards in existing dwelling units that do not exceed 200A.

    (a) True
    (b) False

49. Where equipment operating at 1,000 volts, nominal, or less to ground and likely to require examination, adjustment, servicing, or maintenance while energized is required by installation instructions or function to be located in a space with limited access, and where equipment is installed above a lay-in ceiling, there shall be an opening not smaller than _____.

    (a) 6 in. x 6 in.
    (b) 12 in. x 12 in.
    (c) 22 in. x 22 in.
    (d) 22 in. x 30 in.

50. Where equipment operating at 1,000 volts, nominal, or less to ground and likely to require examination, adjustment, servicing, or maintenance while energized is required by installation instructions or function to be located in a space with limited access, the width of the working space shall be the width of the equipment enclosure or a minimum of _____ in., whichever is greater.

(a) 12
(b) 22
(c) 26
(d) 30

51. Where equipment operating at 1,000 volts, nominal, or less to ground and likely to require examination, adjustment, servicing, or maintenance while energized is required by installation instructions or function to be located in a space with limited access, all enclosure doors or hinged panels shall be capable of opening a minimum of _____ degrees.

(a) 60
(b) 90
(c) 120
(d) 180

52. Where equipment operating at 1,000 volts, nominal, or less to ground and likely to require examination, adjustment, servicing, or maintenance while energized is required by installation instructions or function to be located in a space with limited access, the space in front of the enclosure shall comply with the depth requirements of Table 110.26(A)(1).

(a) True
(b) False

53. Working space shall not be used for _____.

(a) storage
(b) raceways
(c) lighting
(d) accessibility

54. When normally enclosed live parts are exposed for inspection or servicing, the working space, if in a passageway or general open space, shall be suitably _____.

(a) accessible
(b) guarded
(c) open
(d) enclosed

55. For equipment rated 1,200A or more and over 6 ft wide that contains overcurrent devices, switching devices, or control devices, there shall be one entrance to and egress from the required working space not less than 24 in. wide and _____ ft high at each end of the working space.

(a) 5½
(b) 6
(c) 6½
(d) 7

56. For equipment rated 800A or more that contains overcurrent devices, switching devices, or control devices; and where the entrance to the working space has a personnel door(s) less than 25 ft from the nearest edge of the working space, the door shall _____.

(a) open either in or out with simple pressure and shall not have any lock
(b) open in the direction of egress and be equipped with listed panic hardware
(c) be equipped with a locking means
(d) be equipped with an electronic opener

57. Illumination shall be provided for all working spaces about service equipment, switchboards, switchgear, panelboards, or motor control centers _____.

(a) over 600V
(b) installed indoors
(c) rated 1,200A or more
(d) using automatic means of control

58. All switchboards, panelboards, and motor control centers shall be _____.

(a) located in dedicated spaces
(b) protected from damage
(c) in weatherproof enclosures
(d) a and b

59. The minimum height of dedicated equipment space for motor control centers installed indoors is _____ ft above the enclosure, or to the structural ceiling, whichever is lower.

(a) 3
(b) 5
(c) 6
(d) 6½

60. For indoor installations, piping, ducts, leak protection apparatus, or other equipment foreign to the electrical installation shall not be installed in the dedicated space above a panelboard or switchboard.

    (a) True
    (b) False

61. The dedicated equipment space for electrical equipment that is required for panelboards installed indoors is measured from the floor to a height of _____ ft above the equipment, or to the structural ceiling, whichever is lower.

    (a) 3
    (b) 6
    (c) 12
    (d) 30

62. The dedicated space above a panelboard extends to a dropped or suspended ceiling, which is considered a structural ceiling.

    (a) True
    (b) False

63. All switchboards, switchgear, panelboards, and motor control centers shall be located in dedicated spaces and protected from damage, and outdoor installations shall be _____.

    (a) installed in identified enclosures
    (b) protected from accidental contact by unauthorized personnel or by vehicular traffic
    (c) protected from accidental spillage or leakage from piping systems
    (d) all of these

64. All switchboards, switchgear, panelboards, and motor control centers shall be located in dedicated spaces and protected from damage and the working clearance space for outdoor installations shall include the zone described in _____.

    (a) 110.26(A)
    (b) 110.26(B)
    (c) 110.26(C)
    (d) 110.26(D)

65. All switchboards, switchgear, panelboards, and motor control centers shall be located in dedicated spaces and protected from damage and, for outdoor installations, the space equal to the width and depth of the equipment, and extending from grade to a height of _____ ft above the equipment, shall be dedicated to the electrical installation.

    (a) 2
    (b) 4
    (c) 6
    (d) 8

66. Electrical equipment rooms or enclosures housing electrical apparatus that are controlled by a lock(s) shall be considered _____ to qualified persons.

    (a) readily accessible
    (b) accessible
    (c) available
    (d) none of these

67. Live parts operating at 50V to 1,000V, nominal, shall be guarded by being _____.

    (a) located in a room accessible only to qualified persons
    (b) located on a balcony accessible only to qualified persons
    (c) elevated 8 ft or more above the floor or other working surface for 50V to 300V between ungrounded conductors
    (d) any of these

68. Live parts of electrical equipment operating at _____, nominal, shall be guarded against accidental contact by approved enclosures or by suitable permanent, substantial partitions or screens arranged so that only qualified persons have access to the space within reach of the live parts.

    (a) 20V to 40V
    (b) 30V to 100V
    (c) 50V to 1,000V
    (d) 100V to 10,000V

69. In locations where electrical equipment is likely to be exposed to _____, enclosures or guards shall be so arranged and of such strength as to prevent such damage.

    (a) corrosion
    (b) physical damage
    (c) magnetic fields
    (d) weather

70. Entrances to rooms and other guarded locations containing exposed live parts shall be marked with conspicuous _____ forbidding unqualified persons to enter.

    (a) warning signs
    (b) alarms
    (c) a and b
    (d) none of these

71. The term "rainproof" is typically used in conjunction with enclosure type(s) _____.

    (a) 3
    (b) 3R
    (c) 3RX
    (d) b and c

Mike Holt's Electrical Apprenticeship Year 1 Supplement, Based on the 2017 NEC

ARTICLE 250

GROUNDING AND BONDING

Introduction to Article 250—Grounding and Bonding

No other article can match Article 250 for misapplication, violation, and misinterpretation. Terminology used in this article has been a source for much confusion, but that's improved during the last few *NEC* revisions. It's very important to understand the difference between grounding and bonding in order to correctly apply the provisions of Article 250. Pay careful attention to the definitions that apply to grounding and bonding both here and in Article 100 as you begin the study of this important article. Article 250 covers the grounding requirements for providing a path to the earth to reduce overvoltage from lightning, and the bonding requirements for a low-impedance fault current path back to the source of the electrical supply to facilitate the operation of overcurrent protection devices in the event of a ground fault.

Over the past several *Code* cycles, this article was extensively revised to organize it better and make it easier to understand and implement. It's arranged in a logical manner, so it's a good idea to just read through Article 250 to get a big picture view—after you review the definitions. Next, study the article closely so you understand the details. The illustrations will help you understand the key points.

Part I. General

250.1 Scope

Article 250 contains the following grounding and bonding requirements:

(1) What systems and equipment are required to be grounded.

(3) Location of grounding connections.

(4) Types of electrodes and sizes of grounding and bonding conductors.

(5) Methods of grounding and bonding.

250.2 Definition

Bonding Jumper, Supply-Side. The conductor on the supply side of the service or separately derived system overcurrent protection device that ensures electrical conductivity between metal parts and the grounded conductor. ▶Figure 250–1, ▶Figure 250–2, and ▶Figure 250–3

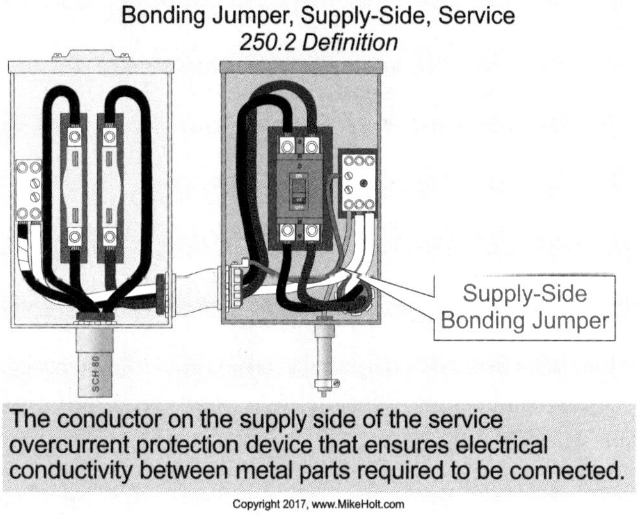

Bonding Jumper, Supply-Side, Service
250.2 Definition

Supply-Side
Bonding Jumper

The conductor on the supply side of the service overcurrent protection device that ensures electrical conductivity between metal parts required to be connected.

Copyright 2017, www.MikeHolt.com

▶Figure 250–1

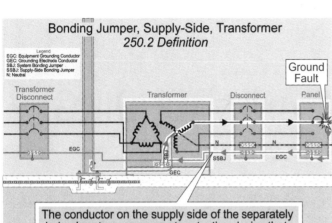

Figure 250–2

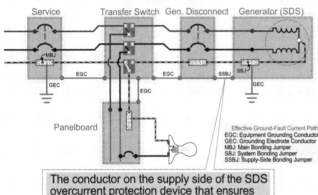

Figure 250–3

250.8 Termination of Grounding and Bonding Conductors

(A) Permitted Methods. Equipment grounding conductors, grounding electrode conductors, and bonding jumpers must terminate in one or more of the following methods:

(1) Listed pressure connectors

(2) Terminal bars

(3) Pressure connectors listed for grounding and bonding

(4) Exothermic welding

(5) Machine screws that engage at least two threads or are secured with a nut ▶Figure 250–4

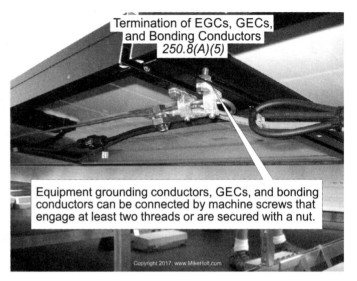

Figure 250–4

(6) Self-tapping machine screws that engage at least two threads ▶Figure 250–5

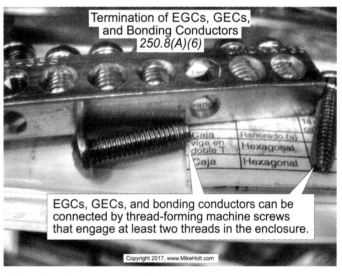

Figure 250–5

(7) Connections that are part of a listed assembly

(8) Other listed means

(B) Methods Not Permitted. Connection devices or fittings that depend solely on solder aren't allowed.

250.10 Protection of Fittings

Where subject to physical damage, grounding and bonding fittings must be protected by enclosing the fittings in metal, wood, or an equivalent protective covering. ▶Figure 250–6

Protection of Ground Clamps and Fittings
250.10

Ground fittings exposed to physical damage must be protected.

Copyright 2017, www.MikeHolt.com

▶Figure 250–6

250.12 Clean Surfaces

Nonconductive coatings, such as paint, must be removed to ensure good electrical continuity, or the termination fittings must be designed so as to make such removal unnecessary [250.53(A) and 250.96(A)].

Author's Comment:

■ Tarnish on copper water pipe needn't be removed before making a termination.

Part III. Grounding Electrode System and Grounding Electrode Conductor

250.50 Grounding Electrode System

Any grounding electrodes described in 250.52(A)(1) through (A)(7) that are present at a building must be bonded together to form the grounding electrode system. ▶Figure 250–7

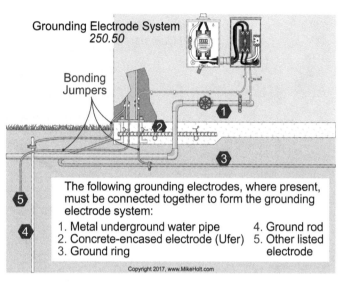

Grounding Electrode System
250.50

Bonding Jumpers

The following grounding electrodes, where present, must be connected together to form the grounding electrode system:
1. Metal underground water pipe
2. Concrete-encased electrode (Ufer)
3. Ground ring
4. Ground rod
5. Other listed electrode

Copyright 2017, www.MikeHolt.com

▶Figure 250–7

Ex: Concrete-encased electrodes aren't required for existing buildings where the conductive steel reinforcing bars aren't accessible without chipping up the concrete. ▶Figure 250–8

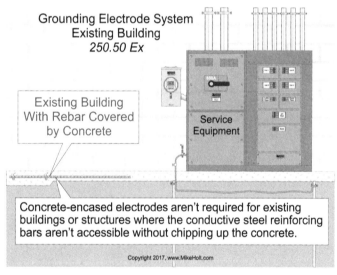

Grounding Electrode System
Existing Building
250.50 Ex

Existing Building With Rebar Covered by Concrete

Service Equipment

Concrete-encased electrodes aren't required for existing buildings or structures where the conductive steel reinforcing bars aren't accessible without chipping up the concrete.

Copyright 2017, www.MikeHolt.com

▶Figure 250–8

Author's Comment:

■ When a concrete-encased electrode is used at a building that doesn't have an underground metal water pipe electrode, no additional electrode is required. ▶Figure 250–9

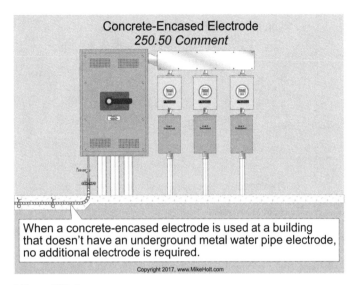

Concrete-Encased Electrode
250.50 Comment

When a concrete-encased electrode is used at a building that doesn't have an underground metal water pipe electrode, no additional electrode is required.

Copyright 2017, www.MikeHolt.com

▶Figure 250–9

250.52 Grounding Electrode Types

(A) Electrodes Permitted for Grounding.

(1) Underground Metal Water Pipe Electrode. Underground metal water pipe in direct contact with the earth for 10 ft or more can serve as a grounding electrode. ▶Figure 250–10

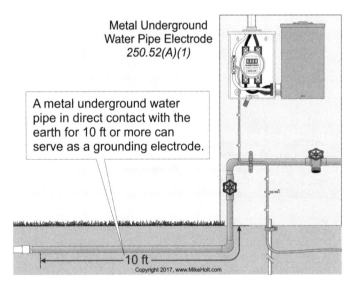

Metal Underground
Water Pipe Electrode
250.52(A)(1)

A metal underground water pipe in direct contact with the earth for 10 ft or more can serve as a grounding electrode.

10 ft

Copyright 2017, www.MikeHolt.com

▶Figure 250–10

Author's Comment:

- Controversy about using metal underground water piping as a grounding electrode has existed since the early 1900s. The water industry believes that neutral current flowing on water piping corrodes the metal. For more information, contact the American Water Works Association about their report—*Effects of Electrical Grounding on Pipe Integrity and Shock Hazard*, Catalog No. 90702, 1.800.926.7337. ▶Figure 250–11

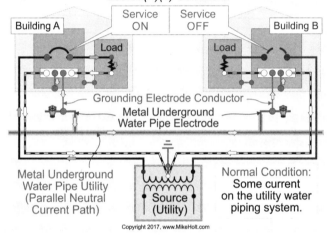

Neutral Current Flow on Metal Water Pipe
250.52(A)(1) Comment

Building A | Service ON | Service OFF | Building B
Load | | | Load

Grounding Electrode Conductor
Metal Underground Water Pipe Electrode

Metal Underground
Water Pipe Utility
(Parallel Neutral
Current Path)

Source
(Utility)

Normal Condition:
Some current
on the utility water
piping system.

Copyright 2017, www.MikeHolt.com

▶Figure 250–11

(2) Metal In-Ground Support Structure(s). Metal in-ground support structure(s) in direct contact with the earth vertically for 10 ft or more can serve as a grounding electrode. ▶Figure 250–12

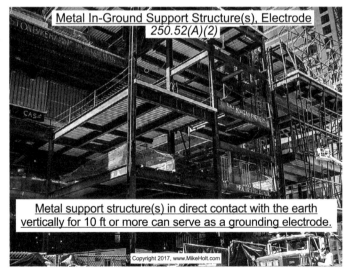

Metal In-Ground Support Structure(s), Electrode
250.52(A)(2)

Metal support structure(s) in direct contact with the earth vertically for 10 ft or more can serve as a grounding electrode.

Copyright 2017, www.MikeHolt.com

▶Figure 250–12

Note: Metal in-ground support structures include, but aren't limited to, pilings, casings, and other structural metal.

(3) Concrete-Encased Electrode. ▸Figure 250–13

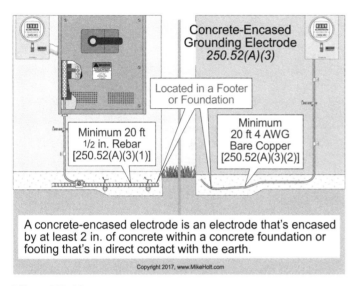

▸Figure 250–13

(1) One or more electrically conductive steel reinforcing bars of not less than ½ in. in diameter, mechanically connected together by steel tie wires, or other effective means to create a 20 ft or greater length can serve as a grounding electrode. ▸Figure 250–14

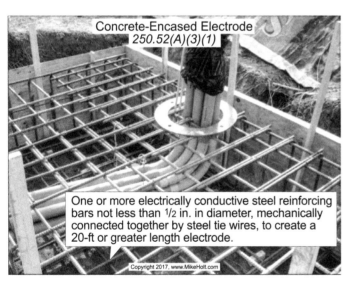

▸Figure 250–14

(2) Bare copper conductor not smaller than 4 AWG of 20 ft or greater length.

The reinforcing bars or bare copper conductor must be encased by at least 2 in. of concrete located horizontally within a concrete footing or vertically within a concrete foundation that's in direct contact with the earth can serve as a grounding electrode.

Where multiple concrete-encased electrodes are present at a building, only one is required to serve as a grounding electrode. ▸Figure 250–15

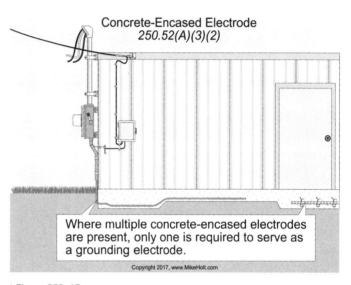

▸Figure 250–15

Note: Concrete separated from the earth because of insulation, vapor barriers, or similar items isn't considered to be in direct contact with the earth. ▸Figure 250–16

▸Figure 250–16

Author's Comment:

■ The grounding electrode conductor to a concrete-encased grounding electrode isn't required to be larger than 4 AWG copper [250.66(B)].

■ The concrete-encased grounding electrode is also called a "Ufer Ground," named after a consultant working for the U.S. Army during World War II. The technique Mr. Ufer came up with was necessary because the site needing grounding had no underground water table and little rainfall. The desert site was a series of bomb storage vaults in the area of Flagstaff, Arizona. This type of grounding electrode generally offers the lowest ground resistance for the cost.

(4) Ground Ring Electrode. A ground ring consisting of at least 20 ft of bare copper conductor not smaller than 2 AWG buried in the earth encircling a building, can serve as a grounding electrode. ▶Figure 250–17

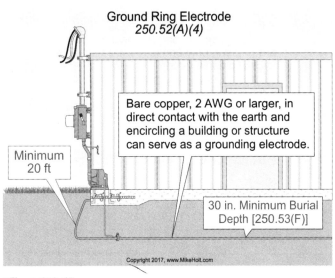

Ground Ring Electrode
250.52(A)(4)

Bare copper, 2 AWG or larger, in direct contact with the earth and encircling a building or structure can serve as a grounding electrode.

Minimum 20 ft

30 in. Minimum Burial Depth [250.53(F)]

Copyright 2017, www.MikeHolt.com

▶Figure 250–17

(5) Rod Electrode. Rod electrodes must have at less 8 ft in length in contact with the earth [250.53(G)].

(b) Rod-type electrodes must have a diameter of at least ⅝ in., unless listed. ▶Figure 250–18

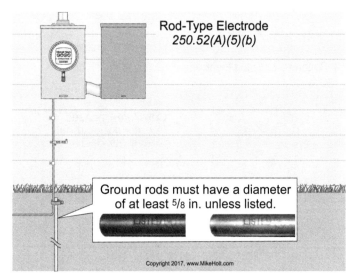

Rod-Type Electrode
250.52(A)(5)(b)

Ground rods must have a diameter of at least ⅝ in. unless listed.

Copyright 2017, www.MikeHolt.com

▶Figure 250–18

Author's Comment:

■ The grounding electrode conductor, if it's the sole connection to the rod(s), isn't required to be larger than 6 AWG copper [250.66(A)].

■ The diameter of a rod has an insignificant effect on the contact resistance of a rod(s) to the earth. However, larger diameter rods (¾ in. and 1 in.) are sometimes installed where mechanical strength is desired, or to compensate for the loss of the electrode's metal due to corrosion.

(6) Listed Electrode. Other listed grounding electrodes can serve as a grounding electrode.

(7) Plate Electrode. Bare or electrically conductive coated iron or steel plate with not less than ¼ in. of thickness, or a solid uncoated copper metal plate not less than 0.06 in. of thickness, with an exposed surface area of not less than 2 sq ft can serve as a grounding electrode.

(8) Metal Underground Systems. Metal underground systems, piping, and well casings can serve as a grounding electrode. ▶Figure 250–19

Author's Comment:

■ The grounding electrode conductor to the metal underground system must be sized in accordance with Table 250.66.

Underground Metal Piping Electrode
250.52(A)(8)

Metal underground systems, such as piping, and well casings can serve as grounding electrodes.

▶Figure 250–19

(B) Not Permitted for Use as a Grounding Electrode.

(1) Underground metal gas-piping systems aren't permitted to be used as a grounding electrode. ▶Figure 250–20

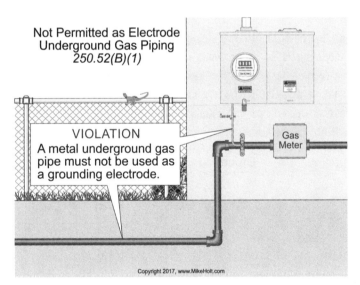

Not Permitted as Electrode
Underground Gas Piping
250.52(B)(1)

VIOLATION
A metal underground gas pipe must not be used as a grounding electrode.

Gas Meter

▶Figure 250–20

(2) Aluminum isn't permitted to be used as a grounding electrode.

(3) Swimming pool reinforcing steel for equipotential bonding in accordance with 680.26(B)(1) and 680.26(B)(2) isn't permitted to be used as a grounding electrode. ▶Figure 250–21

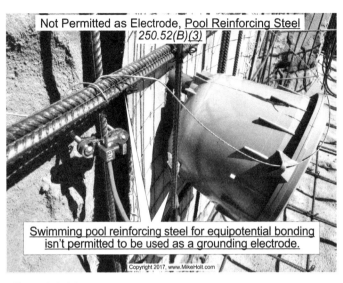

Not Permitted as Electrode, Pool Reinforcing Steel
250.52(B)(3)

Swimming pool reinforcing steel for equipotential bonding isn't permitted to be used as a grounding electrode.

▶Figure 250–21

250.53 Grounding Electrode Installation Requirements

(A) Rod Electrodes.

(1) Below Permanent Moisture Level. If practicable, pipe electrodes must be embedded below the permanent moisture level and be free from nonconductive coatings such as paint or enamel.

(2) Supplemental Electrode. A rod electrode must be supplemented by an additional electrode that's bonded to: ▶Figure 250–22

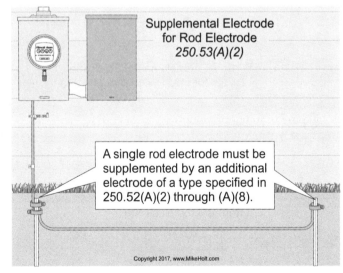

Supplemental Electrode
for Rod Electrode
250.53(A)(2)

A single rod electrode must be supplemented by an additional electrode of a type specified in 250.52(A)(2) through (A)(8).

▶Figure 250–22

(1) Another rod electrode

(2) The grounding electrode conductor

(3) The service neutral conductor

(4) A nonflexible metal service raceway

(5) The service disconnect

Ex: A single rod electrode having a contact resistance to the earth of 25 ohms or less isn't required to have a supplemental electrode.
▶Figure 250–23

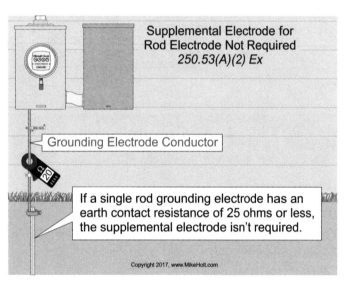

▶Figure 250–23

(3) Spacing. The supplemental electrode for a rod electrode must be installed not less than 6 ft from the rod electrode. ▶Figure 250–24

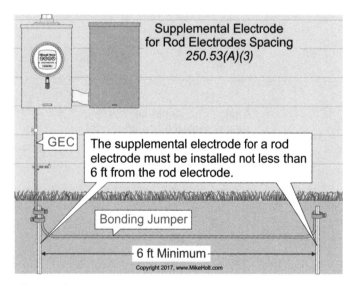

▶Figure 250–24

(B) Electrode Spacing. Electrodes for premises systems must be located no closer than 6 ft from lightning protection system grounding electrodes. Two or more grounding electrodes that are bonded together are considered a single grounding electrode system. ▶Figure 250–25

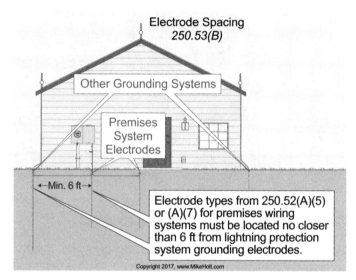

▶Figure 250–25

(C) Grounding Electrode Bonding Jumper. Grounding electrode bonding jumpers must be copper when within 18 in. of the earth [250.64(A)], be securely fastened to the surface, and be protected from physical damage [250.64(B)]. The bonding jumper to each electrode must be sized in accordance with 250.66. ▶Figure 250–26

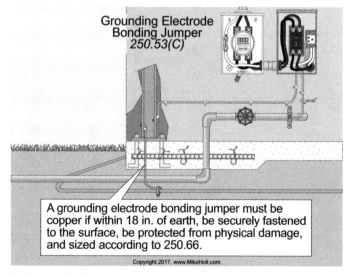

▶Figure 250–26

Author's Comment:

■ The grounding electrode bonding jumpers must terminate by any of the following means in accordance with 250.8(A):

   ◆ Listed pressure connectors

   ◆ Terminal bars

   ◆ Pressure connectors listed as grounding and bonding equipment

   ◆ Exothermic welding

   ◆ Machine screw-type fasteners that engage not less than two threads or are secured with a nut

   ◆ Thread-forming machine screws that engage not less than two threads in the enclosure

   ◆ Connections that are part of a listed assembly

   ◆ Other listed means

When the termination is encased in concrete or buried, the termination fittings must be listed for this purpose [250.70].

(D) Underground Metal Water Pipe Electrode.

(1) Interior Metal Water Piping. The bonding connection for the interior metal water piping system, as required by 250.104(A), isn't permitted to be dependent on water meters, filtering devices, or similar equipment likely to be disconnected for repairs or replacement. When necessary, a bonding jumper must be installed around insulated joints and equipment likely to be disconnected for repairs or replacement. ▶Figure 250–27

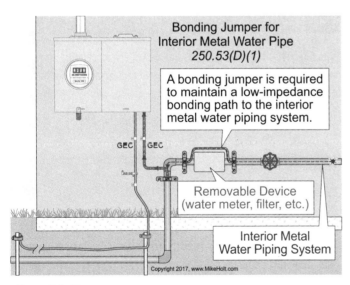

▶Figure 250–27

(2) Underground Metal Water Pipe Supplemental Electrode. When an underground metal water pipe grounding electrode is present, it must be used as part of the grounding electrode system [250.52(A)(1)], and it must be supplemented by any of the following electrodes:

   • Metal frame of the building electrode [250.52(A)(2)]

   • Concrete-encased electrode [250.52(A)(3)]

      ▶Figure 250–28

   • Rod electrode [250.52(A)(5)]

   • Other listed electrode [250.52(A)(6)]

   • Metal underground piping electrode [250.52(A)(8)]

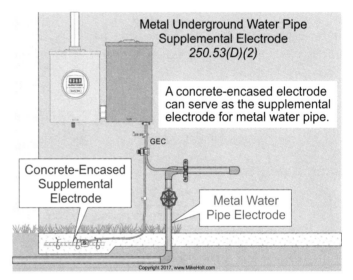

▶Figure 250–28

The supplemental grounding electrode conductor must terminate to any of the following: ▶Figure 250–29

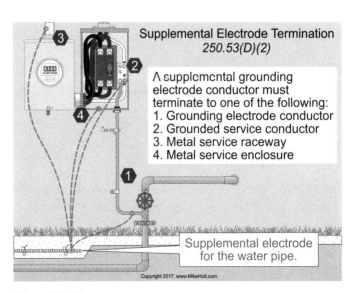

▶Figure 250–29

(1) Grounding electrode conductor

(2) Service neutral conductor

(3) Metal service raceway

(4) Service equipment enclosure

Ex: The supplemental electrode can be bonded to interior metal water piping located not more than 5 ft from the point of entrance to the building [250.68(C)(1)].

(E) Supplemental Rod Electrode. The grounding electrode conductor to a rod(s) that serves as a supplemental electrode isn't required to be larger than 6 AWG copper.

(F) Ground Ring. A bare 2 AWG or larger copper conductor installed not less than 30 in. below the surface of the earth encircling the building [250.52(A)(4)]. ▶Figure 250–30

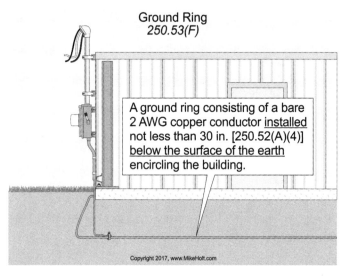

▶Figure 250–30

(G) Rod Electrodes. Rod electrodes must be installed so that not less than 8 ft of length is in contact with the soil. If rock bottom is encountered, the rod must be driven at an angle not to exceed 45 degrees from vertical. If rock bottom is encountered at an angle up to 45 degrees from vertical, the rod can be buried in a minimum 30 in. below the surface of the earth. ▶Figure 250–31

The upper end of the rod must be flush with or underground unless the grounding electrode conductor attachment is protected against physical damage as specified in 250.10.

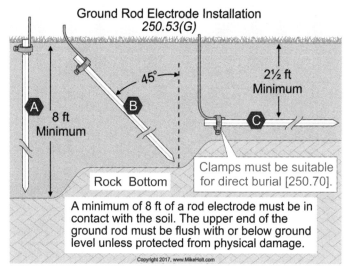

▶Figure 250–31

Author's Comment:

■ When the grounding electrode attachment fitting is located underground, it must be listed for direct soil burial [250.68(A) Ex 1 and 250.70].

Part VI. Equipment Grounding and Equipment Grounding Conductors

250.110 Fixed Equipment Connected by Permanent Wiring Methods—General

Exposed metal parts of fixed equipment likely to become energized must be connected to the circuit equipment grounding conductor where the equipment is:

(1) Within 8 ft vertically or 5 ft horizontally from the surface of the earth or a grounded metal object

(2) Located in a wet or damp location

(3) In electrical contact with metal

(4) In a hazardous (classified) location [Articles 500 through 517]

(5) Supplied by a wiring method that provides an equipment grounding conductor

(6) Supplied by a 277V or 480V circuit

Ex 3: Listed double-insulated equipment isn't required to be connected to the circuit equipment grounding conductor.

250.112 Specific Equipment Fastened in Place or Connected by Permanent Wiring Methods

To remove dangerous voltage from a ground fault, metal parts must be connected to the circuit equipment grounding conductor. ▶Figure 250–32

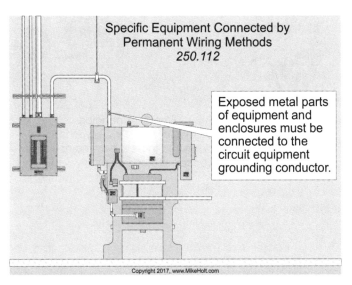

Specific Equipment Connected by Permanent Wiring Methods
250.112

Exposed metal parts of equipment and enclosures must be connected to the circuit equipment grounding conductor.

▶Figure 250–32

(I) Low-Voltage Circuits. Equipment supplied by circuits operating at less than 50V isn't required to be connected to the circuit equipment grounding conductor. ▶Figure 250–33

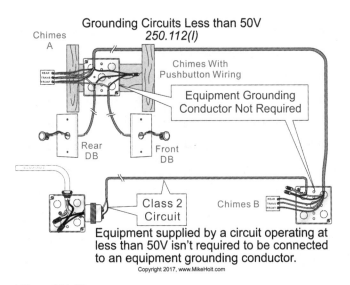

Grounding Circuits Less than 50V
250.112(I)

Chimes A

Chimes With Pushbutton Wiring

Equipment Grounding Conductor Not Required

Rear DB

Front DB

Class 2 Circuit

Chimes B

Equipment supplied by a circuit operating at less than 50V isn't required to be connected to an equipment grounding conductor.

▶Figure 250–33

250.114 Cord-and-Plug-Connected Equipment

To remove dangerous voltage from a ground fault, metal parts must be connected to the circuit equipment grounding conductor. ▶Figure 250–34

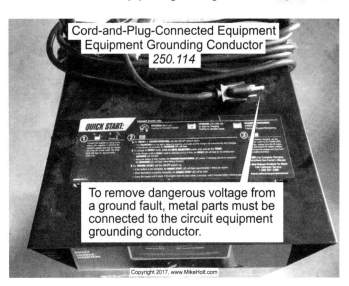

Cord-and-Plug-Connected Equipment
Equipment Grounding Conductor
250.114

To remove dangerous voltage from a ground fault, metal parts must be connected to the circuit equipment grounding conductor.

▶Figure 250–34

Ex: Listed double-insulated equipment isn't required to be connected to the circuit equipment grounding conductor.

250.118 Types of Equipment Grounding Conductors

An equipment grounding conductor can be any one or a combination of the following: ▶Figure 250–35

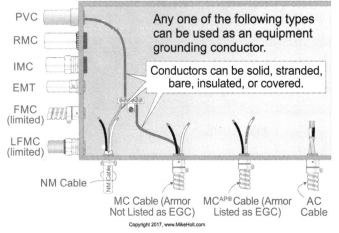

Types of Equipment Grounding Conductors (EGC)
250.118

PVC, RMC, IMC, EMT, FMC (limited), LFMC (limited)

Any one of the following types can be used as an equipment grounding conductor.

Conductors can be solid, stranded, bare, insulated, or covered.

NM Cable

MC Cable (Armor Not Listed as EGC) MC^AP® Cable (Armor Listed as EGC) AC Cable

▶Figure 250–35

Note: The equipment grounding conductor is intended to serve as part of the effective ground-fault current path. See 250.2. ▶Figure 250–36

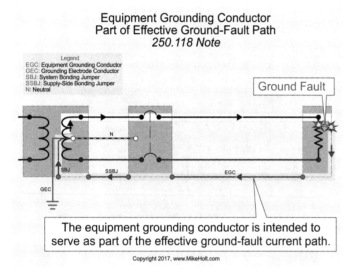

▶Figure 250–36

Author's Comment:

■ The effective ground-fault path is an intentionally constructed low-impedance conductive path designed to carry fault current from the point of a ground fault on a wiring system to the electrical supply source. Its purpose is to quickly remove dangerous voltage from a ground fault by opening the circuit overcurrent protection device [250.2]. ▶Figure 250–37

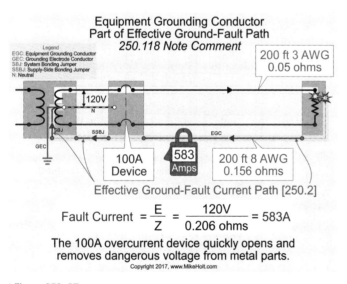

▶Figure 250–37

(1) An equipment grounding conductor of the wire type can be a bare or insulated copper or aluminum conductor. ▶Figure 250–38

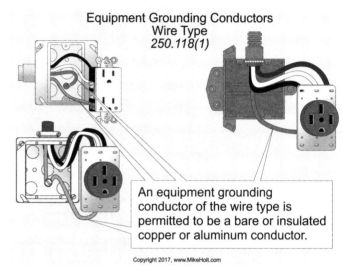

▶Figure 250–38

(2) Rigid metal conduit can serve as an equipment grounding conductor.

(3) Intermediate metal conduit can serve as an equipment grounding conductor.

(4) Electrical metallic tubing can serve as an equipment grounding conductor.

(5) Listed flexible metal conduit (FMC) can serve as an equipment grounding conductor where: ▶Figure 250–39

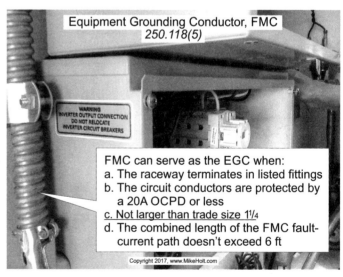

▶Figure 250–39

a. The raceway terminates in listed fittings.

b. The circuit conductors are protected by an overcurrent protection device rated 20A or less.

c. The size of the flexible metal conduit doesn't exceed trade size 1¼.

d. The combined length of the flexible conduit in the same ground-fault current path doesn't exceed 6 ft.

e. If flexibility is required to minimize the transmission of vibration from equipment or to provide flexibility for equipment that requires movement after installation, an equipment grounding conductor of the wire type must be installed with the circuit conductors in accordance with 250.102(E), and it must be sized in accordance with 250.122, based on the rating of the circuit overcurrent protection device. ▶Figure 250–40

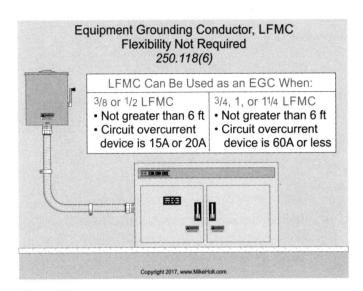

Equipment Grounding Conductor, LFMC
Flexibility Not Required
250.118(6)

LFMC Can Be Used as an EGC When:	
3/8 or 1/2 LFMC	3/4, 1, or 1¼ LFMC
• Not greater than 6 ft	• Not greater than 6 ft
• Circuit overcurrent device is 15A or 20A	• Circuit overcurrent device is 60A or less

Copyright 2017, www.MikeHolt.com

▶Figure 250–41

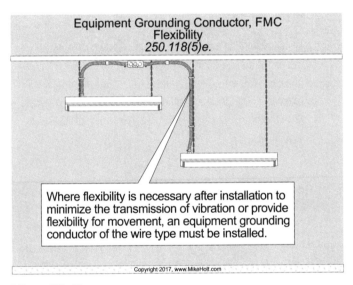

Equipment Grounding Conductor, FMC
Flexibility
250.118(5)e.

Where flexibility is necessary after installation to minimize the transmission of vibration or provide flexibility for movement, an equipment grounding conductor of the wire type must be installed.

Copyright 2017, www.MikeHolt.com

▶Figure 250–40

(6) Listed liquidtight flexible metal conduit (LFMC) can serve as an equipment grounding conductor where: ▶Figure 250–41

a. The raceway terminates in listed fittings.

b. For ⅜ in. through ½ in., the circuit conductors are protected by an overcurrent protection device rated 20A or less.

c. For ¾ in. through 1¼ in., the circuit conductors are protected by an overcurrent protection device rated 60A or less.

d. The combined length of the flexible conduit in the same ground-fault current path doesn't exceed 6 ft.

e. If flexibility is required to minimize the transmission of vibration from equipment or to provide flexibility for equipment that requires movement after installation, an equipment grounding conductor of the wire type must be installed with the circuit conductors in accordance with 250.102(E), and it must be sized in accordance with 250.122, based on the rating of the circuit overcurrent protection device.

(8) The sheath of Type AC cable containing an aluminum bonding strip can serve as an equipment grounding conductor. ▶Figure 250–42

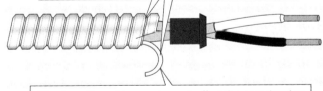

Equipment Grounding Conductor, Type AC Cable
250.118(8)

Type AC cable can be used as an equipment grounding conductor where the combination of the interlocking armor and the bonding strip provides a path for fault current [320.108].

The bonding strip can be cut off at the termination or it can be used to secure the anti-short bushing.

Copyright 2017, www.MikeHolt.com

▶Figure 250–42

Author's Comment:

■ The internal aluminum bonding strip isn't an equipment grounding conductor, but it allows the interlocked armor to serve as an equipment grounding conductor because it reduces the impedance of the armored spirals to ensure that a ground fault will be cleared. It's the aluminum bonding strip in combination with the cable armor that creates the circuit equipment grounding conductor. Once the bonding strip exits the cable, it can be cut off because it no longer serves any purpose.

■ The effective ground-fault current path must be maintained by the use of fittings specifically listed for Type AC cable [320.40]. See 300.12, 300.15, and 320.100.

(9) The copper sheath of Type MI cable can serve as an equipment grounding conductor.

(10) Type MC cable

    a. The interlock type cable that contains an insulated or uninsulated equipment grounding conductor in accordance with 250.118(1) can serve as an equipment grounding conductor. ▶Figure 250–43

Equipment Grounding Conductor
Type MC Cable
250.118(10)a

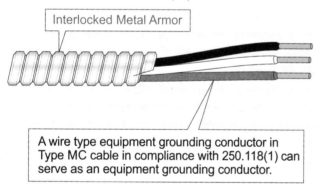

A wire type equipment grounding conductor in Type MC cable in compliance with 250.118(1) can serve as an equipment grounding conductor.

Copyright 2017, www.MikeHolt.com

▶Figure 250–43

    b. The combined metallic sheath and uninsulated equipment grounding/bonding conductor of interlocked metal that's listed and identified as an equipment grounding conductor can serve as an equipment grounding conductor. ▶Figure 250–44

Equipment Grounding Conductor
Type MC Cable
250.118(10)b

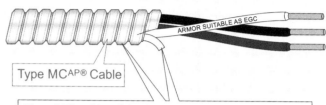

Type MC cable of the interlocked type can serve as an equipment grounding conductor if the combined metallic sheath and uninsulated equipment grounding/bonding conductor is listed and identified as an equipment grounding conductor.

Copyright 2017, www.MikeHolt.com

▶Figure 250–44

Author's Comment:

■ Once the bare aluminum grounding/bonding conductor exits the cable, it can be cut off because it no longer serves any purpose. The effective ground-fault current path must be maintained by the use of fittings specifically listed for Type MC^AP® cable [330.40]. See 300.12, 300.15, and 330.100. ▶Figure 250–45

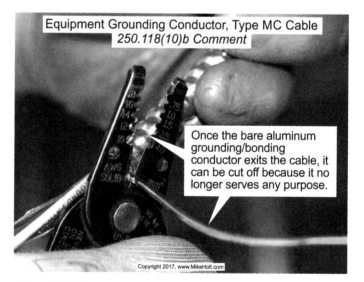

Equipment Grounding Conductor, Type MC Cable
250.118(10)b Comment

Once the bare aluminum grounding/bonding conductor exits the cable, it can be cut off because it no longer serves any purpose.

Copyright 2017, www.MikeHolt.com

▶Figure 250–45

    c. The metallic sheath of the smooth or corrugated tube-type MC cable that's listed and identified as an equipment grounding conductor can serve as an equipment grounding conductor.

(11) Metal cable trays can serve as an equipment grounding conductor if continuous maintenance and supervision ensure only qualified persons will service the cable tray, with cable tray and fittings identified for grounding and the cable tray, fittings [392.10], and raceways are bonded together using bolted mechanical connectors or bonding jumpers sized and installed in accordance with 250.102 [392.60]. ▶Figure 250–46

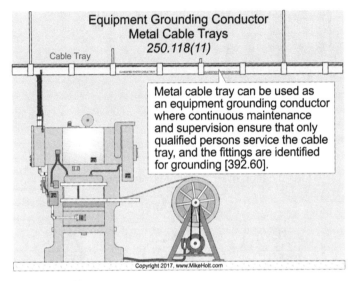

Equipment Grounding Conductor
Metal Cable Trays
250.118(11)

Cable Tray

Metal cable tray can be used as an equipment grounding conductor where continuous maintenance and supervision ensure that only qualified persons service the cable tray, and the fittings are identified for grounding [392.60].

Copyright 2017, www.MikeHolt.com

▶Figure 250–46

(13) Listed electrically continuous metal raceways, such as metal wireways [Article 376] or strut-type channel raceways [384.60] can serve as an equipment grounding conductor. ▶Figure 250–47

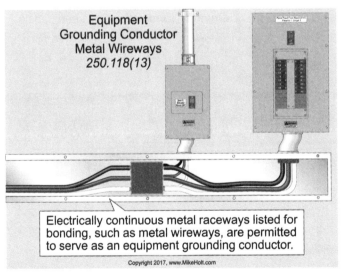

Equipment
Grounding Conductor
Metal Wireways
250.118(13)

Electrically continuous metal raceways listed for bonding, such as metal wireways, are permitted to serve as an equipment grounding conductor.

Copyright 2017, www.MikeHolt.com

▶Figure 250–47

(14) Surface metal raceways listed for grounding [Article 386] can serve as an equipment grounding conductor.

250.119 Identification of Equipment Grounding Conductors

Unless required to be insulated, equipment grounding conductors can be bare or covered. Insulated equipment grounding conductors 6 AWG and smaller must have a continuous outer finish that's either green or green with one or more yellow stripes. ▶Figure 250–48

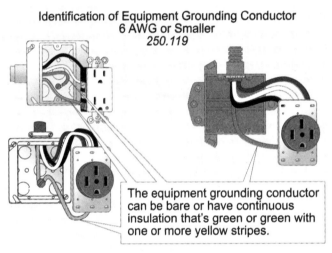

Identification of Equipment Grounding Conductor
6 AWG or Smaller
250.119

The equipment grounding conductor can be bare or have continuous insulation that's green or green with one or more yellow stripes.

Copyright 2017, www.MikeHolt.com

▶Figure 250–48

Conductors with insulation that's green, or green with one or more yellow stripes, aren't permitted be used for an ungrounded or neutral conductor. ▶Figure 250–49

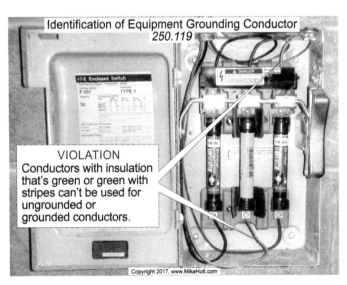

Identification of Equipment Grounding Conductor
250.119

VIOLATION
Conductors with insulation that's green or green with stripes can't be used for ungrounded or grounded conductors.

Copyright 2017, www.MikeHolt.com

▶Figure 250–49

Author's Comment:

■ The *NEC* neither requires nor prohibits the use of the color green for the identification of grounding electrode conductors. ▶Figure 250–50

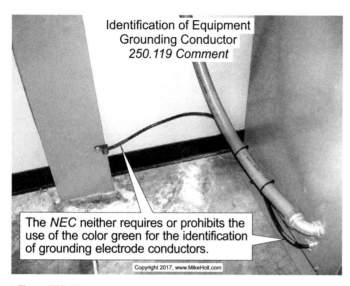

Identification of Equipment
Grounding Conductor
250.119 Comment

The *NEC* neither requires or prohibits the use of the color green for the identification of grounding electrode conductors.

▶Figure 250–50

Ex 3: Conductors with green insulation can be used as ungrounded signal conductors for traffic signal control and traffic signal indicating heads. The circuit must still include an equipment grounding conductor, and if it's of the wire type it must be bare or green with one or more yellow stripes.

(A) Conductors 4 AWG and Larger.

(1) Identified if Accessible. Insulated equipment grounding conductors 4 AWG and larger can be permanently reidentified at the time of installation at every point where the conductor is accessible. ▶Figure 250–51

Ex: Identification of equipment grounding conductors 4 AWG and larger in conduit bodies isn't required.

(2) Identification Method. ▶Figure 250–52

a. Removing the insulation at termination

b. Coloring the insulation green at termination

c. Marking the insulation at termination with green tape or green adhesive labels

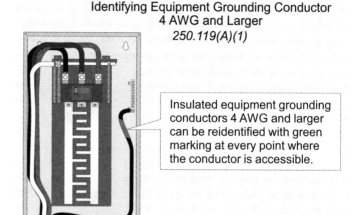

Identifying Equipment Grounding Conductor
4 AWG and Larger
250.119(A)(1)

Insulated equipment grounding conductors 4 AWG and larger can be reidentified with green marking at every point where the conductor is accessible.

Copyright 2017, www.MikeHolt.com

▶Figure 250–51

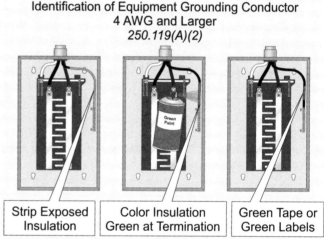

Identification of Equipment Grounding Conductor
4 AWG and Larger
250.119(A)(2)

| Strip Exposed Insulation | Color Insulation Green at Termination | Green Tape or Green Labels |

Copyright 2017, www.MikeHolt.com

▶Figure 250–52

250.120 Equipment Grounding Conductor Installation

An equipment grounding conductor must be installed as follows:

(A) Raceway, Cable Trays, Cable Armor, Cablebus, or Cable Sheaths. If it consists of a raceway, cable tray, cable armor, cablebus framework, or cable sheath, fittings for joints and terminations must be made tight using suitable tools.

(B) Aluminum Conductors. Aluminum equipment grounding conductors must comply with the following:

(1) Bare or covered aluminum equipment grounding conductors are not permitted to be in contact with masonry or earth.

(2) Aluminum equipment grounding conductors within 18 in. of the earth are permitted to terminate within listed enclosures identified for outdoor use.

(3) Aluminum equipment grounding conductors located outdoors must be insulated when within 18 in. of the earth. The terminal must be listed as a sealed wire-connector system for grounding and bonding equipment.

(C) Equipment Grounding Conductors Smaller Than 6 AWG. If not routed with circuit conductors as permitted in 250.130(C) and 250.134(B) Ex 2, equipment grounding conductors smaller than 6 AWG must be installed within a raceway or cable if subject to physical damage. ▶Figure 250–53

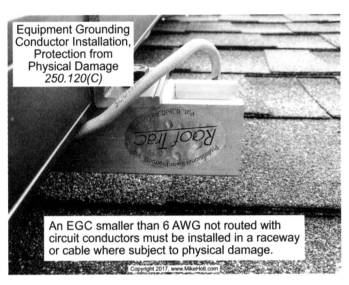

▶Figure 250–53

250.121 Use of Equipment Grounding Conductors

An equipment grounding conductor isn't permitted to be used as a grounding electrode conductor. ▶Figure 250–54

Ex: Equipment grounding conductors of the wire type can be used as a grounding electrode conductor provided they meet all of the rules for both.

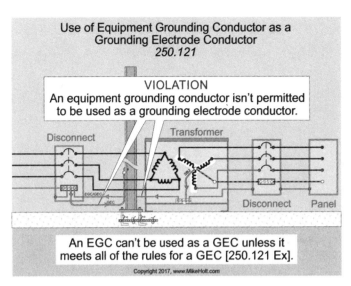

▶Figure 250–54

250.122 Sizing Equipment Grounding Conductor

(A) General. Equipment grounding conductors of the wire type must be sized not smaller than shown in Table 250.122, based on the rating of the circuit overcurrent protection device; however, the circuit equipment grounding conductor isn't required to be larger than the circuit conductors. ▶Figure 250–55 and ▶Figure 250–56

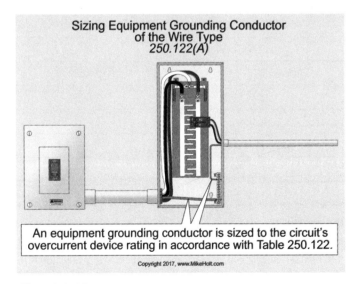

▶Figure 250–55

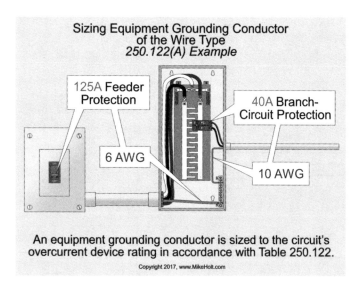

Sizing Equipment Grounding Conductor
of the Wire Type
250.122(A) Example

125A **Feeder Protection**

40A **Branch-Circuit Protection**

6 AWG

10 AWG

An equipment grounding conductor is sized to the circuit's overcurrent device rating in accordance with Table 250.122.

Copyright 2017, www.MikeHolt.com

▶Figure 250–56

Table 250.122 Sizing Equipment Grounding Conductor

Overcurrent Protection Device Rating	Copper Conductor
15A	14 AWG
20A	12 AWG
25A—60A	10 AWG
70A—100A	8 AWG
110A—200A	6 AWG
225A—300A	4 AWG
350A—400A	3 AWG
450A—500A	2 AWG
600A	1 AWG
700A—800A	1/0 AWG
1,000A	2/0 AWG
1,200A	3/0 AWG

(B) Increased in Size. If ungrounded conductors are increased in size for any reason from the minimum size that has sufficient ampacity for the intended installation before the application of any adjustment or correction factor(s), wire-type equipment grounding conductors must be at least proportionately increased in size according to the circular mil area of the ungrounded conductors.

Author's Comment:

■ Ungrounded conductors are sometimes increased in size to accommodate conductor voltage drop, harmonic current heating, short-circuit rating, or simply for future capacity.

Example: *If the ungrounded conductors for a 40A circuit (with 75°C terminals) are increased in size from 8 AWG to 6 AWG due to voltage drop, the circuit equipment grounding conductor must be increased in size from 10 AWG to what size?* ▶Figure 250–57

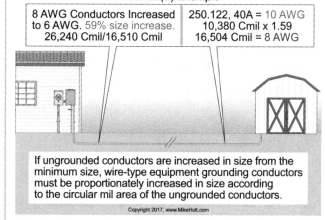

Size of Wire-Type Equipment Grounding Conductor
250.122(B) Example

8 AWG Conductors Increased to 6 AWG. 59% size increase. 26,240 Cmil/16,510 Cmil

250.122, 40A = 10 AWG
10,380 Cmil x 1.59
16,504 Cmil = 8 AWG

If ungrounded conductors are increased in size from the minimum size, wire-type equipment grounding conductors must be proportionately increased in size according to the circular mil area of the ungrounded conductors.

Copyright 2017, www.MikeHolt.com

▶Figure 250–57

Solution: *The circuit equipment grounding conductor must be increased to size 8 AWG.*

Conductor Size = 10,380 Cmil × 1.59
Conductor Size = 16,504 Cmil

Answer: *The circuit equipment grounding conductor must be increased to 8 AWG [Chapter 9, Table 8].*

The circular mil area of 6 AWG is 59 percent more than 8 AWG (26,240 Cmil/16,510 Cmil) [Chapter 9, Table 8]. According to Table 250.122, the circuit equipment grounding conductor for a 40A overcurrent protection device will be 10 AWG (10,380 Cmil), but the circuit equipment grounding conductor for this circuit must be increased in size by a multiplier of 1.59.

(C) Multiple Circuits. When multiple circuits are installed in the same raceway, cable, or cable tray, one equipment grounding conductor sized in accordance with 250.122, based on the rating of the largest circuit overcurrent protection device is sufficient. ▶Figure 250–58 and ▶Figure 250–59

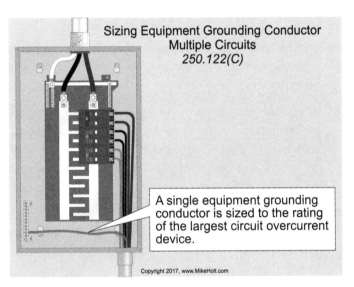

Figure 250–58

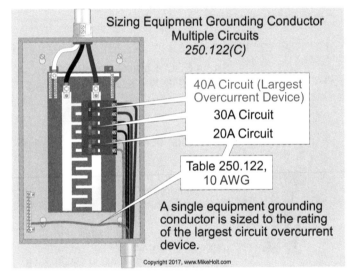

Figure 250–59

(D) Motor Branch Circuits.

(1) General. The equipment grounding conductor of the wire type must be sized in accordance with Table 250.122, based on the rating of the motor circuit branch-circuit short-circuit and ground-fault overcurrent protection device, but this conductor isn't required to be larger than the circuit conductors [250.122(A)]. ▶Figure 250–60

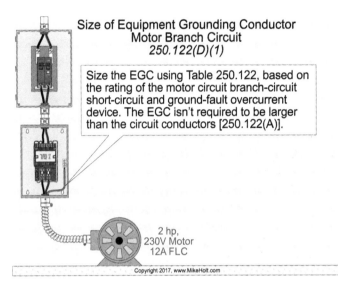

Figure 250–60

Example: *What size equipment grounding conductor of the wire type is required for a 14 AWG motor branch circuit [430.22], protected with a 2-pole, 30A circuit breaker in accordance with 430.22 and 430.52(C)(1)?* ▶Figure 250–61

Answer: *The equipment grounding conductor isn't required to be larger than the 14 AWG motor branch circuit conductors [250.122(D)(1) and 250.122(A)].*

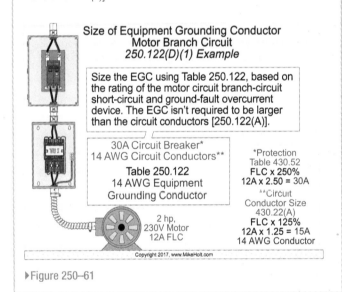

Figure 250–61

(F) Parallel Runs. If circuit conductors are installed in parallel as permitted by 310.10(H), an equipment grounding conductor must be installed for each parallel conductor set in accordance with the following:

(1) Raceways or Cable Trays.

(a) Parallel Feeder Runs in a Single Raceway or Cable Tray. The single wire-type equipment grounding conductor is required in each raceway or cable tray. It must be sized in accordance with Table 250.122, based on the rating of the circuit overcurrent protection device.

(b) Parallel Feeder Runs in Multiple Raceways. The equipment grounding conductor in each parallel run raceway must be sized in accordance with Table 250.122, based on the rating of the feeder overcurrent protection device. ▶Figure 250–62 and ▶Figure 250–63

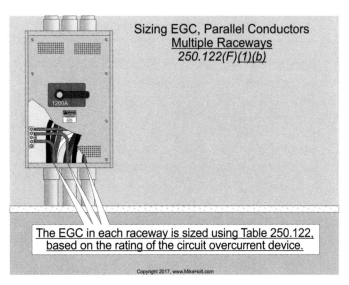

The EGC in each raceway is sized using Table 250.122, based on the rating of the circuit overcurrent device.

▶Figure 250–62

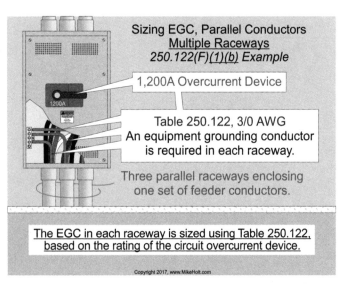

The EGC in each raceway is sized using Table 250.122, based on the rating of the circuit overcurrent device.

▶Figure 250–63

(2) Parallel Feeder Runs Using Multiconductor Cables.

(a) Multiconductor cables used in parallel must have the equipment grounding conductors of all cables electrically paralleled with each other.

(b) Parallel multiconductor cables in a single raceway or cable tray are permitted to have a single equipment grounding conductor connected to the equipment grounding conductors within the multiconductor cables. This single equipment grounding conductor must be sized in accordance with 250.122, based on the rating of the feeder overcurrent protection device.

(c) Equipment grounding conductors installed in cable trays must comply with 392.10(B)(1)(c).

(d) Parallel multiconductor cables not installed in a raceway or cable tray must have an equipment grounding conductor of the wire type in each cable sized in accordance with 250.122, based on the rating of the circuit overcurrent protection device. ▶Figure 250–64

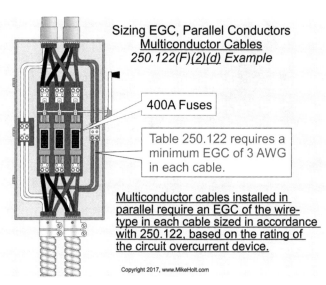

400A Fuses

Table 250.122 requires a minimum EGC of 3 AWG in each cable.

Multiconductor cables installed in parallel require an EGC of the wire-type in each cable sized in accordance with 250.122, based on the rating of the circuit overcurrent device.

▶Figure 250–64

(G) Feeder Tap Conductors. Equipment grounding conductors for feeder taps must be sized in accordance with Table 250.122, based on the ampere rating of the overcurrent protection device ahead of the feeder, but in no case is it required to be larger than the feeder tap conductors. ▶Figure 250–65

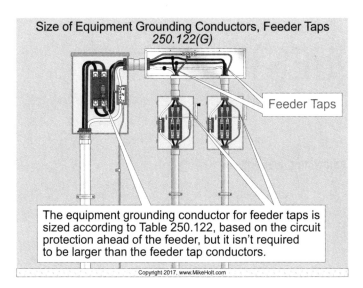

Size of Equipment Grounding Conductors, Feeder Taps
250.122(G)

Feeder Taps

The equipment grounding conductor for feeder taps is sized according to Table 250.122, based on the circuit protection ahead of the feeder, but it isn't required to be larger than the feeder tap conductors.

Copyright 2017, www.MikeHolt.com

▶Figure 250–65

ARTICLE
250

PRACTICE QUESTIONS

Please use the 2017 _Code_ book to answer the following questions.

Part I. General

1. A conductor installed on the supply side of a service or within a service equipment enclosure, or for a separately derived system, to ensure the required electrical conductivity between metal parts required to be electrically connected is known as the "____."

    (a) supply-side bonding jumper
    (b) ungrounded conductor
    (c) electrical supply source
    (d) grounding electrode conductor

2. Equipment grounding conductors, grounding electrode conductors, and bonding jumpers shall be connected by ____.

    (a) listed pressure connectors
    (b) terminal bars
    (c) exothermic welding
    (d) any of these

3. Grounding and bonding connection devices that depend solely on ____ shall not be used.

    (a) pressure connections
    (b) solder
    (c) lugs
    (d) approved clamps

4. Ground clamps and fittings that are exposed to physical damage shall be enclosed in ____ or equivalent protective covering.

    (a) metal
    (b) wood
    (c) concrete
    (d) a or b

5. ____ on equipment to be grounded shall be removed from contact surfaces to ensure good electrical continuity.

    (a) Paint
    (b) Lacquer
    (c) Enamel
    (d) any of these

Part III. Grounding Electrode System and Grounding Electrode Conductor

6. Concrete-encased electrodes of ____ shall not be required to be part of the grounding electrode system where the steel reinforcing bars or rods aren't accessible for use without disturbing the concrete.

    (a) hazardous (classified) locations
    (b) health care facilities
    (c) existing buildings or structures
    (d) agricultural buildings with equipotential planes

7. In order for a metal underground water pipe to be used as a grounding electrode, it shall be in direct contact with the earth for ____.

    (a) 5 ft
    (b) 10 ft or more
    (c) less than 10 ft
    (d) 20 ft or more

8. One or more metal in-ground support structure(s) in direct contact with the earth vertically for _____ ft or more, with or without concrete encasement is permitted to be a grounding electrode in accordance with 250.52.

   (a) 4
   (b) 6
   (c) 8
   (d) 10

9. A bare 4 AWG copper conductor installed horizontally near the bottom or vertically, and within that portion of a concrete foundation or footing that is in direct contact with the earth, can be used as a grounding electrode when the conductor is at least _____ ft in length.

   (a) 10
   (b) 15
   (c) 20
   (d) 25

10. An electrode encased by at least 2 in. of concrete, located horizontally near the bottom or vertically and within that portion of a concrete foundation or footing that is in direct contact with the earth, shall be permitted as a grounding electrode when it consists of _____.

   (a) at least 20 ft of ½ in. or larger steel reinforcing bars or rods
   (b) at least 20 ft of bare copper conductor of 4 AWG or larger
   (c) a or b
   (d) none of these

11. Reinforcing bars for use as a concrete-encased electrode can be bonded together by the usual steel tie wires or other effective means.

   (a) True
   (b) False

12. Where more than one concrete-encased electrode is present at a building or structure, it shall be permitted to bond only one into the grounding electrode system.

   (a) True
   (b) False

13. A ground ring encircling the building or structure can be used as a grounding electrode when the _____.

   (a) ring is in direct contact with the earth
   (b) ring consists of at least 20 ft of bare copper conductor
   (c) bare copper conductor is not smaller than 2 AWG
   (d) all of these

14. Grounding electrodes of the rod type less than _____ in. in diameter shall be listed.

   (a) ½
   (b) ⅝
   (c) ¾
   (d) 1

15. A buried iron or steel plate used as a grounding electrode shall expose not less than _____ sq ft of surface area to exterior soil.

   (a) 2
   (b) 4
   (c) 9
   (d) 10

16. Grounding electrodes of bare or electrically conductive coated iron or steel plates shall be at least _____ in. thick.

   (a) ⅛
   (b) ¼
   (c) ½
   (d) ¾

17. Local metal underground systems or structures such as _____ are permitted to serve as grounding electrodes.

   (a) piping systems
   (b) underground tanks
   (c) underground metal well casings that are not bonded to a metal water pipe
   (d) all of these

18. _____ shall not be used as grounding electrodes.

   (a) Metal underground gas piping systems
   (b) Aluminum
   (c) Metal well casings
   (d) a and b

19. Swimming pool structures and structural _____ [680.26(B)(1) and (B)(2)] shall not be used as a grounding electrode.

    (a) reinforcing steel
    (b) equipotential planes
    (c) a or b
    (d) none of these

20. Where practicable, rod, pipe, and plate electrodes shall be installed _____.

    (a) directly below the electrical meter
    (b) on the north side of the building
    (c) below permanent moisture level
    (d) all of these

21. Where the resistance-to-ground of 25 ohms or less is not achieved for a single rod electrode, _____.

    (a) other means besides electrodes shall be used in order to provide grounding
    (b) the single rod electrode shall be supplemented by one additional electrode
    (c) no additional electrodes are required
    (d) none of these

22. Two or more grounding electrodes bonded together are considered a single grounding electrode system.

    (a) True
    (b) False

23. Where a metal underground water pipe is used as a grounding electrode, the continuity of the grounding path or the bonding connection to interior piping shall not rely on _____ and similar equipment.

    (a) bonding jumpers
    (b) water meters or filtering devices
    (c) grounding clamps
    (d) all of these

24. Where the supplemental electrode is a rod, that portion of the bonding jumper that is the sole connection to the supplemental grounding electrode shall not be required to be larger than _____ AWG copper wire.

    (a) 8
    (b) 6
    (c) 4
    (d) 1

25. When a ground ring is used as a grounding electrode, it shall be installed at a depth below the earth's surface of not less than _____.

    (a) 18 in.
    (b) 24 in.
    (c) 30 in.
    (d) 8 ft

26. Ground rod electrodes shall be installed so that at least _____ of the length is in contact with the soil.

    (a) 5 ft
    (b) 8 ft
    (c) one-half
    (d) 80 percent

27. Where rock bottom is encountered when driving a ground rod at an angle up to 45 degrees, the electrode can be buried in a trench that is at least _____ deep.

    (a) 18 in.
    (b) 30 in.
    (c) 4 ft
    (d) 8 ft

28. The upper end of a ground rod electrode shall be _____ ground level unless the aboveground end and the grounding electrode conductor attachment are protected against physical damage.

    (a) above
    (b) flush with
    (c) below
    (d) b or c

Part VI. Equipment Grounding and Equipment Grounding Conductors

29. Exposed normally noncurrent-carrying metal parts of fixed equipment likely to become energized shall be connected to the equipment grounding conductor where located _____.

    (a) within 8 ft vertically or 5 ft horizontally of ground or grounded metal objects and subject to contact by persons
    (b) in wet or damp locations and not isolated
    (c) in electrical contact with metal
    (d) any of these

30. Listed FMC can be used as the equipment grounding conductor if the length in any ground return path does not exceed 6 ft and the circuit conductors contained in the conduit are protected by overcurrent devices rated at _____ or less.

    (a) 15A
    (b) 20A
    (c) 30A
    (d) 60A

31. Listed FMC can be used as the equipment grounding conductor if the conduit does not exceed trade size _____.

    (a) 1¼
    (b) 1½
    (c) 2
    (d) 2¼

32. Listed FMC and LFMC shall contain an equipment grounding conductor if the raceway is installed for the reason of _____.

    (a) physical protection
    (b) flexibility after installation
    (c) minimizing transmission of vibration from equipment
    (d) b or c

33. The *NEC* requires the installation of an equipment grounding conductor of the wire type in _____.

    (a) rigid metal conduit (RMC)
    (b) intermediate metal conduit (IMC)
    (c) electrical metallic tubing (EMT)
    (d) none of these

34. Listed liquidtight flexible metal conduit (LFMC) is acceptable as an equipment grounding conductor when it terminates in listed fittings and is protected by an overcurrent device rated 60A or less for trade sizes ⅜ through ½.

    (a) True
    (b) False

35. The armor of Type AC cable is recognized by the *NEC* as an equipment grounding conductor.

    (a) True
    (b) False

36. Type MC cable provides an effective ground-fault current path and is recognized by the *NEC* as an equipment grounding conductor when _____.

    (a) it contains an insulated or uninsulated equipment grounding conductor in compliance with 250.118(1)
    (b) the combined metallic sheath and uninsulated equipment grounding/bonding conductor of interlocked metal tape-type MC cable is listed and identified as an equipment grounding conductor
    (c) only when it is hospital grade Type MC cable
    (d) a or b

37. An equipment grounding conductor shall be identified by _____.

    (a) a continuous outer finish that is green
    (b) being bare
    (c) a continuous outer finish that is green with one or more yellow stripes
    (d) any of these

38. Conductors with the color _____ insulation shall not be used for ungrounded or grounded conductors.

    (a) green
    (b) green with one or more yellow stripes
    (c) a or b
    (d) white

39. A wire-type equipment grounding conductor is permitted to be used as a grounding electrode conductor if it meets all of the requirements of Parts II, III, and VI of Article 250.

    (a) True
    (b) False

40. Equipment grounding conductors of the wire type shall not be required to be larger than the circuit conductors.

    (a) True
    (b) False

41. When ungrounded circuit conductors are increased in size to account for voltage drop, the wire-type equipment grounding conductor shall be proportionately increased in size according to the increase in size of the ungrounded conductors using their _____.

    (a) ampacity
    (b) circular mil area
    (c) diameter
    (d) none of these

42. When a single equipment grounding conductor is used for multiple circuits in the same raceway, cable, or cable tray, the single equipment grounding conductor shall be sized according to the _____.

    (a) combined rating of all the overcurrent devices
    (b) largest overcurrent device of the multiple circuits
    (c) combined rating of all the loads
    (d) any of these

43. Equipment grounding conductors for motor branch circuits shall be sized in accordance with Table 250.122, based on the rating of the _____ device.

    (a) motor overload
    (b) motor over-temperature
    (c) branch-circuit short-circuit and ground-fault protective
    (d) feeder overcurrent protection

44. If circuit conductors are installed in parallel in the same raceway or cable tray, a single wire-type conductor shall be permitted as the equipment grounding conductor and sized in accordance with 250.122, based on the _____.

    (a) feeder
    (b) branch circuit
    (c) overcurrent protective device
    (d) none of these

45. Where circuit conductors are installed in parallel in multiple raceways or cables and include an EGC of the wire type, the equipment grounding conductor shall be installed in parallel in each raceway or cable, sized in compliance with 250.122 based on the overcurrent protective device for the feeder or branch circuit.

    (a) True
    (b) False

46. If multiconductor cables are installed in parallel in the same raceway, auxiliary gutter, or cable tray, _____ equipment grounding conductor(s) that is(are) sized in accordance with 250.122 shall be permitted in combination with the equipment grounding conductors provided within the multiconductor cables and shall all be connected together.

    (a) one
    (b) two
    (c) three
    (d) four

47. Except as provided in 250.122(F)(2)(b) for raceway or cable tray installations, the equipment grounding conductor in each multiconductor cable shall be sized in accordance with 250.122 based on the _____.

    (a) largest circuit conductor
    (b) overcurrent protective device for the feeder or branch circuit
    (c) smallest branch-circuit conductor
    (d) overcurrent protective device for the service

48. Equipment grounding conductors for feeder taps are not required to be larger than the tap conductors.

    (a) True
    (b) False

ARTICLE 300

GENERAL REQUIREMENTS FOR WIRING METHODS AND MATERIALS

Introduction to Article 300—General Requirements for Wiring Methods and Materials

Article 300 contains the general requirements for all wiring methods included in the *NEC*. However, it doesn't apply to communications systems (twisted wire, antennas, and coaxial cable), which are covered in Chapter 8, except when Article 300 is specifically referenced in Chapter 8.

This article is primarily concerned with how to install, route, splice, protect, and secure conductors and raceways. How well you conform to the requirements of Article 300 will generally be evident in the finished work, because many of the requirements tend to determine the appearance of the installation. Because of this, it's often easy to spot Article 300 problems if you're looking for *Code* violations. For example, you can easily see when someone runs an equipment grounding conductor outside a raceway instead of grouping all conductors of a circuit together, as required by 300.3(B).

A good understanding of Article 300 will start you on the path to correctly installing the wiring methods included in Chapter 3. Be sure to carefully consider the accompanying illustrations, and refer to the definitions in Article 100 as needed.

Part I. General

300.1 Scope

(A) Wiring Installations. Article 300 contains the general requirements for wiring methods and materials for power and lighting. ▶Figure 300–1

Author's Comment:

■ The requirements contained in Article 300 don't apply to the wiring methods for Class 2 and 3 circuits, fire alarm circuits, and communications systems (twisted wire, antennas, and coaxial cable), except where there's a specific reference in Chapters 7 or 8 to a rule in Article 300.

  ◆ Class 2 and 3 Remote Control and Signaling, 725.3
  ◆ Communications Cables and Raceways, 800.133(A)(2)
  ◆ Coaxial Circuits, 820.3
  ◆ Fire Alarm Circuits, 760.3

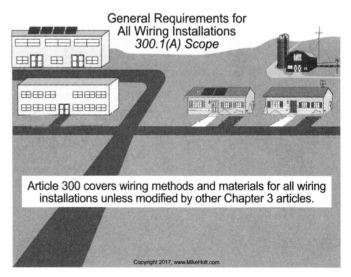

General Requirements for
All Wiring Installations
300.1(A) Scope

Article 300 covers wiring methods and materials for all wiring installations unless modified by other Chapter 3 articles.

Copyright 2017, www.MikeHolt.com

▶Figure 300–1

(B) Integral Parts of Equipment. The requirements contained in Article 300 don't apply to the internal parts of electrical equipment. ▶**Figure 300–2**

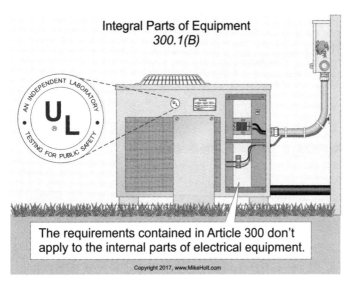

Integral Parts of Equipment
300.1(B)

The requirements contained in Article 300 don't apply to the internal parts of electrical equipment.

Copyright 2017, www.MikeHolt.com

▶Figure 300–2

(C) Trade Sizes. Designators for raceway trade sizes are given in Table 300.1(C).

Author's Comment:

■ Industry practice is to describe raceways using inch sizes, such as ½ in., 2 in., and so on; however, the proper reference is to use "Trade Size ½," or "Trade Size 2." In this textbook we use the term "Trade Size."

300.3 Conductors

(A) Conductors. Single conductors must be installed within a Chapter 3 wiring method, such as a raceway, cable, or enclosure. ▶**Figure 300–3**

Ex: Overhead conductors can be installed in accordance with 225.6.

(B) Circuit Conductors Grouped Together. Conductors of a circuit and, where used, the neutral and equipment grounding and bonding conductors must be installed in the same raceway, cable, trench, cord, or cable tray, except as permitted by (1) through (4).

(1) Paralleled Installations. Conductors installed in parallel in accordance with 310.10(H) must have all circuit conductors within the same raceway, cable tray, trench, or cable. ▶**Figure 300–4**

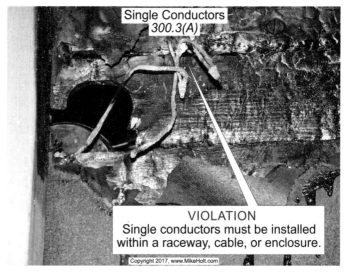

Single Conductors
300.3(A)

VIOLATION
Single conductors must be installed within a raceway, cable, or enclosure.

Copyright 2017, www.MikeHolt.com

▶Figure 300–3

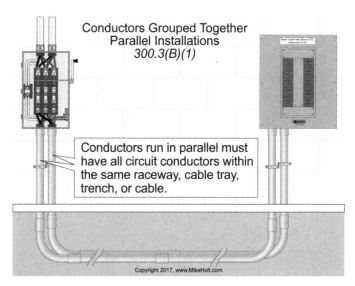

Conductors Grouped Together
Parallel Installations
300.3(B)(1)

Conductors run in parallel must have all circuit conductors within the same raceway, cable tray, trench, or cable.

Copyright 2017, www.MikeHolt.com

▶Figure 300–4

Author's Comment:

■ To minimize induction heating of ferrous metal raceways and ferrous metal enclosures for alternating-current circuits, and to maintain an effective ground-fault current path, all conductors of a circuit must be installed in the same raceway, cable, trench, cord, or cable tray. See 250.102(E), 300.3(B), 300.5(I), 300.20(A), and 392.8(D). ▶**Figure 300–5** and ▶**Figure 300–6**

Ex: Parallel phase and neutral conductors can be installed in individual underground nonmetallic raceways (Phase A in raceway 1, Phase B in raceway 2, and so forth) as permitted by 300.5(I) Ex 2, if the installation complies with 300.20(B). ▶**Figure 300–7**

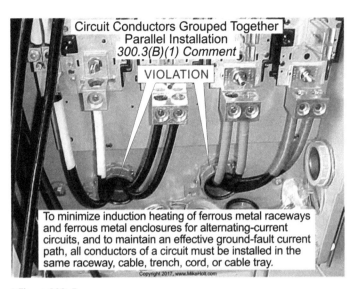

▶Figure 300–5

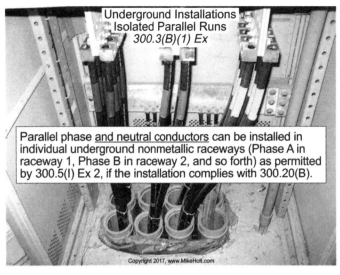

▶Figure 300–7

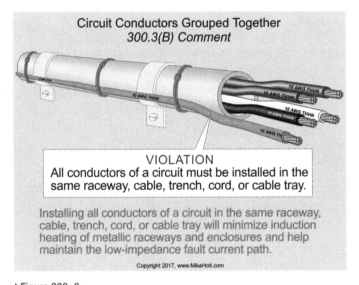

▶Figure 300–6

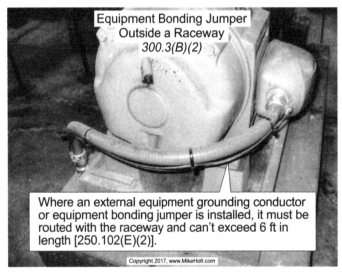

▶Figure 300–8

(2) Outside a Raceway or an Enclosure. Equipment grounding jumpers can be located outside of a flexible raceway if the bonding jumper is installed in accordance with 250.102(E)(2). ▶**Figure 300–8**

For dc circuits, the equipment grounding conductor can be run separately from the circuit conductors in accordance with 250.134(B) Ex 2. ▶**Figure 300–9**

(3) Nonferrous Wiring Methods. Circuit conductors can be installed in different raceways (Phase A in raceway 1, Phase B in raceway 2, and so on) if, in order to reduce or eliminate inductive heating, the raceway is nonmetallic or nonmagnetic and the installation complies with 300.20(B). See 300.3(B)(1) and 300.5(I) Ex 2.

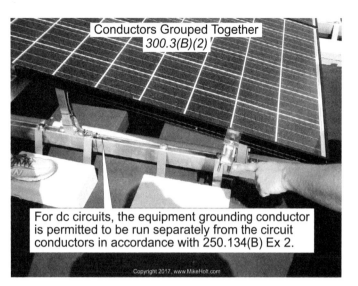

▶Figure 300–9

(C) Conductors of Different Systems.

(1) Mixing. Power conductors of alternating-current and direct-current systems rated 1,000V or less can occupy the same raceway, cable, or enclosure if all conductors have an insulation voltage rating not less than the maximum circuit voltage. ▶Figure 300–10

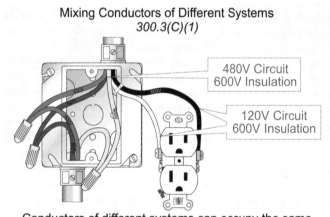

Conductors of different systems can occupy the same raceway, cable, or enclosure if the insulation voltage rating isn't less than the maximum circuit voltage.

Copyright 2017, www.MikeHolt.com

▶Figure 300–10

Note 1: See 725.136(A) for Class 2 and Class 3 circuit conductors. ▶Figure 300–11

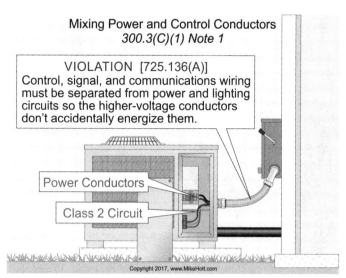

▶Figure 300–11

Author's Comment:

■ Control, signal, and communications wiring must be separated from power and lighting circuits so the higher-voltage conductors don't accidentally energize the control, signal, or communications wiring:

  ◆ Class 1 control circuits, 725.48
  ◆ Class 2 and Class 3 Control Circuits, 725.136(A)
  ◆ Communications Circuits, 800.133(A)(1)(c)
  ◆ Coaxial Cable, 820.133(A)
  ◆ Fire Alarm Circuits, 760.136(A)
  ◆ Sound Circuits, 640.9(C)

■ Class 1 circuit conductors can be installed with associated power conductors [725.48(B)(1)] if all conductors have an insulation voltage rating not less than the maximum circuit voltage [300.3(C)(1)].

■ A Class 2 circuit that's been reclassified as a Class 1 circuit [725.130(A) Ex 2] can be installed with associated power conductors [725.48(B)(1)] if all conductors have an insulation voltage rating not less than the maximum circuit voltage [300.3(C)(1)]. ▶Figure 300–12

300.4 Protection Against Physical Damage

Where subject to physical damage, conductors, raceways, and cables must be protected in accordance with (A) through (H).

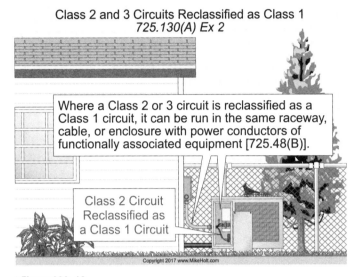

Class 2 and 3 Circuits Reclassified as Class 1
725.130(A) Ex 2

Where a Class 2 or 3 circuit is reclassified as a Class 1 circuit, it can be run in the same raceway, cable, or enclosure with power conductors of functionally associated equipment [725.48(B)].

Class 2 Circuit Reclassified as a Class 1 Circuit

Copyright 2017 www.MikeHolt.com

▶Figure 300–12

Note: Minor superficial damage to a raceway, cable armor, or cable insulation doesn't necessarily violate the integrity of either the contained conductors or the conductors' insulation.

(A) Cables and Raceways Through Wood Members. When the following wiring methods are installed through wood members, they must comply with (1) and (2). ▶Figure 300–13

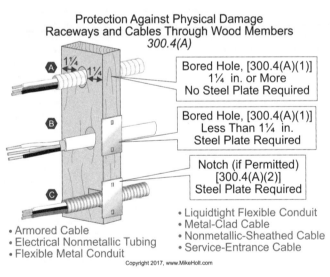

Protection Against Physical Damage Raceways and Cables Through Wood Members
300.4(A)

Ⓐ 1¼ 1¼

Bored Hole, [300.4(A)(1)] 1¼ in. or More No Steel Plate Required

Ⓑ

Bored Hole, [300.4(A)(1)] Less Than 1¼ in. Steel Plate Required

Ⓒ

Notch (if Permitted) [300.4(A)(2)] Steel Plate Required

• Armored Cable
• Electrical Nonmetallic Tubing
• Flexible Metal Conduit

• Liquidtight Flexible Conduit
• Metal-Clad Cable
• Nonmetallic-Sheathed Cable
• Service-Entrance Cable

Copyright 2017, www.MikeHolt.com

▶Figure 300–13

- Armored Cable, Article 320
- Electrical Nonmetallic Tubing, Article 362
- Flexible Metal Conduit, Article 348
- Liquidtight Flexible Metal Conduit, Article 350
- Liquidtight Flexible Nonmetallic Conduit, Article 356

- Metal-Clad Cable, Article 330
- Nonmetallic-Sheathed Cable, Article 334
- Service-Entrance Cable, Article 338
- Underground Feeder and Branch-Circuit Cable, Article 340

(1) Holes in Wood Members. Holes through wood framing members for the above cables or raceways must be not less than 1¼ in. from the edge of the wood member. If the edge of a drilled hole in a wood framing member is less than 1¼ in. from the edge, a ¹⁄₁₆ in. thick steel plate of sufficient length and width must be installed to protect the wiring method from screws and nails. ▶Figure 300–14

Cables Through Wood Members, Bored Holes
300.4(A)(1)

If the edge of a drilled hole in a wood framing member is less than 1¼ in. from the edge, a ¹⁄₁₆ in. thick steel plate must be installed to protect the wiring method from screws and nails.

Copyright 2017, www.MikeHolt.com

▶Figure 300–14

Ex 1: A steel plate isn't required to protect rigid metal conduit, intermediate metal conduit, PVC conduit, or electrical metallic tubing.

(2) Notches in Wood Members. If notching of wood framing members for cables and raceways are permitted by the building code, a ¹⁄₁₆ in. thick steel plate of sufficient length and width must be installed to protect the wiring method laid in these wood notches from screws and nails.

⚠ **CAUTION:** *When drilling or notching wood members, be sure to check with the building inspector to ensure you don't damage or weaken the structure and violate the building code.*

Ex 1: A steel plate isn't required to protect rigid metal conduit, intermediate metal conduit, PVC conduit, or electrical metallic tubing.

Ex 2: A listed and marked steel plate less than 1/16 in. thick that provides equal or better protection against nail or screw penetration is permitted. ▶Figure 300–15

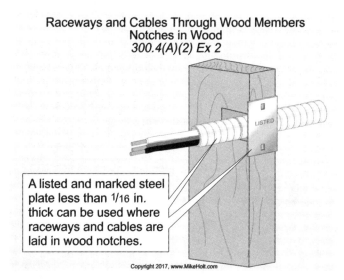

Raceways and Cables Through Wood Members
Notches in Wood
300.4(A)(2) Ex 2

LISTED

A listed and marked steel plate less than 1/16 in. thick can be used where raceways and cables are laid in wood notches.

Copyright 2017, www.MikeHolt.com

▶Figure 300–15

(B) Nonmetallic-Sheathed Cable and Electrical Nonmetallic Tubing Through Metal Framing Members.

(1) Nonmetallic-Sheathed Cable (NM). If Type NM cables pass through factory or field openings in metal framing members, the cable must be protected by listed bushings or listed grommets that cover all metal edges. The protection fitting must be securely fastened in the opening before the installation of the cable. ▶Figure 300–16

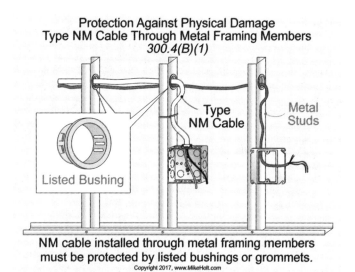

Protection Against Physical Damage
Type NM Cable Through Metal Framing Members
300.4(B)(1)

Type
NM Cable

Metal
Studs

Listed Bushing

NM cable installed through metal framing members must be protected by listed bushings or grommets.
Copyright 2017, www.MikeHolt.com

▶Figure 300–16

(2) Type NM Cable and Electrical Nonmetallic Tubing. If nails or screws are likely to penetrate Type NM cable or electrical nonmetallic tubing, a steel sleeve, steel plate, or steel clip not less than 1/16 in. in thickness must be installed to protect the cable or tubing.

Ex: A listed and marked steel plate less than 1/16 in. thick that provides equal or better protection against nail or screw penetration is permitted.

(C) Behind Suspended Ceilings. Wiring methods, such as boxes, enclosures, cables, or raceways, installed behind panels designed to allow access must be supported in accordance with its applicable article. ▶Figure 300–17

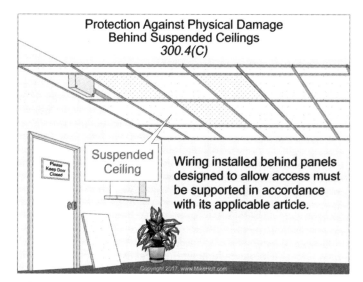

Protection Against Physical Damage
Behind Suspended Ceilings
300.4(C)

Please
Keep Door
Closed

Suspended
Ceiling

Wiring installed behind panels designed to allow access must be supported in accordance with its applicable article.

Copyright 2017, www.MikeHolt.com

▶Figure 300–17

Author's Comment:

- Similar support requirements are contained in Chapters 6, 7, and 8 as follows:
  - ◆ Audio Cable, 640.6(B)
  - ◆ Communications (twisted pair) Cable, 800.21
  - ◆ Control and Signaling Cable, 725.21 and 725.24
  - ◆ Coaxial Cable, 820.21 and 820.24
  - ◆ Optical Fiber Cable, 770.21 and 770.24

(D) Cables and Raceways Parallel to Framing Members and Furring Strips. Cables or raceways run parallel to framing members or furring strips must be protected if they're likely to be penetrated by nails or screws, by installing the wiring method so it isn't less than 1¼ in. from the nearest edge of the framing member or furring strip. If the edge of the framing member or furring strip is less than 1¼ in. away, a 1/16 in. thick steel plate of sufficient length and width must be installed to protect the wiring method from screws and nails. ▶Figure 300–18

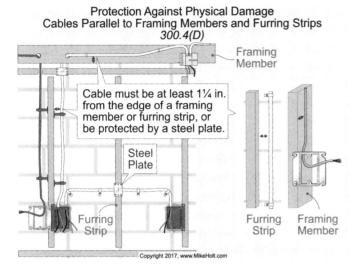

Protection Against Physical Damage
Cables Parallel to Framing Members and Furring Strips
300.4(D)

▶Figure 300–18

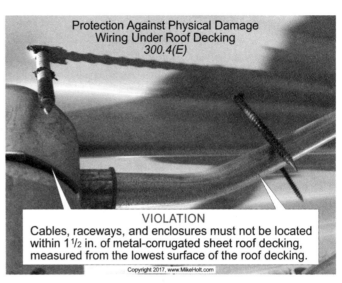

Protection Against Physical Damage
Wiring Under Roof Decking
300.4(E)

▶Figure 300–19

Author's Comment:

- This rule doesn't apply to control, signaling, and communications cables, but similar requirements are contained in Chapters 6, 7, and 8 as follows:

  ◆ Communications Cable, 800.24
  ◆ Control and Signaling Cable, 725.24
  ◆ Coaxial Cable, 820.24
  ◆ Optical Fiber Cable, 770.24
  ◆ Fire Alarm Cable, 760.24
  ◆ Audio Cable, 640.6(B)

Ex 1: Protection isn't required for rigid metal conduit, intermediate metal conduit, PVC conduit, or electrical metallic tubing.

Ex 2: For concealed work in finished buildings, or finished panels for prefabricated buildings if such supporting is impracticable, the cables can be fished between access points.

Ex 3: A listed and marked steel plate less than ¹⁄₁₆ in. thick that provides equal or better protection against nail or screw penetration is permitted.

(E) Wiring Under Roof Decking. Where subject to physical damage, cables, raceways, and enclosures under metal-corrugated sheet roof decking aren't permitted to be located within 1½ in. of the roof decking, measured from the lowest surface of the roof decking to the top of the cable, raceway, or box. ▶Figure 300–19

In addition, cables, raceways, and enclosures aren't permitted in concealed locations of metal-corrugated sheet decking type roofing.

Author's Comment:

- This requirement also applies to luminaires installed in or under roof decking [410.10(F)].

Note: Roof decking material will be installed or replaced after the initial raceway or cabling which may be penetrated by the screws or other mechanical devices designed to provide "hold down" strength of the waterproof membrane or roof insulating material.

Ex: Spacing from roof decking doesn't apply to rigid metal conduit and intermediate metal conduit.

(F) Cables and Raceways Installed in Grooves. Cables and raceways installed in a groove must be protected by a ¹⁄₁₆ in. thick steel plate or sleeve, or by 1¼ in. of free space.

Author's Comment:

- An example is Type NM cable installed in a groove cut into the Styrofoam-type insulation building block structure and then covered with wallboard.

Ex 1: Protection isn't required if the cable is installed in rigid metal conduit, intermediate metal conduit, PVC conduit, or electrical metallic tubing.

Ex 2: A listed and marked steel plate less than ¹⁄₁₆ in. thick that provides equal or better protection against nail or screw penetration is permitted.

(G) Insulating Fittings. If raceways contain insulated circuit conductors 4 AWG and larger that enter an enclosure, the conductors must be protected from abrasion during and after installation by a fitting identified to provide a smooth, rounded insulating surface, such as an insulating bushing. ▶Figure 300–20

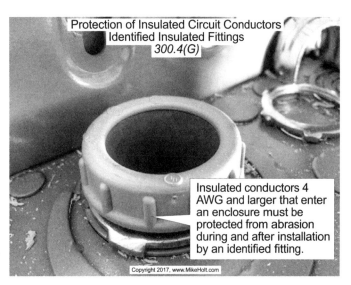

Protection of Insulated Circuit Conductors
Identified Insulated Fittings
300.4(G)

Insulated conductors 4 AWG and larger that enter an enclosure must be protected from abrasion during and after installation by an identified fitting.

Copyright 2017, www.MikeHolt.com

▶Figure 300–20

Author's Comment:

- If IMC or RMC conduit enters an enclosure without a connector, a bushing must be provided, regardless of the conductor size [342.46 and 344.46].

- An insulated fitting isn't required for a bare grounding electrode conductor.

Ex: Insulating bushings aren't required if a raceway terminates in a threaded raceway entry that provides a smooth, rounded, or flared surface for the conductors, such as a hub.

(H) Structural Joints. A listed expansion/deflection fitting or other means approved by the authority having jurisdiction must be used where a raceway crosses a structural joint intended for expansion, contraction or deflection.

300.5 Underground Installations

(A) Minimum Burial Depths. When cables or raceways are installed underground, they must have a minimum cover in accordance with Table 300.5. ▶Figure 300–21

Underground Installations, Minimum Cover Depths
Table 300.5

	Column 1 UF or USE Cables or Conductors	Column 2 RMC or IMC	Column 3 Nonmetallic Raceways not Encased in Concrete	Column 4 Residential 15A & 20A GFCI 120V Branch Ckts
Dwelling Unit	24 in.	6 in.	18 in.	12 in.
Dwelling Unit Driveway and Parking Area	18 in.	18 in.	18 in.	12 in.
Under Roadway Driveway Parking Lot	24 in.	24 in.	24 in.	24 in.
Other Locations	24 in.	6 in.	18 in.	12 in.

Copyright 2017, www.MikeHolt.com

▶Figure 300–21

Table 300.5 Minimum Cover Requirements in Inches

Location	Column 1 Buried Cables	Column 2 RMC or IMC	Column 3 Nonmetallic Raceway
Under Building	0	0	0
Dwelling Unit	24/12*	6	18
Dwelling Unit Driveway	18/12*	6	18/12*
Under Roadway	24	24	24
Other Locations	24	6	18

*Residential branch circuits rated 120V or less with GFCI protection and maximum protection of 20A.

See the table in the NEC for full details.

a. Lesser depth is permitted where specified in the installation instructions of a listed low-voltage lighting system. ▶Figure 300–22

b. A depth of 6 in. is permitted for pool, spa, and fountain lighting wiring installed in a nonmetallic raceway, where part of a listed 30V lighting system. ▶Figure 300–23

Note 1 to Table 300.5 defines "Cover" as the distance from the top of the underground cable or raceway to the top surface of finished grade. ▶Figure 300–24

Author's Comment:

- Table 300.5 Notes a and b only pertain to Column 5. Refer to the *NEC* for the complete table.

Underground Burial Depth
Irrigation and Landscape Lighting
Table 300.5, Column 5, <u>Note a</u>

A lesser burial depth than specified in Column 5
is permitted where specified in the installation
instructions of a listed low voltage lighting system.

Copyright 2017, www.MikeHolt.com

▶Figure 300–22

Underground Installations
Minimum Cover Depths
Table 300.5, Note 1

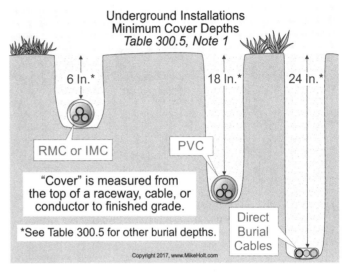

"Cover" is measured from
the top of a raceway, cable, or
conductor to finished grade.

*See Table 300.5 for other burial depths.

Copyright 2017, www.MikeHolt.com

▶Figure 300–24

Underground Burial Depth
Pool, Spa, and Fountain Lighting, 30V or Less
Table 300.5, Column 5, <u>Note b</u>

A depth of 6 in. is permitted for pool,
spa, and fountain lighting wiring installed
in a nonmetallic raceway, where part of
a listed lighting system 30V or less.

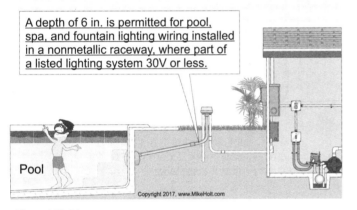

Copyright 2017, www.MikeHolt.com

▶Figure 300–23

Underground Burial Depth
Irrigation and Landscape Lighting
Table 300.5, Column 5

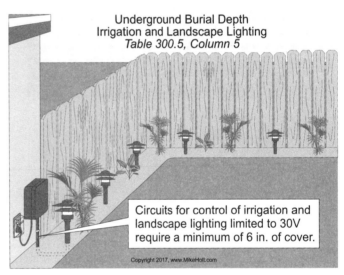

Circuits for control of irrigation and
landscape lighting limited to 30V
require a minimum of 6 in. of cover.

Copyright 2017, www.MikeHolt.com

▶Figure 300–25

Author's Comment:

- Circuits for control of irrigation and landscape lighting limited to 30V require a minimum of 6 in. of cover: ▶Figure 300–25
- There are no cover requirements for raceways under a building: ▶Figure 300–26
- The cover requirements contained in 300.5 don't apply to signaling, communications, and other power-limited wiring systems: ▶Figure 300–27
  - Class 2 and 3 Circuits, 725.3
  - Communications Cables and Raceways, 90.3
  - Coaxial Cable, 90.3
  - Fire Alarm Circuits, 760.3
  - Optical Fiber Cables and Raceways, 770.3

(B) Wet Locations. The interior of enclosures or raceways installed in an underground installation are considered to be a wet location. Cables and insulated conductors installed in underground enclosures or raceways must comply with 310.10(C).

Author's Comment:

- The definition of a "Wet Location" as contained in Article 100, includes installations underground, in concrete slabs in direct contact with the earth, locations subject to saturation with water, and unprotected locations exposed to weather. If raceways are installed in wet locations above grade, the interior of these raceways is also considered to be a wet location [300.9].

▶Figure 300–26

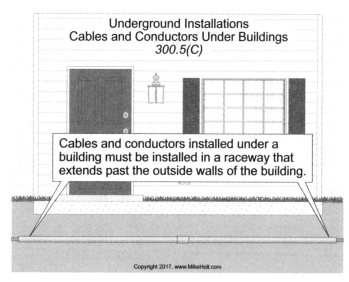

▶Figure 300–28

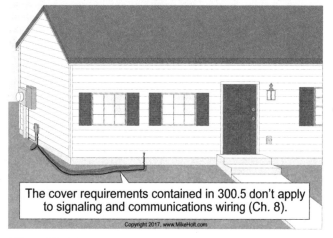

▶Figure 300–27

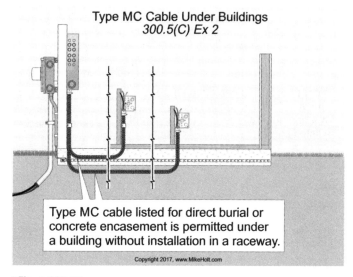

▶Figure 300–29

(C) Cables and Conductors Under Buildings. Cables and conductors installed under a building must be installed within a raceway that extends past the outside walls of the building. ▶Figure 300–28

Ex 2: Type MC Cable listed for direct burial is permitted under a building without installation within a raceway [330.10(A)(5)]. ▶Figure 300–29

(D) Protecting Underground Cables and Conductors. Direct-buried conductors and cables such as Types MC, UF, and USE installed underground must be protected from damage in accordance with (1) through (4).

(1) Emerging from Grade. Direct-buried cables or conductors that emerge from grade must be installed in an enclosure or raceway to protect against physical damage. Protection isn't required to extend more than 18 in. below grade, and protection above ground must extend to a height of not less than 8 ft. ▶Figure 300–30

(2) Conductors Entering Buildings. Underground conductors and cables that enter a building must be protected to the point of entrance.

(3) Service Conductors. Underground service conductors must have their location identified by a warning ribbon placed in the trench at least 12 in. above the underground conductor installation. ▶Figure 300–31

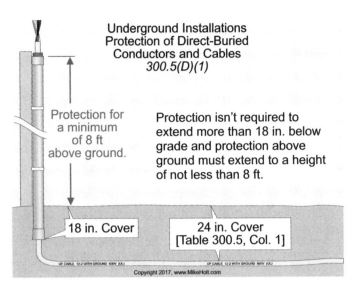

Underground Installations
Protection of Direct-Buried
Conductors and Cables
300.5(D)(1)

Protection for a minimum of 8 ft above ground.

Protection isn't required to extend more than 18 in. below grade and protection above ground must extend to a height of not less than 8 ft.

18 in. Cover

24 in. Cover [Table 300.5, Col. 1]

Copyright 2017, www.MikeHolt.com

▶Figure 300–30

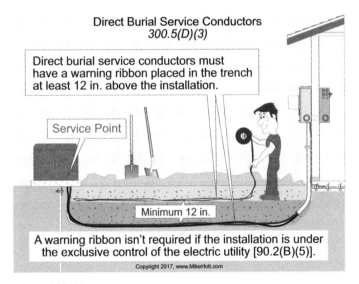

Direct Burial Service Conductors
300.5(D)(3)

Direct burial service conductors must have a warning ribbon placed in the trench at least 12 in. above the installation.

Service Point

Minimum 12 in.

A warning ribbon isn't required if the installation is under the exclusive control of the electric utility [90.2(B)(5)].

Copyright 2017, www.MikeHolt.com

▶Figure 300–31

Author's Comment:

- Although a warning ribbon isn't required by the *NEC* if the underground service conductors are under the exclusive control of the utility, it may be required by the local utility.

(4) Raceway Damage. Where a raceway is subject to physical damage, the conductors must be installed in EMT, RMC, IMC, RTRC-XW, or Schedule 80 PVC conduit.

(E) Underground Splices and Taps. Direct-buried conductors or cables can be spliced or tapped underground without a splice box [300.15(G)], if the splice or tap is made in accordance with 110.14(B). ▶**Figure 300–32**

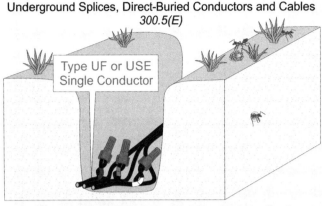

Underground Splices, Direct-Buried Conductors and Cables
300.5(E)

Type UF or USE Single Conductor

Direct-buried conductors or cables can be spliced or tapped underground without a splice box if the splice or tap device is listed for direct burial.

Copyright 2017, www.MikeHolt.com

▶Figure 300–32

(F) Backfill. Backfill material for underground wiring must not damage underground raceways, cables, or conductors. ▶**Figure 300–33**

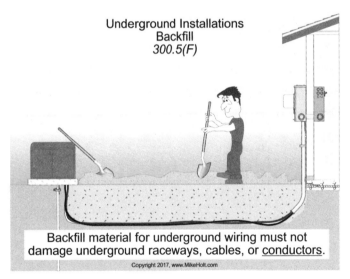

Underground Installations
Backfill
300.5(F)

Backfill material for underground wiring must not damage underground raceways, cables, or conductors.

Copyright 2017, www.MikeHolt.com

▶Figure 300–33

Author's Comment:

- Large rocks, chunks of concrete, steel rods, mesh, and other sharp-edged objects aren't permitted to be used for backfill material, because they can damage the underground conductors, cables, or raceways.

(G) Raceway Seals. If moisture could contact energized live parts from an underground raceway, including spare raceways, a seal identified for use with the cable or conductor insulation must be installed at either or both ends of the raceway [225.27 and 230.8]. ▶**Figure 300–34**

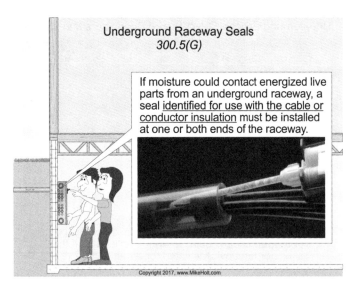

▶Figure 300–34

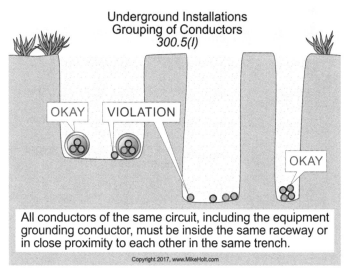

▶Figure 300–35

Author's Comment:

■ This is a common problem for equipment located downhill from the supply, or in underground equipment rooms. See 230.8 for service raceway seals and 300.7(A) for different temperature area seals.

Note: Hazardous explosive gases or vapors make it necessary to seal underground raceways that enter the building in accordance with 501.15.

Author's Comment:

■ It isn't the intent of this Note to imply that sealing fittings of the types required in hazardous locations be installed in unclassified locations, except as required in Chapter 5. This also doesn't imply that the sealing material provides a watertight seal, but only that it prevents moisture from entering the raceways.

(H) Bushing. Raceways that terminate underground must have a bushing or fitting at the end of the raceway to protect emerging cables or conductors.

(I) Conductors Grouped Together. Underground conductors of the same circuit, including the equipment grounding conductor, must be inside the same raceway, or in close proximity to each other in the same trench. See 300.3(B). ▶Figure 300–35

Ex 1: Conductors can be installed in parallel in raceways, multiconductor cables, or direct-buried single-conductor cables. Each raceway or multiconductor cable must contain all conductors of the same circuit including the equipment grounding conductor. Each direct-buried single-conductor cable must be located in close proximity in the trench to the other single-conductors cables in the same parallel set of conductors, including equipment grounding conductors.

Ex 2: Parallel circuit conductors installed in accordance with 310.10(H) of the same phase or neutral can be installed in underground PVC conduits, if inductive heating at raceway terminations is reduced by the use of aluminum locknuts and cutting a slot between the individual holes through which the conductors pass as required by 300.20(B). ▶**Figure 300–36**

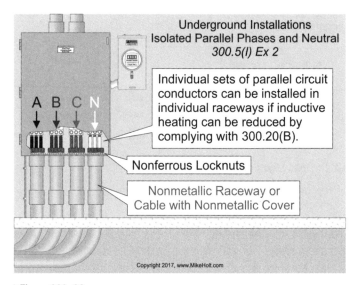

▶Figure 300–36

Author's Comment:

- Installing ungrounded and neutral conductors in different PVC conduits makes it easier to terminate larger parallel sets of conductors, but it will result in higher levels of electromagnetic fields (EMF).

(J) Earth Movement. Direct-buried conductors, cables, or raceways that are subject to movement by settlement or frost must be arranged to prevent damage to conductors or equipment connected to the wiring. ▶Figure 300–37

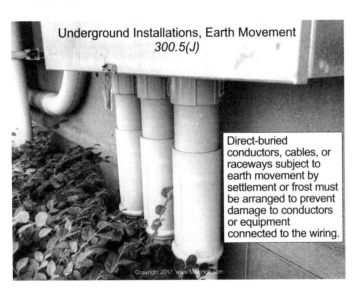

Underground Installations, Earth Movement
300.5(J)

Direct-buried conductors, cables, or raceways subject to earth movement by settlement or frost must be arranged to prevent damage to conductors or equipment connected to the wiring.

Copyright 2017, www.MikeHolt.com

▶Figure 300–37

Note: "S" loops in underground direct burial cables and conductors, raceway expansion fittings, and flexible connections to equipment can serve this purpose.

(K) Directional Boring. Cables or raceways installed using directional boring equipment must be approved by the authority having jurisdiction for this purpose.

Author's Comment:z

- Directional boring technology uses a directional drill, which is steered continuously from point "A" to point "B." When the drill head comes out of the earth at point "B," it's replaced with a back-reamer and the duct or raceway being installed is attached to it. The size of the boring rig (hp, torque, and pull-back power) comes into play, along with the types of soil, in determining the type of raceways required. For telecommunications work, multiple poly innerducts are pulled in at one

time. At major crossings, such as expressways, railroads, or rivers, outerduct may be installed to create a permanent sleeve for the innerducts.

- "Innerduct" and "outerduct" are terms usually associated with optical fiber cable installations, while "unitduct" comes with factory installed conductors. Galvanized rigid metal conduit, Schedule 40 and Schedule 80 PVC, HDPE conduit, and nonmetallic underground conduit with conductors (NUCC) are common wiring methods used with directional boring installations.

300.6 Protection Against Corrosion and Deterioration

Raceways, cable trays, cablebus, cable armor, boxes, cable sheathing, cabinets, elbows, couplings, fittings, supports, and support hardware must be suitable for the environment. ▶Figure 300–38

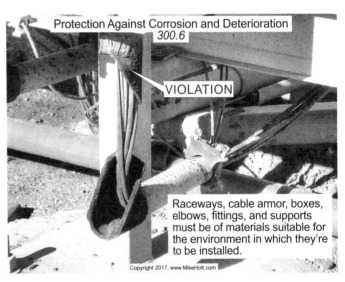

Protection Against Corrosion and Deterioration
300.6

VIOLATION

Raceways, cable armor, boxes, elbows, fittings, and supports must be of materials suitable for the environment in which they're to be installed.

Copyright 2017, www.MikeHolt.com

▶Figure 300–38

(A) Ferrous Metal Equipment. Ferrous metal raceways, enclosures, cables, cable trays, fittings, and support hardware must be protected against corrosion by a coating of listed corrosion-resistant material. Where conduit is threaded in the field, the threads must be coated with an approved electrically conductive, corrosion-resistant compound, such as cold zinc.

Note: Field-cut threads are those threads that are cut anywhere other than at the factory.

Author's Comment:

- Nonferrous metal raceways, such as aluminum rigid metal conduit, don't have to meet the provisions of this section.

(1) Protected from Corrosion Solely by Enamel. If ferrous metal parts are protected from corrosion solely by enamel, they aren't permitted to be used outdoors or in wet locations as described in 300.6(D).

(2) Organic Coatings on Boxes or Cabinets. Boxes or cabinets having a system of organic coatings marked "Raintight," "Rainproof," or "Outdoor Type," can be installed outdoors.

(3) In Concrete or in Direct Contact with the Earth. Ferrous metal raceways, cable armor, boxes, cable sheathing, cabinets, elbows, couplings, nipples, fittings, supports, and support hardware can be installed in concrete or in direct contact with the earth, or in areas subject to severe corrosive influences if made of material approved for the condition, or if provided with corrosion protection approved for the condition.

Author's Comment:

- Galvanized electrical metallic tubing can be installed in concrete at grade level and in direct contact with the earth, but supplementary corrosion protection is usually required (UL White Book, *Guide Information for Electrical Equipment*). Electrical metallic tubing can be installed in concrete above the ground floor slab generally without supplementary corrosion protection.

(B) Aluminum Equipment. Aluminum raceways, cable trays, cablebus, cable armor, boxes, cable sheathing, cabinets, elbows, couplings, nipples, fittings, supports, and support hardware embedded or encased in concrete or in direct contact with the earth must be provided with supplementary corrosion protection.

(C) Nonmetallic Equipment. Nonmetallic raceways, cable trays, cablebus, boxes, cables with a nonmetallic outer jacket and internal metal armor or jacket, cable sheathing, cabinets, elbows, couplings, nipples, fittings, supports, and support hardware must be made of material identified for the condition, and must comply with (1) and (2). ▶Figure 300–39

(1) Exposed to Sunlight. If exposed to sunlight, the materials must be listed or identified as sunlight resistant.

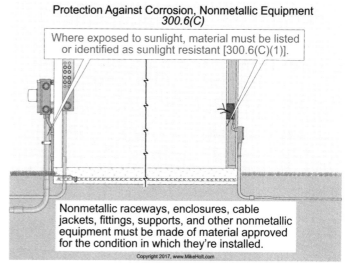

Protection Against Corrosion, Nonmetallic Equipment 300.6(C)

Where exposed to sunlight, material must be listed or identified as sunlight resistant [300.6(C)(1)].

Nonmetallic raceways, enclosures, cable jackets, fittings, supports, and other nonmetallic equipment must be made of material approved for the condition in which they're installed.

Copyright 2017, www.MikeHolt.com

▶Figure 300–39

(2) Chemical Exposure. If subject to exposure to chemical solvents, vapors, splashing, or immersion, materials or coatings must either be inherently resistant to chemicals based upon their listing, or be identified for the specific chemical.

(D) Indoor Wet Locations. In portions of dairy processing facilities, laundries, canneries, and other indoor wet locations, and in locations where walls are frequently washed or where there are surfaces of absorbent materials, such as damp paper or wood, the entire wiring system, where installed exposed, including all boxes, fittings, raceways, and cables, must be mounted so there's at least ¼ in. of airspace between it and the wall or supporting surface.

Author's Comment:

- See the definitions of "Exposed" and "Location, Wet" in Article 100.

Ex: Nonmetallic raceways, boxes, and fittings are permitted without the airspace on a concrete, masonry, tile, or similar surface.

Note: Areas where acids and alkali chemicals are handled and stored may present corrosive conditions, particularly when wet or damp. Severe corrosive conditions may also be present in portions of meatpacking plants, tanneries, glue houses, and some stables; in installations immediately adjacent to a seashore or swimming pool, spa, hot tub, and fountain areas; in areas where chemical deicers are used; and in storage cellars or rooms for hides, casings, fertilizer, salt, and bulk chemicals.

300.7 Raceways Exposed to Different Temperatures

 Scan this QR code to watch Mike explain this topic; it's a sample video clip from Mike's *Understanding the NEC Volume 1* DVDs.

(A) Sealing. If a raceway is subjected to different temperatures, and where condensation is known to be a problem, the raceway must be filled with a material approved by the authority having jurisdiction that will prevent the circulation of warm air to a colder section of the raceway. An explosionproof seal isn't required for this purpose. ▶Figure 300–40

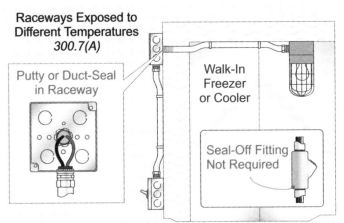

Raceways Exposed to Different Temperatures
300.7(A)

Putty or Duct-Seal in Raceway

Walk-In Freezer or Cooler

Seal-Off Fitting Not Required

Raceways must be sealed to prevent the circulation of warm air to a colder section of the raceway or sleeve.
Copyright 2017, www.MikeHolt.com

▶Figure 300–40

(B) Expansion, Expansion-Deflection, and Deflection Fittings. Raceways must be provided with expansion, expansion-deflection, and deflection fittings where necessary to compensate for thermal expansion, deflection, and contraction. ▶Figure 300–41

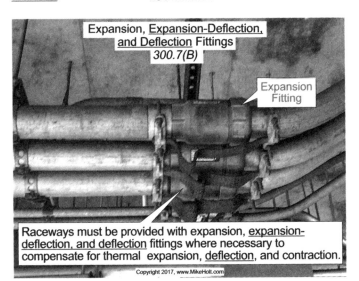

Expansion, Expansion-Deflection, and Deflection Fittings
300.7(B)

Expansion Fitting

Raceways must be provided with expansion, expansion-deflection, and deflection fittings where necessary to compensate for thermal expansion, deflection, and contraction.
Copyright 2017, www.MikeHolt.com

▶Figure 300–41

Note: Table 352.44 provides the expansion characteristics for PVC conduit. The expansion characteristics for steel conduit are determined by multiplying the values from Table 352.44 by 0.20, and the expansion characteristics for aluminum raceways are determined by multiplying the values from Table 352.44 by 0.40. Table 354.44 provides the expansion characteristics for reinforced thermosetting resin conduit (RTRC). ▶Figure 300–42

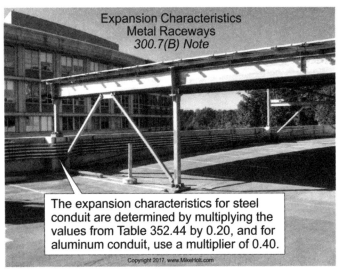

Expansion Characteristics Metal Raceways
300.7(B) Note

The expansion characteristics for steel conduit are determined by multiplying the values from Table 352.44 by 0.20, and for aluminum conduit, use a multiplier of 0.40.
Copyright 2017, www.MikeHolt.com

▶Figure 300–42

300.8 Not Permitted in Raceways

Raceways are designed for the exclusive use of electrical conductors and cables, and aren't permitted to contain nonelectrical components, such as pipes or tubes for steam, water, air, gas, drainage, and so forth. ▶Figure 300–43

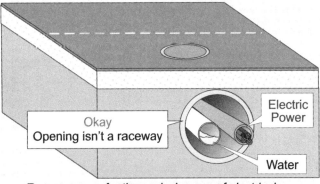

Not Permitted in Raceways
300.8

Okay
Opening isn't a raceway

Electric Power

Water

Raceways are for the exclusive use of electrical conductors and cables, and must not contain piping for steam, water, air, gas, or drainage.
Copyright 2017, www.MikeHolt.com

▶Figure 300–43

300.9 Raceways in Wet Locations Above Grade

Insulated conductors and cables installed in raceways in aboveground wet locations must be listed for use in wet locations in accordance with 310.10(C).

300.10 Electrical Continuity

Metal raceways, cable armor, and other metal enclosures must be metallically joined together into a continuous electrical conductor to provide effective electrical continuity [110.10 and 250.4(A)(3)]. ▶Figure 300–44

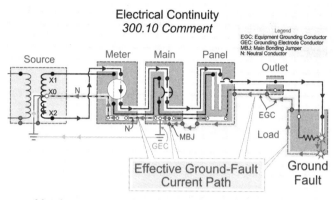

Metal raceways and enclosures for conductors must be metallically joined together to form an effective ground-fault current path to facilitate the operation of the circuit overcurrent protection device.

Copyright 2017, www.MikeHolt.com

▶Figure 300–45

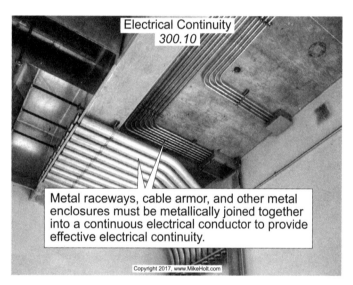

▶Figure 300–44

Author's Comment:

■ The purpose of effective electrical continuity is to establish an effective ground-fault current path necessary to facilitate the operation of the circuit overcurrent protection device in the event of a ground fault [250.4(A)(3)]. ▶Figure 300–45

Ex 1: Short lengths of metal raceways used for the support or protection of cables aren't required to be electrically continuous, nor are they required to be connected to an equipment grounding conductor [250.86 Ex 2 and 300.12 Ex]. ▶Figure 300–46

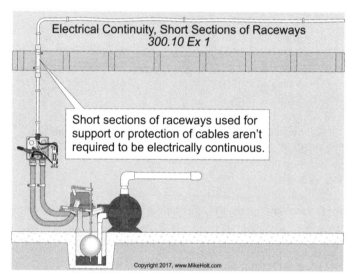

▶Figure 300–46

300.11 Securing and Supporting

(A) Secured in Place. Raceways, cable assemblies, and enclosures must be securely fastened in place.

(B) Wiring Systems Installed Above Suspended Ceilings. The ceiling-support wires or ceiling grid aren't permitted to be used to support raceways and cables (power, signaling, or communications). However, independent support wires that are secured at both ends and provide secure support are permitted. ▶Figure 300–47

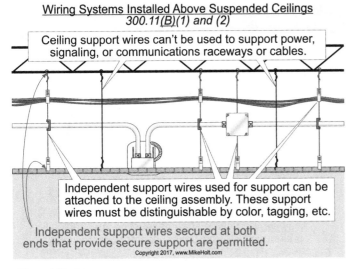

Wiring Systems Installed Above Suspended Ceilings
300.11(B)(1) and (2)

Ceiling support wires can't be used to support power, signaling, or communications raceways or cables.

Independent support wires used for support can be attached to the ceiling assembly. These support wires must be distinguishable by color, tagging, etc.

Independent support wires secured at both ends that provide secure support are permitted.
Copyright 2017, www.MikeHolt.com

▶Figure 300–47

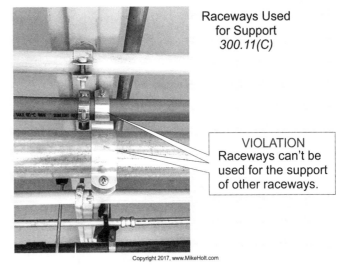

Raceways Used for Support
300.11(C)

VIOLATION
Raceways can't be used for the support of other raceways.

Copyright 2017, www.MikeHolt.com

▶Figure 300–48

Author's Comment:

- Outlet boxes [314.23(D)] and luminaires can be secured to the suspended-ceiling grid if securely fastened to the ceiling-framing members by mechanical means such as bolts, screws, or rivets, or by the use of clips or other securing means identified for use with the type of ceiling-framing member(s) used [410.36(B)].

(1) Fire-Rated Ceiling Assembly. Electrical wiring within the cavity of a fire-rated floor-ceiling or roof-ceiling assembly can be supported by independent support wires attached to the ceiling assembly. The independent support wires must be distinguishable from the suspended-ceiling support wires by color, tagging, or other effective means.

(2) Nonfire-Rated Ceiling Assembly. Wiring in a nonfire-rated floor-ceiling or roof-ceiling assembly can be supported by independent support wires attached to the ceiling assembly. The independent support wires must be distinguishable from the suspended-ceiling support wires by color, tagging, or other effective means.

(C) Raceways Used for Support. Raceways aren't permitted to be used as a means of support for other raceways, cables, or nonelectrical equipment, except as permitted in (1) through (3). ▶Figure 300–48 and ▶Figure 300–49

(1) Identified. If the raceway or means of support is identified as a means of support.

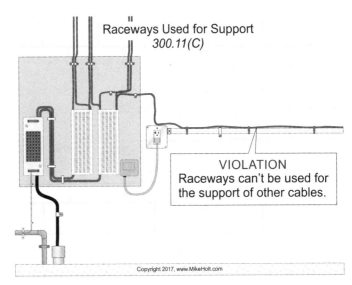

Raceways Used for Support
300.11(C)

VIOLATION
Raceways can't be used for the support of other cables.

Copyright 2017, www.MikeHolt.com

▶Figure 300–49

(2) Class 2 and 3 Circuits. Class 2 and 3 cables can be supported by the raceway that supplies power to the equipment controlled by the Class 2 or 3 circuit. ▶Figure 300–50

(3) Boxes Supported by Raceways. Raceways are permitted as a means of support for threaded boxes and conduit bodies in accordance with 314.23(E) and (F), or to support luminaires in accordance with 410.36(E).

(D) Cables Not Used as Means of Support. Cables aren't permitted to be used to support other cables, raceways, or nonelectrical equipment. ▶Figure 300–51

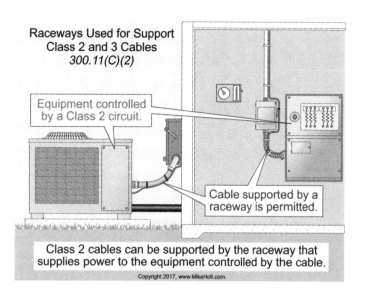

Raceways Used for Support
Class 2 and 3 Cables
300.11(C)(2)

Equipment controlled by a Class 2 circuit.

Cable supported by a raceway is permitted.

Class 2 cables can be supported by the raceway that supplies power to the equipment controlled by the cable.

Copyright 2017, www.MikeHolt.com

▶Figure 300–50

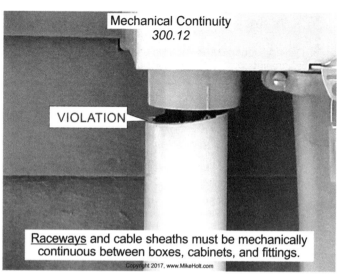

Mechanical Continuity
300.12

VIOLATION

Raceways and cable sheaths must be mechanically continuous between boxes, cabinets, and fittings.

Copyright 2017, www.MikeHolt.com

▶Figure 300–52

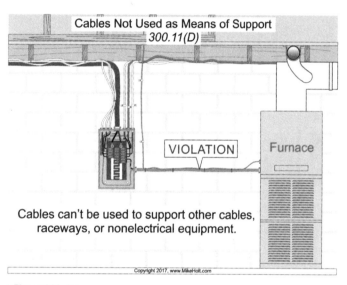

Cables Not Used as Means of Support
300.11(D)

VIOLATION

Furnace

Cables can't be used to support other cables, raceways, or nonelectrical equipment.

Copyright 2017, www.MikeHolt.com

▶Figure 300–51

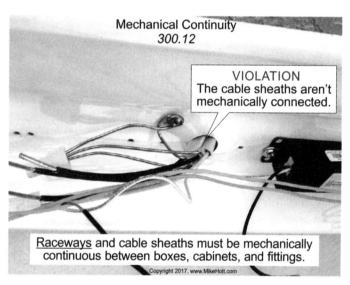

Mechanical Continuity
300.12

VIOLATION
The cable sheaths aren't mechanically connected.

Raceways and cable sheaths must be mechanically continuous between boxes, cabinets, and fittings.

Copyright 2017, www.MikeHolt.com

▶Figure 300–53

300.12 Mechanical Continuity

Raceways and cable sheaths must be mechanically continuous between boxes, cabinets, and fittings. ▶Figure 300–52 and ▶Figure 300–53

Ex 1: Short sections of raceways used to provide support or protection of cable from physical damage aren't required to be mechanically continuous [250.86 Ex 2 and 300.10 Ex 1]. ▶Figure 300–54

Ex 2: Raceways at the bottom of open-bottom equipment, such as switchboards, motor control centers, and transformers, aren't required to be mechanically secured to the equipment. ▶Figure 300–55

Author's Comment:

■ When raceways are stubbed into an open-bottom switchboard, the raceway, including the end fitting, can't rise more than 3 in. above the bottom of the switchboard enclosure [408.5].

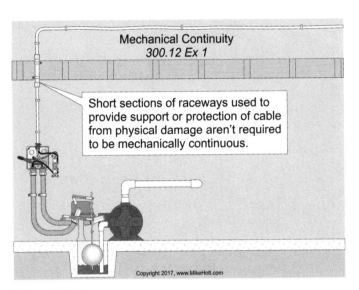

▶Figure 300–54

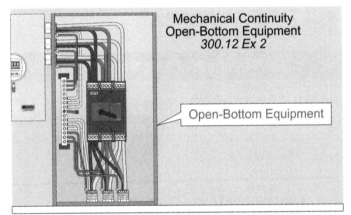

▶Figure 300–55

300.13 Splices and Pigtails

(A) Conductor Splices. Splices must be in enclosures in accordance with 300.15 and aren't permitted in raceways, except as permitted by 376.56, 386.56, or 388.56. ▶Figure 300–56

(B) Device Removal—Neutral Continuity. Continuity of the neutral conductor of a multiwire branch circuit isn't permitted to be interrupted by the removal of a wiring device. In these applications, the neutral conductors must be spliced together, and a pigtail must be provided for the wiring device. ▶Figure 300–57

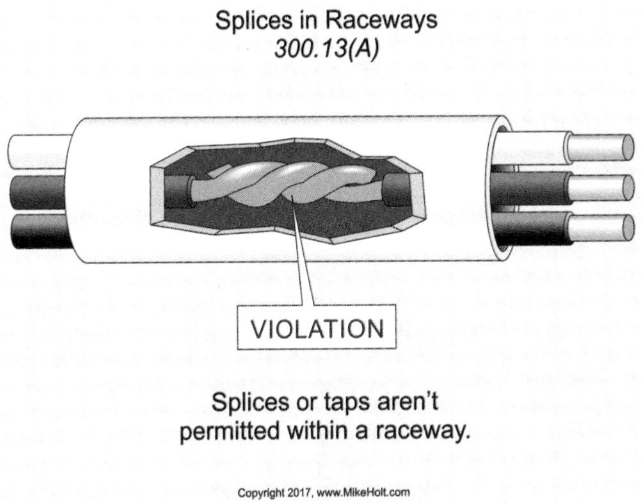

Splices in Raceways
300.13(A)

VIOLATION

Splices or taps aren't
permitted within a raceway.

Copyright 2017, www.MikeHolt.com

▶Figure 300–56

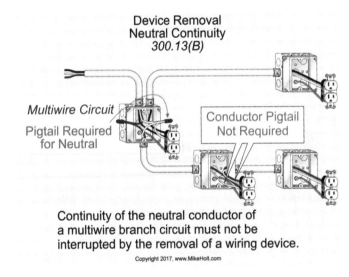

▶Figure 300–57

Author's Comment:

■ The opening of the ungrounded conductors, or the neutral conductor of a 2-wire circuit during the replacement of a device doesn't cause a safety hazard, so pigtailing these conductors isn't required [110.14(B)].

⚠ **CAUTION:** *If the continuity of the neutral conductor of a multiwire circuit is interrupted (opened), the resultant over- or undervoltage can cause a fire and/or destruction of electrical equipment.*

▶ Hazard of Open Neutral

Example: If the neutral conductor is interrupted on a 3-wire, 120/240V multiwire circuit that supplies a 1,200W, 120V hair dryer and a 600W, 120V television, it will cause the 120V television to operate at 160V for an instant before it burns up. We can determine this as follows: ▶Figure 300–58 and ▶Figure 300–59

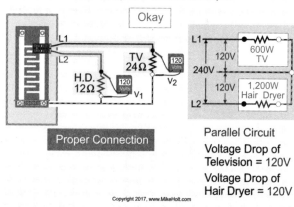

Danger of an Open Neutral
on a Multiwire Circuit, Example

▶Figure 300–58

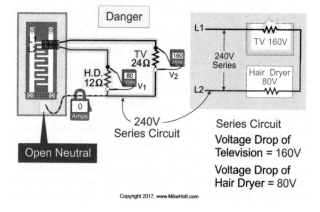

Danger of an Open Neutral
on a Multiwire Circuit, Example

▶Figure 300–59

Step 1: Determine the resistance of each appliance:

$R = E^2/P$

R of the hair dryer = $120V^2/1,200W$

R of the hair dryer = 12 ohms

R of the television = $120V^2/600W$

R of the television = 24 ohms

Step 2: Determine the current of the circuit:

$I = E/R$

E = 240V

R = 36 ohms (12 ohms + 24 ohms)

I = 240V/36 ohms

I = 6.70A

Step 3: Determine the operating voltage for each appliance:

$E = I \times R$

I = 6.70A

R = 12 ohms for hair dryer and 24 ohms for TV

Voltage of hair dryer = 6.70A × 12 ohms

Voltage of hair dryer = 80V

Voltage of television = 6.70A × 24 ohms

Voltage of television = 160V

300.14 Length of Free Conductors

At least 6 in. of free conductor, measured from the point in the box where the conductors enter the enclosure, must be left at each outlet, junction, and switch point for splices or terminations of luminaires or devices. ▶Figure 300–60

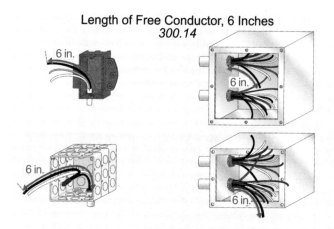

Length of Free Conductor, 6 Inches
300.14

At least 6 in. of free conductor is required at each box.

▶Figure 300–60

Boxes that have openings less than 8 in. in any dimension, must have at least 6 in. of free conductor, measured from the point where the conductors enter the box, and at least 3 in. of free conductor outside the box opening. ▶Figure 300–61

Length of Free Conductor, 3 Inches Outside Opening
300.14

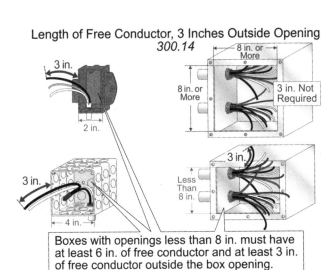

Boxes with openings less than 8 in. must have at least 6 in. of free conductor and at least 3 in. of free conductor outside the box opening.

Copyright 2017, www.MikeHolt.com

▶Figure 300–61

Ex: Six in. of free conductor aren't required for conductors that pass through a box without a splice or termination.

300.15 Boxes or Conduit Bodies

Fittings can only be used with the specific wiring methods for which they're listed and designed. For example, Type NM cable connectors aren't permitted to be used with Type AC cable, and electrical metallic tubing fittings aren't permitted to be used with rigid metal conduit or intermediate metal conduit, unless listed for the purpose. ▶Figure 300–62

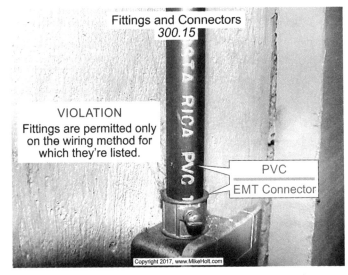

Fittings and Connectors
300.15

VIOLATION
Fittings are permitted only on the wiring method for which they're listed.

PVC
EMT Connector

Copyright 2017, www.MikeHolt.com

▶Figure 300–62

Author's Comment:

- PVC conduit couplings and connectors are permitted with electrical nonmetallic tubing if the proper glue is used in accordance with manufacturer's instructions [110.3(B)]. See 362.48.

A box or conduit body must be installed at each splice or termination point, except as permitted for by 310.15(A) through (L): ▶Figure 300–63 and ▶Figure 300–64

- Cabinets, 312.8
- Luminaires, 410.64
- Surface Raceways, 386.56 and 388.56
- Wireways, 376.56

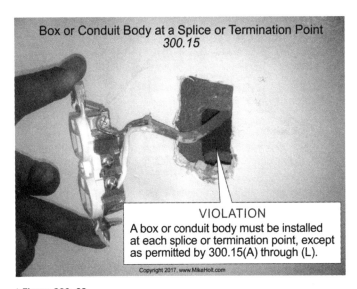

Box or Conduit Body at a Splice or Termination Point
300.15

VIOLATION
A box or conduit body must be installed at each splice or termination point, except as permitted by 300.15(A) through (L).

Copyright 2017, www.MikeHolt.com

▶Figure 300–63

Splice and Termination Points
Conduit Body
300.15

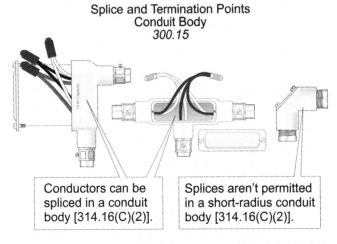

Conductors can be spliced in a conduit body [314.16(C)(2)].

Splices aren't permitted in a short-radius conduit body [314.16(C)(2)].

Copyright 2017, www.MikeHolt.com

▶Figure 300–64

Author's Comment:

- Boxes aren't required for the following signaling and communications cables or raceways: ▶ **Figure 300–65**

    ◆ Class 2 and 3 Control and Signaling, 725.3

    ◆ Communications, 90.3

    ◆ Coaxial Cable, 90.3

    ◆ Optical Fiber, 770.3

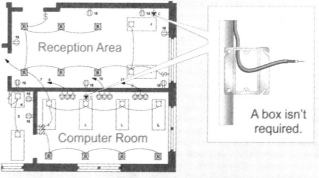

▶ Figure 300–65

(C) Raceways for Support or Protection. When a raceway is used for the support or protection of cables, a fitting to reduce the potential for abrasion must be placed at the location the cables enter the raceway. ▶ **Figure 300–66**

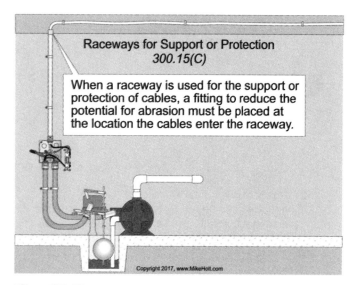

▶ Figure 300–66

(F) Fitting. A fitting is permitted in lieu of a box or conduit body where conductors aren't spliced or terminated within the fitting if it's accessible after installation. ▶ **Figure 300–67**

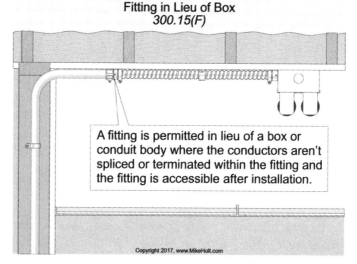

▶ Figure 300–67

(G) Underground Splices. A box or conduit body isn't required where a splice is made underground if the conductors are spliced with a splicing device listed for direct burial. See 110.14(B) and 300.5(E).

Author's Comment:

- See the definition of "Conduit Body" in Article 100.

(H) NM Cable Interconnection Devices. A box or conduit body isn't required where a listed nonmetallic-sheathed cable interconnector device is used for any exposed cable wiring or for concealed cable wiring in existing buildings in accordance with 334.40(B). ▶ **Figure 300–68**

(I) Enclosures. A box or conduit body isn't required where a splice is made in a cabinet containing switches or overcurrent protection devices if the splices or taps don't fill the wiring space at any cross section to more than 75 percent, and the wiring at any cross section doesn't exceed 40 percent. See 312.8 and 404.3(B). ▶ **Figure 300–69**

(L) Handhole Enclosures. A box or conduit body isn't required for conductors installed in a handhole enclosure. Splices must be made in accordance with 314.30. ▶ **Figure 300–70**

NM Cable Interconnection Devices
300.15(H)

A box isn't required where a listed NM cable interconnector device is used in accordance with 334.40(B).

▶Figure 300–68

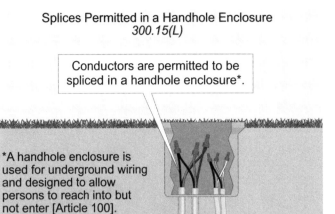

Splices Permitted in a Handhole Enclosure
300.15(L)

Conductors are permitted to be spliced in a handhole enclosure*.

*A handhole enclosure is used for underground wiring and designed to allow persons to reach into but not enter [Article 100].

▶Figure 300–70

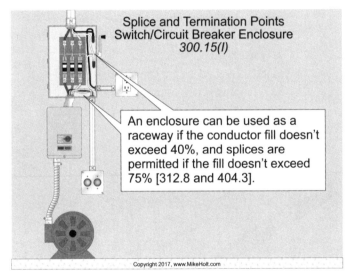

Splice and Termination Points
Switch/Circuit Breaker Enclosure
300.15(I)

An enclosure can be used as a raceway if the conductor fill doesn't exceed 40%, and splices are permitted if the fill doesn't exceed 75% [312.8 and 404.3].

▶Figure 300–69

Author's Comment:

■ Splices or terminations within a handhole must be accomplished using fittings listed as suitable for wet locations [110.14(B) and 314.30(C)].

300.16 Raceway or Cable to Open or Concealed Wiring

(B) Bushing. A bushing is permitted in lieu of a box or terminal where the conductors emerge from a raceway and enter or terminate at equipment such as open switchboards, unenclosed control equipment, or similar equipment.

300.17 Raceway Sizing

Raceways must be large enough to permit the installation and removal of conductors without damaging the conductors' insulation.

Author's Comment:

■ When all conductors within a raceway are the same size and of the same insulation type, the number of conductors permitted can be determined by Annex C.

Example: *How many 12 THHN conductors can be installed in trade size ¾ electrical metallic tubing?* ▶Figure 300–71

Answer: *16 conductors [Annex C, Table C.1]*

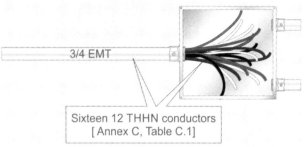

Raceway Sizing
300.17 Example

3/4 EMT

Sixteen 12 THHN conductors
[Annex C, Table C.1]

When all conductors in a raceway are the same size and insulation type, the number of conductors permitted can be determined by Annex C.

Copyright 2017, www.MikeHolt.com

▶Figure 300–71

Author's Comment:

- When different size conductors are installed within a raceway, conductor fill is limited to the percentages in Table 1 of Chapter 9.
  ▶Figure 300–72

Raceway Fill Limitation
Chapter 9, Table 1

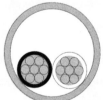

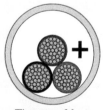

One Conductor	Two Conductors	Three or More Conductors
53% Fill	**31% Fill**	**40% Fill**

When conductors are installed in a raceway, conductor fill is limited to the above percentages.

Copyright 2017, www.MikeHolt.com

▶Figure 300–72

Table 1, Chapter 9	
Number	**Percent Fill**
1 Conductor	53%
2 Conductors	31%
3 or More	40%

The above percentages are based on conditions where the length of the conductor and number of raceway bends are within reasonable limits [Chapter 9, Table 1, Note 1].

Author's Comment:

- Follow these steps for sizing raceways:
  - **Step 1:** When sizing a raceway, first determine the total area of conductors (Chapter 9, Table 5 for insulated conductors and Chapter 9, Table 8 for bare conductors).
    ▶Figure 300–73
  - **Step 2:** Select the raceway from Chapter 9, Table 4, in accordance with the percent fill listed in Chapter 9, Table 1.
    ▶Figure 300–74

Conductor Cross-Sectional Area
Chapter 9, Tables 5 and 8 Example

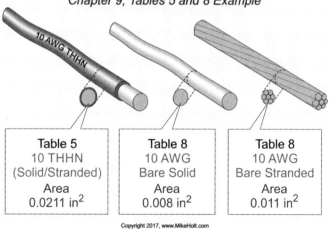

Table 5 10 THHN (Solid/Stranded) Area 0.0211 in²	Table 8 10 AWG Bare Solid Area 0.008 in²	Table 8 10 AWG Bare Stranded Area 0.011 in²

Copyright 2017, www.MikeHolt.com

▶Figure 300–73

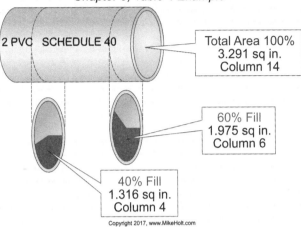

Raceway Cross-Sectional Area
Chapter 9, Table 4 Example

2 PVC SCHEDULE 40

Total Area 100%
3.291 sq in.
Column 14

60% Fill
1.975 sq in.
Column 6

40% Fill
1.316 sq in.
Column 4

Copyright 2017, www.MikeHolt.com

▶Figure 300–74

Example: What trade size Schedule 40 PVC conduit is required for the following conductors? ▶**Figure 300–75**

3—500 THHN
1—250 THHN
1—3 THHN

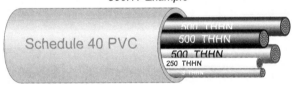

Raceway Sizing
300.17 Example

Schedule 40 PVC

500 THHN
500 THHN
500 THHN
250 THHN
3 THHN

Step 1. Determine the conductor area, Chapter 9, Table 5.

500 kcmil = 0.7073 in.² x 3 conductors = 2.1219 in.²
250 kcmil = 0.3970 in.² x 1 conductor   = 0.3970 in.²
  3 AWG = 0.0973 in.² x 1 conductor   = 0.0973 in.²
        Total area of the conductors = 2.6162 in.²

Step 2. Size the raceway at 40% fill, Chapter 9, Table 4.

Trade Size 3 PVC at 40 percent fill = 2.907 in.²

Copyright 2017, www.MikeHolt.com

▶Figure 300–75

Solution:

Step 1: Determine the total area of conductors [Chapter 9, Table 5]:

500 THHN	0.7073 × 3 =	2.1219 in²
250 THHN	0.3970 × 1 =	0.3970 in²
3 THHN	0.0973 × 1 =	+ 0.0973 in²
Total Area =		2.6162 in²

Step 2: Select the raceway at 40 percent fill [Chapter 9, Table 4]

Answer: Trade size 3 Schedule 40 PVC because there's 2.907 sq in. of conductor fill at 40 percent.

300.18 Inserting Conductors in Raceways

(A) Complete Runs. To protect conductor insulation from abrasion during installation, raceways must be mechanically completed between the pulling points before conductors are installed. See 300.10 and 300.12. ▶Figure 300–76

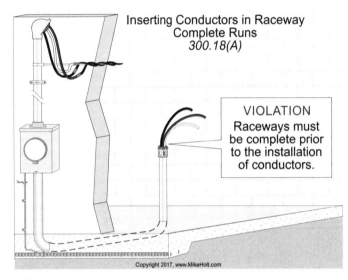

Inserting Conductors in Raceway
Complete Runs
300.18(A)

VIOLATION
Raceways must be complete prior to the installation of conductors.

Copyright 2017, www.MikeHolt.com

▶Figure 300–76

Ex: Short sections of raceways used for the protection of cables from physical damage aren't required to be installed complete between outlet, junction, or splicing points. ▶Figure 300–77

(B) Welding. Metal raceways aren't permitted to be supported, terminated, or connected by welding to the raceway.

300.19 Supporting Conductors in Vertical Raceways

(A) Spacing Intervals. If the vertical rise of a raceway exceeds the values of Table 300.19(A), each conductor must be supported at the top, or as close to the top as practical. Intermediate support must also be provided in increments that don't exceed the values of Table 300.19(A). ▶Figure 300–78

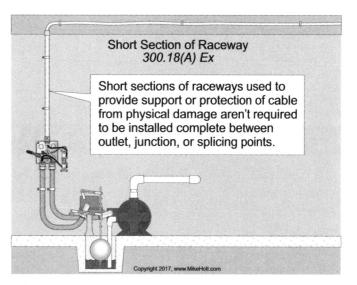

Short Section of Raceway
300.18(A) Ex

Short sections of raceways used to provide support or protection of cable from physical damage aren't required to be installed complete between outlet, junction, or splicing points.

▶Figure 300–77

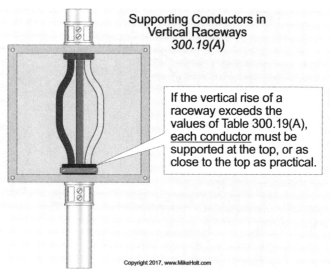

Supporting Conductors in
Vertical Raceways
300.19(A)

If the vertical rise of a raceway exceeds the values of Table 300.19(A), underline each conductor must be supported at the top, or as close to the top as practical.

▶Figure 300–78

Author's Comment:

■ The weight of long vertical runs of conductors can cause the conductors to actually drop out of the raceway if they aren't properly secured. There've been many cases where conductors in a vertical raceway were released from the pulling "basket" or "grip" (at the top) without being secured, and the conductors fell down and out of the raceway, injuring those at the bottom of the installation.

300.20 Induced Currents in Ferrous Metal Enclosures and Raceways

(A) Conductors Grouped Together. To minimize induction heating of ferrous metal raceways and ferrous metal enclosures for alternating-current circuits, and to maintain an effective ground-fault current path, all conductors of a circuit must be installed in the same raceway, cable, trench, cord, or cable tray. See 250.102(E), 300.3(B), 300.5(I), and 392.8(D). ▶Figure 300–79 and ▶Figure 300–80

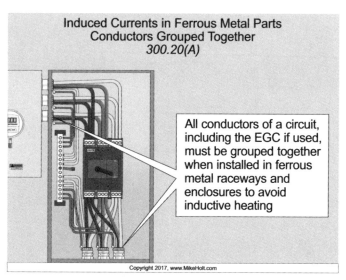

Induced Currents in Ferrous Metal Parts
Conductors Grouped Together
300.20(A)

All conductors of a circuit, including the EGC if used, must be grouped together when installed in ferrous metal raceways and enclosures to avoid inductive heating

▶Figure 300–79

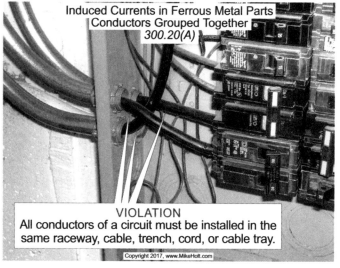

Induced Currents in Ferrous Metal Parts
Conductors Grouped Together
300.20(A)

VIOLATION
All conductors of a circuit must be installed in the same raceway, cable, trench, cord, or cable tray.

▶Figure 300–80

Author's Comment:

- When alternating current (ac) flows through a conductor, a pulsating or varying magnetic field is created around the conductor. This magnetic field is constantly expanding and contracting with the amplitude of the ac current. In the United States, the frequency is 60 cycles per second (Hz). Since ac reverses polarity 120 times per second, the magnetic field that surrounds the conductor also reverses its direction 120 times per second. This expanding and collapsing magnetic field induces eddy currents in the ferrous metal parts that surround the conductors, causing them to heat up from hysteresis heating.

- Magnetic materials naturally resist the rapidly changing magnetic fields. The resulting friction produces its own heat—hysteresis heating—in addition to eddy current heating. A metal which offers high resistance is said to have high magnetic "permeability." Permeability can vary on a scale of 100 to 500 for magnetic materials; nonmagnetic materials have a permeability of one.

- Simply put, the molecules of steel and iron align to the polarity of the magnetic field and when the magnetic field reverses, the molecules reverse their polarity as well. This back-and-forth alignment of the molecules heats up the metal, and the more the current flows, the more the heat rises in the ferrous metal parts. ▶Figure 300–81

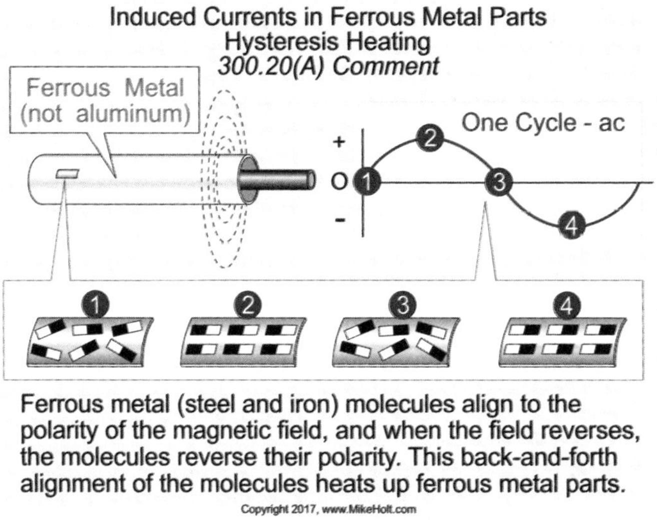

Induced Currents in Ferrous Metal Parts
Hysteresis Heating
300.20(A) Comment

Ferrous metal (steel and iron) molecules align to the polarity of the magnetic field, and when the field reverses, the molecules reverse their polarity. This back-and-forth alignment of the molecules heats up ferrous metal parts.

Copyright 2017, www.MikeHolt.com

▶Figure 300–81

- When conductors of the same circuit are grouped together, the magnetic fields of the different conductors tend to cancel each other out, resulting in a reduced magnetic field around them. The lower magnetic field reduces induced currents in the ferrous metal raceways or enclosures, which reduces the hysteresis heating of the surrounding metal enclosure.

WARNING: *There's been much discussion in the press on the effects of electromagnetic fields on humans. According to the Institute of Electrical and Electronics Engineers (IEEE), there's insufficient information at this time to define an unsafe electromagnetic field level.*

(B) Single Conductors. When single conductors are installed in nonmetallic raceways as permitted in 300.5(I) Ex 2, the inductive heating of the metal enclosure must be minimized using aluminum locknuts and by cutting a slot between the individual holes through which the conductors pass. ▶Figure 300–82

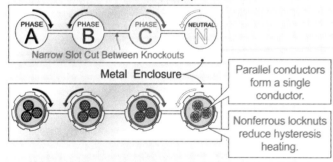

Induced Currents in Ferrous Metal Parts
Single Conductors
300.20(B)

When single conductors are installed in a nonmetallic raceway, inductive heating of the metal enclosure must be minimized by cutting a slot between the individual holes through which the conductors pass.

Copyright 2017, www.MikeHolt.com

▶Figure 300–82

Note: Because aluminum is a nonmagnetic metal, aluminum parts don't heat up due to hysteresis heating.

Author's Comment:

- Aluminum conduit, locknuts, and enclosures carry eddy currents, but because aluminum is nonferrous, it doesn't heat up [300.20(B) Note].

300.21 Spread of Fire or Products of Combustion

Electrical circuits and equipment must be installed in such a way that the spread of fire or products of combustion won't be substantially increased. Openings into or through fire-rated walls, floors, and ceilings for electrical equipment must be fire-stopped using methods approved by the authority having jurisdiction to maintain the fire-resistance rating of the fire-rated assembly. ▶Figure 300–83

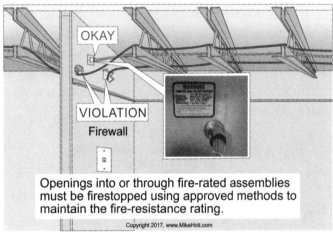

Spread of Fire or Products of Combustion
300.21

OKAY

VIOLATION
Firewall

Openings into or through fire-rated assemblies must be firestopped using approved methods to maintain the fire-resistance rating.

Copyright 2017, www.MikeHolt.com

▶Figure 300–83

Author's Comment:

■ Fire-stopping materials are listed for the specific types of wiring methods and the construction of the assembly that they penetrate. ▶Figure 300–84

Note: Directories of electrical construction materials published by qualified testing laboratories contain listing and installation restrictions necessary to maintain the fire-resistive rating of assemblies. Outlet boxes must have a horizontal separation of not less than 24 in. when installed in a fire-rated assembly, unless an outlet box is listed for closer spacing or protected by fire-resistant "putty pads" in accordance with manufacturer's instructions. ▶Figure 300–85 and ▶Figure 300–86

Author's Comment:

■ Boxes installed in fire-resistance-rated assemblies must be listed for the purpose. If steel boxes are used, they must be secured to the framing member, so cut-in type boxes aren't permitted (UL White Book, *Guide Information for Electrical Equipment*).

Spread of Fire or Products of Combustion
Examples of Approved Firestopping Methods.
300.21 Comment

Putty Pad in a
Metal Box

Cables in a
Ready Sleeve

Fire-stopping materials are listed for the specific types of wiring methods and the construction of the assembly that they penetrate.

Copyright 2017, www.MikeHolt.com

▶Figure 300–84

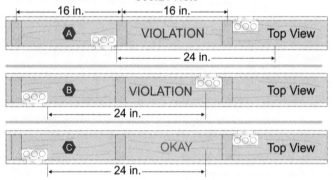

Spread of Fire or Products of Combustion
300.21 Note

16 in. — 16 in.

Ⓐ VIOLATION Top View
24 in.

Ⓑ VIOLATION Top View
24 in.

Ⓒ OKAY Top View
24 in.

3 examples (top view of wall) of outlet boxes installed on opposite sides of studs in a fire-rated assembly. 24 in. minimum horizontal separation is required unless protected by fire-resistant "putty pads."

Copyright 2017, www.MikeHolt.com

▶Figure 300–85

■ This rule also applies to control, signaling, and communications cables or raceways.

◆ Communications, 800.26
◆ Control and Signaling, 725.25
◆ Coaxial Cable, 820.26
◆ Fire Alarm, 760.3(A)
◆ Optical Fiber, 770.26
◆ Sound Systems, 640.3(A)

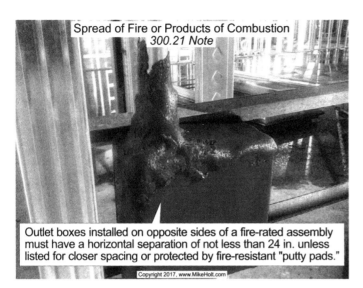

Outlet boxes installed on opposite sides of a fire-rated assembly must have a horizontal separation of not less than 24 in. unless listed for closer spacing or protected by fire-resistant "putty pads."

Copyright 2017, www.MikeHolt.com

▶Figure 300–86

300.22 Wiring in Ducts and Plenum Spaces

This section applies to the installation and uses of electrical wiring and equipment in ducts used for dust, loose stock, or vapor removal; ducts specifically fabricated for environmental air; and plenum spaces used for environmental air.

(A) Ducts Used for Dust, Loose Stock, or Vapor. Ducts that transport dust, loose stock, or vapors must not have any wiring method installed within them. ▶Figure 300–87

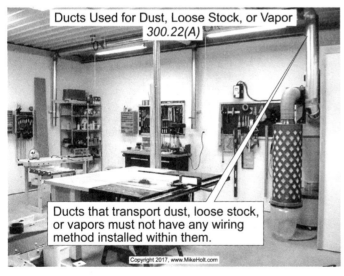

Ducts Used for Dust, Loose Stock, or Vapor
300.22(A)

Ducts that transport dust, loose stock, or vapors must not have any wiring method installed within them.

Copyright 2017, www.MikeHolt.com

▶Figure 300–87

(B) Ducts Specifically Fabricated for Environmental Air. If necessary for direct action upon, or sensing of, the contained air, Type MC cable that has a smooth or corrugated impervious metal sheath without an overall nonmetallic covering, electrical metallic tubing, flexible metallic tubing, intermediate metal conduit, or rigid metal conduit without an overall nonmetallic covering can be installed in ducts specifically fabricated to transport environmental air. Flexible metal conduit in lengths not exceeding 4 ft can be used to connect physically adjustable equipment and devices within the fabricated duct.

Equipment is only permitted within the duct specifically fabricated to transport environmental air if necessary for the direct action upon, or sensing of, the contained air. Equipment, devices, and/or illumination are only permitted to be installed in the duct if necessary to facilitate maintenance and repair. ▶Figure 300–88

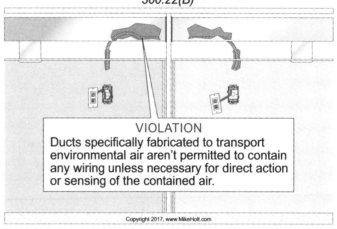

Wiring in Ducts Specifically Fabricated
for Environmental Air
300.22(B)

VIOLATION
Ducts specifically fabricated to transport environmental air aren't permitted to contain any wiring unless necessary for direct action or sensing of the contained air.

Copyright 2017, www.MikeHolt.com

▶Figure 300–88

Ex: Wiring methods and cables listed for plenum spaces can be installed in ducts specifically fabricated for environmental air-handling purposes under the following conditions: ▶Figure 300–89

(1) The wiring method or cabling is necessary to connect to equipment or devices associated with the direct action upon or sensing of the contained air, and

(2) The total length of such wiring method or cabling doesn't exceed 4 ft.

Author's Comment:

■ Class 2 and Class 3 cables selected in accordance with Table 725.154 and installed in accordance with 725.135(B) are permitted to be installed in ducts specifically fabricated for environmental air [725.3(C) Ex. 1].

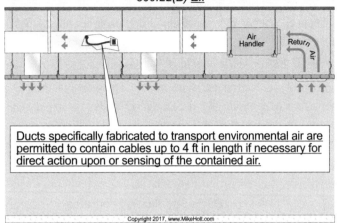

Wiring in Ducts Specifically Fabricated
for Environmental Air
300.22(B) Ex

Ducts specifically fabricated to transport environmental air are permitted to contain cables up to 4 ft in length if necessary for direct action upon or sensing of the contained air.

Copyright 2017, www.MikeHolt.com

▶Figure 300–89

- Power-limited fire alarm cables selected in accordance with Table 760.154 and installed in accordance with 760.135(B) are permitted to be installed in ducts specifically fabricated for environmental air [760.3(C) Ex. 1].

(C) Plenum Space for Environmental Air. This subsection applies only to plenum spaces (space above a suspended ceiling or below a raised floor used for environmental air), it doesn't apply to habitable rooms or areas of buildings, the prime purpose of which isn't air handling. ▶Figure 300–90

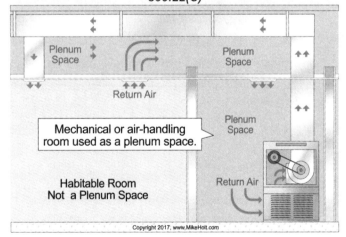

Other Spaces Used as a Plenum Space
300.22(C)

Plenum Space

Plenum Space

Return Air

Mechanical or air-handling room used as a plenum space.

Plenum Space

Return Air

Habitable Room
Not a Plenum Space

Copyright 2017, www.MikeHolt.com

▶Figure 300–90

Note 1: The spaces above a suspended ceiling or below a raised floor used for environmental air are examples of the type of plenum spaces to which this section applies. ▶Figure 300–91

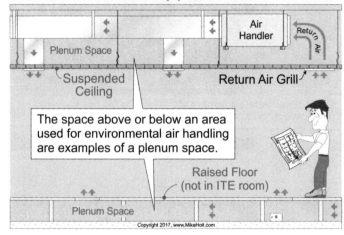

Other Spaces Used as a Plenum Space
300.22(C) Note 1

Air Handler

Return Air

Plenum Space

Suspended Ceiling

Return Air Grill

The space above or below an area used for environmental air handling are examples of a plenum space.

Raised Floor
(not in ITE room)

Plenum Space

Copyright 2017, www.MikeHolt.com

▶Figure 300–91

Ex: In a dwelling unit, this section doesn't apply to the space between joists or studs where the wiring passes through that space perpendicular to the long dimension of that space. ▶Figure 300–92

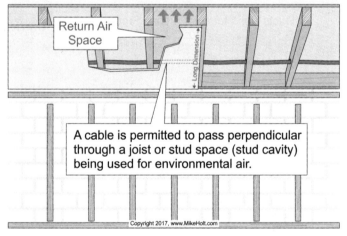

Other Spaces Used as a Plenum Space, Dwelling
300.22(C) Ex

Return Air Space

Long Dimension

A cable is permitted to pass perpendicular through a joist or stud space (stud cavity) being used for environmental air.

Copyright 2017, www.MikeHolt.com

▶Figure 300–92

(1) Wiring Methods. Electrical metallic tubing, rigid metal conduit, intermediate metal conduit, armored cable, metal-clad cable without a nonmetallic cover, and flexible metal conduit can be installed in a plenum space. Surface metal raceways or metal wireways with metal covers can be installed in a plenum space. ▶Figure 300–93

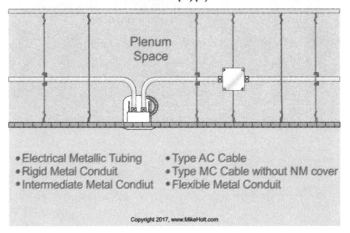

Wiring Methods Permitted in a Plenum Space
300.22(C)(1)

Plenum Space

• Electrical Metallic Tubing
• Rigid Metal Conduit
• Intermediate Metal Condiut
• Type AC Cable
• Type MC Cable without NM cover
• Flexible Metal Conduit

Copyright 2017, www.MikeHolt.com

▶Figure 300–93

Cable ties for securing and supporting must be listed for use in a plenum space. ▶Figure 300–94

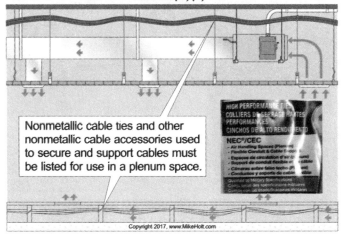

Cable Ties Used in a Plenum Space
300.22(C)(1)

Nonmetallic cable ties and other nonmetallic cable accessories used to secure and support cables must be listed for use in a plenum space.

Copyright 2017, www.MikeHolt.com

▶Figure 300–94

Author's Comment:

- PVC conduit [Article 352], electrical nonmetallic tubing [Article 362], liquidtight flexible conduit, and nonmetallic cables aren't permitted to be installed in plenum spaces because they give off deadly toxic fumes when burned or superheated.

- Plenum-rated control, signaling, and communications cables and raceways are permitted in plenum spaces according to the following: ▶Figure 300–95

  ◆ Communications, Table 800.154(a)
  ◆ Control and Signaling, 725.3(C) Ex 2
  ◆ Coaxial Cable, Table 820.154(a)
  ◆ Fire Alarm, Table 760.3(C) Ex 2
  ◆ Optical Fiber Cables and Raceways, Table 770.154(a)
  ◆ Sound Systems, 640.9(C) and Table 725.154

- Any wiring method suitable for the condition can be used in a space not used for environmental air-handling purposes. ▶Figure 300–96

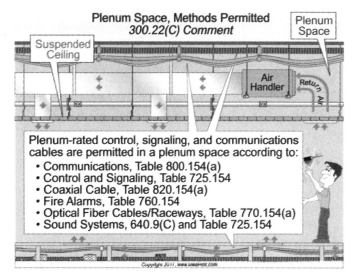

Plenum Space, Methods Permitted
300.22(C) Comment

Plenum Space

Suspended Ceiling

Air Handler

Plenum-rated control, signaling, and communications cables are permitted in a plenum space according to:
• Communications, Table 800.154(a)
• Control and Signaling, Table 725.154
• Coaxial Cable, Table 820.154(a)
• Fire Alarms, Table 760.154
• Optical Fiber Cables/Raceways, Table 770.154(a)
• Sound Systems, 640.9(C) and Table 725.154

▶Figure 300–95

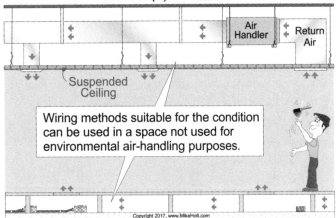

▶Figure 300–96

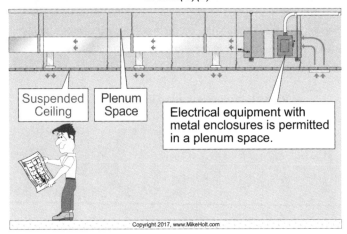

▶Figure 300–98

(2) Cable Tray Systems.

(a) Metal Cable Tray Systems. Metal cable tray systems can be installed to support the wiring methods and equipment permitted to be installed in a plenum space. ▶**Figure 300–97**

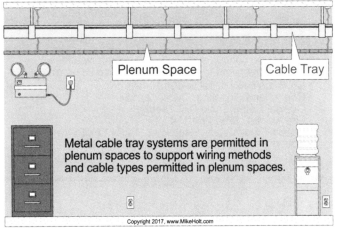

▶Figure 300–97

(3) Equipment. Electrical equipment with a metal enclosure can be installed in a plenum space. ▶**Figure 300–98**

Author's Comment:

■ Examples of electrical equipment permitted in plenum spaces are air-handlers, junction boxes, and dry-type transformers; however, transformers must not be rated over 50 kVA when located in hollow spaces [450.13(B)].

(D) Information Technology Equipment. Wiring methods beneath raised floors for information technology equipment can be installed as permitted in Article 645. ▶**Figure 300–99**

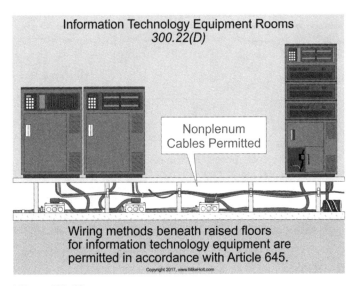

▶Figure 300–99

300.23 Panels Designed to Allow Access

Wiring, cables, and equipment installed behind panels must be located so the panels can be removed to give access to electrical equipment.
▶Figure 300–100

Author's Comment:

■ Access to equipment must not be hindered by an accumulation of cables that prevents the removal of suspended-ceiling panels. Control, signaling, and communications cables must be located and supported so the suspended-ceiling panels can be moved to provide access to electrical equipment.

 ◆ Communications Cable, 800.21
 ◆ Control and Signaling Cable, 725.21
 ◆ Coaxial Cable, 820.21
 ◆ Fire Alarm Cable, 760.21
 ◆ Optical Fiber Cable, 770.21
 ◆ Audio Cable, 640.5

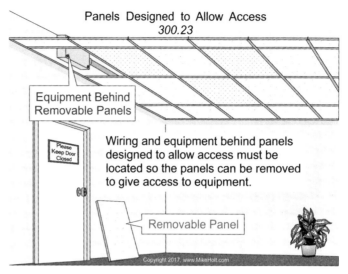

▶Figure 300–100

ARTICLE
300 PRACTICE QUESTIONS

Please use the 2017 *Code* book to answer the following questions.

1. All conductors of the same circuit, including the grounded and equipment grounding conductors and bonding conductors shall be contained within the same _____, unless otherwise permitted elsewhere in the *NEC*.

    (a) raceway
    (b) cable
    (c) trench
    (d) all of these

2. Conductors installed in nonmetallic raceways run underground shall be permitted to be arranged as _____ installations. The raceways shall be installed in close proximity, and the conductors shall comply with the provisions of 300.20(B).

    (a) neutral
    (b) grounded conductor
    (c) isolated phase
    (d) all of these

3. Conductors of ac and dc circuits, rated 1,000V or less, shall be permitted to occupy the same _____ provided that all conductors have an insulation rating equal to the maximum voltage applied to any conductor.

    (a) enclosure
    (b) cable
    (c) raceway
    (d) any of these

4. Where cables or nonmetallic raceways are installed through bored holes in joists, rafters, or wood members, holes shall be bored so that the edge of the hole is _____ the nearest edge of the wood member.

    (a) not less than 1¼ in. from
    (b) immediately adjacent to
    (c) not less than ¹⁄₁₆ in. from
    (d) 90 degrees away from

5. Cables laid in wood notches require protection against nails or screws by using a steel plate at least _____ in. thick, installed before the building finish is applied.

    (a) ¹⁄₁₆
    (b) ⅛
    (c) ¼
    (d) ½

6. Where Type NM cable passes through factory or field openings in metal members, it shall be protected by _____ bushings or _____ grommets that cover metal edges.

    (a) approved
    (b) identified
    (c) listed
    (d) none of these

7. Where Type NM cables pass through cut or drilled slots or holes in metal members, the cable shall be protected by _____ which are installed in the opening prior to the installation of the cable and which securely cover all metal edges.

   (a) listed bushings
   (b) listed grommets
   (c) plates
   (d) a or b

8. Where nails or screws are likely to penetrate nonmetallic-sheathed cable or ENT installed through metal framing members, a steel sleeve, steel plate, or steel clip not less than _____ in. in thickness shall be used to protect the cable or tubing.

   (a) $\frac{1}{16}$
   (b) $\frac{1}{8}$
   (c) $\frac{1}{2}$
   (d) $\frac{3}{4}$

9. Wiring methods installed behind panels that allow access shall be _____ according to their applicable articles.

   (a) supported
   (b) painted
   (c) in a metal raceway
   (d) all of these

10. Where cables and nonmetallic raceways are installed parallel to framing members, the nearest outside surface of the cable or raceway shall be _____ the nearest edge of the framing member where nails or screws are likely to penetrate.

    (a) not less than $1\frac{1}{4}$ in. from
    (b) immediately adjacent to
    (c) not less than $\frac{1}{16}$ in. from
    (d) 90 degrees away from

11. A cable, raceway, or box installed under metal-corrugated sheet roof decking shall be supported so the top of the cable, raceway, or box is not less than _____ in. from the lowest surface of the roof decking to the top of the cable, raceway, or box.

    (a) $\frac{1}{2}$
    (b) 1
    (c) $1\frac{1}{2}$
    (d) 2

12. When installed under metal-corrugated sheet roof decking, cables, raceways, and enclosures are permitted in concealed locations of metal-corrugated sheet decking type roofing if they are at least 2 in. away from a structural support member.

    (a) True
    (b) False

13. When installed under metal-corrugated sheet roof decking, the rules for spacing from roof decking apply equally to rigid metal conduit and intermediate metal conduit.

    (a) True
    (b) False

14. Where raceways contain insulated circuit conductors _____ AWG and larger, the conductors shall be protected from abrasion during and after installation by a fitting that provides a smooth, rounded insulating surface.

    (a) 8
    (b) 6
    (c) 4
    (d) 2

15. A listed expansion/deflection fitting or other approved means shall be used where a raceway crosses a _____ intended for expansion, contraction or deflection used in buildings, bridges, parking garages, or other structures.

    (a) junction box
    (b) structural joint
    (c) cable tray
    (d) unistrut hanger

16. What is the minimum cover requirement for direct burial Type UF cable installed outdoors that supplies a 120V, 30A circuit?

    (a) 6 in.
    (b) 12 in.
    (c) 18 in.
    (d) 24 in.

17. Rigid metal conduit that is directly buried outdoors shall have at least _____ in. of cover.

    (a) 6
    (b) 12
    (c) 18
    (d) 24

18. When installing PVC conduit underground without concrete cover, there shall be a minimum of _____ in. of cover.

    (a) 6
    (b) 12
    (c) 18
    (d) 22

19. What is the minimum cover requirement for Type UF cable supplying power to a 120V, 15A GFCI-protected circuit outdoors under a driveway of a one-family dwelling?

    (a) 6 in.
    (b) 12 in.
    (c) 16 in.
    (d) 24 in.

20. Type UF cable used with a 24V landscape lighting system can have a minimum cover of _____ in.

    (a) 6
    (b) 12
    (c) 18
    (d) 24

21. For locations not specifically identified in Table 300.5, a lesser cover depth than required in Column 5 shall be permitted where specified in the installation instructions of a(n) _____ low-voltage lighting system.

    (a) approved
    (b) labeled
    (c) listed
    (d) none of these

22. For locations not specifically identified in Table 300.5, a cover depth of _____ in. shall be permitted for pool, spa, and fountain lighting, installed in a nonmetallic raceway, limited to not more than 30V where part of a listed low-voltage lighting system.

    (a) 6
    (b) 12
    (c) 18
    (d) 24

23. "_____" is defined as the shortest distance measured between a point on the top surface of direct-burial cable and the top surface of the finished grade.

    (a) Notch
    (b) Cover
    (c) Gap
    (d) none of these

24. The interior of underground raceways shall be considered a _____ location.

    (a) wet
    (b) dry
    (c) damp
    (d) corrosive

25. Type MC Cable listed for _____ is permitted to be installed underground under a building without installation in a raceway.

    (a) direct burial
    (b) damp and wet locations
    (c) rough service
    (d) b and c

26. Where direct-buried conductors and cables emerge from grade, they shall be protected by enclosures or raceways to a point at least _____ ft above finished grade.

    (a) 3
    (b) 6
    (c) 8
    (d) 10

27. Direct-buried service conductors that are not encased in concrete and that are buried 18 in. or more below grade shall have their location identified by a warning ribbon placed in the trench at least _____ in. above the underground installation.

    (a) 6
    (b) 10
    (c) 12
    (d) 18

28. Direct-buried conductors or cables can be spliced or tapped without the use of splice boxes when the splice or tap is made in accordance with 110.14(B).

    (a) True
    (b) False

29. Backfill used for underground wiring shall not damage _____ or prevent adequate compaction of fill or contribute to corrosion.

   (a) raceways
   (b) cables
   (c) conductors
   (d) all of these

30. Conduits or raceways through which moisture may contact live parts shall be _____ at either or both ends.

   (a) sealed
   (b) plugged
   (c) bushed
   (d) a or b

31. Spare or unused raceways shall be sealed with sealants _____ for use with the cable insulation, conductor insulation, bare conductor, shield, or other components.

   (a) listed
   (b) identified
   (c) approved
   (d) any of these

32. A _____, with an integral bushed opening shall be used at the end of a conduit or other raceway that terminates underground where the conductors or cables emerge as a direct burial wiring method.

   (a) splice kit
   (b) terminal fitting
   (c) bushing
   (d) b or c

33. All conductors of the same circuit shall be _____, unless otherwise specifically permitted in the NEC.

   (a) in the same raceway or cable
   (b) in close proximity in the same trench
   (c) the same size
   (d) a or b

34. Each direct-buried single conductor cable shall be located _____ in the trench to the other single conductor cables in the same parallel set of conductors, including equipment grounding conductors.

   (a) perpendicular
   (b) bundled together
   (c) in close proximity
   (d) spaced apart

35. Direct-buried conductors, cables, or raceways, which are subject to movement by settlement or frost, shall be arranged to prevent damage to the _____ or to equipment connected to the raceways.

   (a) siding of the building mounted on
   (b) landscaping around the cable or raceway
   (c) enclosed conductors
   (d) expansion fitting

36. "S" loops in underground direct burial _____ to raceway transitions, expansion fittings in raceway risers to fixed equipment, and, generally, the provision of flexible connections to equipment subject to settlement or frost heaves are recognized by the NEC.

   (a) feeders and circuits
   (b) cables and conductors
   (c) wireways and cable trays
   (d) none of these

37. Cables or raceways installed using directional boring equipment shall be _____ for this purpose.

   (a) marked
   (b) listed
   (c) labeled
   (d) approved

38. Raceways, cable trays, cablebus, auxiliary gutters, cable armor, boxes, cable sheathing, cabinets, elbows, couplings, fittings, supports, and support hardware shall be of materials suitable for _____.

   (a) corrosive locations
   (b) wet locations
   (c) the environment in which they are to be installed
   (d) none of these

39. Where corrosion protection is necessary for ferrous metal equipment and the conduit is threaded in the field, the threads shall be coated with a(n) _____ electrically conductive, corrosion-resistant compound.

   (a) marked
   (b) listed
   (c) labeled
   (d) approved

40. Which of the following metal parts shall be protected from corrosion?

    (a) Ferrous metal raceways.
    (b) Ferrous metal elbows.
    (c) Ferrous boxes.
    (d) all of these

41. Ferrous metal raceways, boxes, fittings, supports, and support hardware can be installed in concrete or in direct contact with the earth or other areas subject to severe corrosive influences, where _____ approved for the condition.

    (a) the soil is
    (b) made of material
    (c) the qualified installer is
    (d) none of these

42. Aluminum raceways, cable trays, cablebus, auxiliary gutters, cable armor, boxes, cable sheathing, cabinets, elbows, couplings, nipples, fittings, supports, and support hardware _____ shall be provided with supplementary corrosion protection.

    (a) embedded or encased in concrete
    (b) in direct contact with the earth
    (c) likely to become energized
    (d) a or b

43. Where exposed to sunlight, nonmetallic raceways, cable trays, boxes, cables with a nonmetallic outer jacket, fittings, and support hardware shall be _____.

    (a) listed as sunlight resistant
    (b) identified as sunlight resistant
    (c) a and b
    (d) a or b

44. Where nonmetallic wiring methods are subject to exposure to chemical solvents or vapors, they shall be inherently resistant to chemicals based upon their being _____ for the specific chemical reagent.

    (a) listed
    (b) identified
    (c) a and b
    (d) a or b

45. An exposed wiring system for indoor wet locations where walls are frequently washed shall be mounted so that there is at least a _____ between the mounting surface and the electrical equipment.

    (a) ¼-in. airspace
    (b) separation by insulated bushings
    (c) separation by noncombustible tubing
    (d) none of these

46. In general, areas where acids and alkali chemicals are handled and stored may present corrosive conditions, particularly when wet or damp.

    (a) True
    (b) False

47. Where portions of a cable raceway or sleeve are subjected to different temperatures and condensation is known to be a problem, the _____ shall be filled with an approved material to prevent the circulation of warm air to a colder section of the raceway or sleeve.

    (a) raceway
    (b) sleeve
    (c) a or b
    (d) none of these

48. Raceways shall be provided with expansion, expansion-deflection, or deflection fittings where necessary to compensate for thermal expansion, deflection, and contraction.

    (a) True
    (b) False

49. Raceways or cable trays containing electric conductors shall not contain any pipe or tube for steam, water, air, gas, drainage, or any service other than _____.

    (a) as permitted by the authority having jurisdiction
    (b) electrical
    (c) pneumatic
    (d) as designed by the engineer

50. Where raceways are installed in wet locations above grade, the interior of these raceways shall be considered a _____ location.

    (a) wet
    (b) dry
    (c) damp
    (d) corrosive

51. Metal raceways, cable armor, and other metal enclosures shall be _____ joined together into a continuous electric conductor so as to provide effective electrical continuity.

    (a) electrically
    (b) permanently
    (c) metallically
    (d) none of these

52. Raceways, cable assemblies, boxes, cabinets, and fittings shall be securely fastened in place.

    (a) True
    (b) False

53. Where independent support wires of a suspended ceiling assembly are used to support raceways, cable assemblies, or boxes above a ceiling, they shall be secured at _____ end(s).

    (a) one
    (b) both
    (c) a or b
    (d) none of these

54. Electrical wiring within the cavity of a fire-rated floor-ceiling or roof-ceiling assembly shall not be supported by the ceiling assembly or ceiling support wires.

    (a) True
    (b) False

55. The independent support wires for supporting electrical wiring methods in a fire-rated ceiling assembly shall be distinguishable from fire-rated suspended-ceiling framing support wires by _____.

    (a) color
    (b) tagging
    (c) other effective means
    (d) any of these

56. Independent support wires used for the support of electrical raceways and cables within nonfire-rated assemblies shall be distinguishable from the suspended-ceiling framing support wires.

    (a) True
    (b) False

57. Raceways can be used as a means of support of Class 2 circuit conductors or cables that connect to the same equipment.

    (a) True
    (b) False

58. Cable wiring methods shall not be used as a means of support for _____.

    (a) other cables
    (b) raceways
    (c) nonelectrical equipment
    (d) all of these

59. Raceways and cables installed into the _____ of open bottom equipment shall not be required to be mechanically secured to the equipment.

    (a) bottom
    (b) sides
    (c) top
    (d) any of these

60. Conductors in raceways shall be _____ between outlets, boxes, devices, and so forth.

    (a) continuous
    (b) installed
    (c) copper
    (d) in conduit

61. In multiwire branch circuits, the continuity of the _____ conductor shall not be dependent upon the device connections.

    (a) ungrounded
    (b) grounded
    (c) grounding electrode
    (d) a and b

62. When the opening to an outlet, junction, or switch point is less than 8 in. in any dimension, each conductor shall be long enough to extend at least _____ in. outside the opening of the enclosure.

    (a) 1
    (b) 3
    (c) 6
    (d) 12

63. Fittings and connectors shall be used only with the specific wiring methods for which they are designed and listed.

    (a) True
    (b) False

64. A box or conduit body shall not be required where cables enter or exit from conduit or tubing that is used to provide cable support or protection against physical damage.

    (a) True
    (b) False

65. A box or conduit body shall not be required for splices and taps in direct-buried conductors and cables as long as the splice is made with a splicing device that is identified for the purpose.

    (a) True
    (b) False

66. A box or conduit body shall not be required for conductors in hand-hole enclosures, except where connected to electrical equipment.

    (a) True
    (b) False

67. A bushing shall be permitted in lieu of a box or terminal where the conductors emerge from a raceway and enter or terminate at equipment such as open switchboards, unenclosed control equipment, or similar equipment.

    (a) True
    (b) False

68. The number and size of conductors permitted in a raceway is limited to _____.

    (a) permit heat to dissipate
    (b) prevent damage to insulation during installation
    (c) prevent damage to insulation during removal of conductors
    (d) all of these

69. Raceways shall be _____ between outlet, junction, or splicing points prior to the installation of conductors.

    (a) installed complete
    (b) tested for ground faults
    (c) a minimum of 80 percent complete
    (d) none of these

70. Prewired raceway assemblies shall be used only where specifically permitted in the *NEC* for the applicable wiring method.

    (a) True
    (b) False

71. Short sections of raceways used for _____ shall not be required to be installed complete between outlet, junction, or splicing points.

    (a) meter to service enclosure connection
    (b) protection of cables from physical damage
    (c) nipples
    (d) separately derived systems

72. Metal raceways shall not be _____ by welding to the raceway.

    (a) supported
    (b) terminated
    (c) connected
    (d) all of these

73. At least _____ support method(s) shall be provided for each conductor at the top of the vertical raceway or as close to the top as practical if the vertical rise exceeds the values in Table 300.19(A).

    (a) one
    (b) two
    (c) three
    (d) four

74. A vertical run of 4/0 AWG copper shall be supported at intervals not exceeding _____.

    (a) 40 ft
    (b) 80 ft
    (c) 100 ft
    (d) 120 ft

75. Conductors in ferrous metal raceways or enclosures shall be arranged so as to avoid heating the surrounding ferrous metal by alternating-current induction. To accomplish this, the _____ conductor(s) shall be grouped together.

    (a) phase
    (b) grounded
    (c) equipment grounding
    (d) all of these

76. _____ is a nonferrous, nonmagnetic metal that has no heating due to hysteresis heating.

    (a) Steel
    (b) Iron
    (c) Aluminum
    (d) all of these

77. Electrical installations in hollow spaces, vertical shafts, and ventilation or air-handling ducts shall be made so that the possible spread of fire or products of combustion is not _____.

    (a) substantially increased
    (b) allowed
    (c) inherent
    (d) possible

78. Openings around electrical penetrations into or through fire-resistant-rated walls, partitions, floors, or ceilings shall _____ to maintain the fire-resistance rating.

    (a) be documented
    (b) not be permitted
    (c) be firestopped using approved methods
    (d) be enlarged

79. No wiring of any type shall be installed in ducts used to transport _____.

    (a) dust
    (b) flammable vapors
    (c) loose stock
    (d) all of these

80. Equipment and devices shall only be permitted within ducts or plenum chambers specifically fabricated to transport environmental air if necessary for their direct action upon, or sensing of, the _____.

    (a) contained air
    (b) air quality
    (c) air temperature
    (d) none of these

81. Wiring methods and cabling systems, listed for use in other spaces used for environmental air (plenums), shall be permitted to be installed in ducts specifically fabricated for environmental air-handling purposes _____.

    (a) only if necessary to connect to equipment or devices associated with the direct action upon or sensing of the contained air
    (b) if the total length of such wiring methods or cabling systems does not exceed 4 ft
    (c) a and b
    (d) none of these

82. The space above a hung ceiling used for environmental air-handling purposes is an example of _____, and the wiring limitations of _____ apply.

    (a) a specifically fabricated duct used for environmental air, 300.22(B)
    (b) other space used for environmental air (plenum), 300.22(C)
    (c) a supply duct used for environmental air, 300.22(B)
    (d) none of these

83. A(n) _____ is not a plenum space.

    (a) office space
    (b) mechanical room
    (c) space over a hung ceiling used for environmental air-handling purposes
    (d) a and b

84. Wiring methods permitted in the ceiling areas used for environmental air include _____.

    (a) electrical metallic tubing
    (b) FMC of any length
    (c) RMC without an overall nonmetallic covering
    (d) all of these

85. _____ shall be permitted to support the wiring methods and equipment permitted to be used in other spaces used for environmental air (plenum).

    (a) Metal cable tray systems
    (b) Nonmetallic wireways
    (c) PVC conduit
    (d) Surface nonmetallic raceways

86. Electrical equipment with _____ and having low smoke and heat release properties, and associated wiring material suitable for the ambient temperature can be installed within an air-handling space (plenum).

    (a) a metal enclosure
    (b) a nonmetallic enclosure listed for use within an air-handling (plenum) space
    (c) any type of enclosure
    (d) a or b

87. Wiring methods and equipment installed behind suspended-ceiling panels shall be arranged and secured to allow access to the electrical equipment.

    (a) True
    (b) False

ARTICLE 310

CONDUCTORS FOR GENERAL WIRING

Introduction to Article 310—Conductors for General Wiring

This article contains the general requirements for conductors, such as insulation markings, ampacity ratings, and conditions of use. Article 310 doesn't apply to conductors that are part of flexible cords, fixture wires, or to conductors that are an integral part of equipment [90.7 and 300.1(B)].

People often make mistakes in applying the ampacity tables contained in Article 310. If you study the explanations carefully, you'll avoid common errors such as applying Table 310.15(B)(17) when you should be applying Table 310.15(B)(16).

Why so many tables? Why does Table 310.15(B)(17) list the ampacity of 6 THHN as 105A, while Table 310.15(B)(16) lists the same conductor as having an ampacity of only 75A? To answer that, go back to Article 100 and review the definition of ampacity. Notice the phrase "conditions of use." These tables set a maximum current value at which premature failure of the conductor insulation shouldn't occur during normal use, under the conditions described in the tables.

The designations THHN, THHW, RHH, and so on, are insulation types. Every type of insulation has a limit as to how much heat it can withstand. When current flows through a conductor, it creates heat. How well the insulation around a conductor can dissipate that heat depends on factors such as whether the conductor is in free air or not. Think about what happens when you put on a sweater, a jacket, and then a coat—all at the same time. You heat up. Your skin can't dissipate heat with all that clothing on nearly as well as it dissipates heat in free air. The same principle applies to conductors.

Conductor insulation also fails with age. That's why we conduct cable testing and take other measures to predict failure and replace certain conductors (for example, feeders or critical equipment conductors) while they're still within design specifications. But conductor insulation failure takes decades under normal use—and it's a maintenance issue. However, if a conductor is forced to exceed the ampacity listed in the appropriate table, and as a result its design temperature is exceeded, insulation failure happens much more rapidly—often catastrophically. Consequently, exceeding the allowable ampacity of a conductor is a serious safety issue.

Part I. General

310.1 Scope

Article 310 contains the general requirements for conductors, such as insulation markings, ampacity ratings, and their use. ▶Figure 310–1

Part II. Installation

310.10 Uses Permitted

(B) Dry and Damp Locations. Insulated conductors typically used in dry and damp locations include THHN, THHW, THWN, or THWN-2.

Conductors for General Wiring
310.1 Scope

Article 310 covers general requirements for conductors and their type designations, insulations, markings, strength ampacity ratings and their use.

Copyright 2017, www.MikeHolt.com

▶Figure 310–1

Author's Comment:

■ Refer to Table 310.104 for a complete list of conductors that may be installed in dry or damp locations.

(C) Wet Locations. Insulated conductors typically used in wet locations include:

(2) Types THHW, THWN, THWN-2, XHHW, or XHHW-2

Author's Comment:

■ Refer to Table 310.104 for a complete list of conductors that may be installed in wet locations.

(D) Locations Exposed to Direct Sunlight. Insulated conductors and cables exposed to the direct rays of the sun must be:

(1) Listed as sunlight resistant or marked as being sunlight resistant. ▶Figure 310–2

Author's Comment:

■ SE cable and the conductors contained in the cable are listed as sunlight resistant. However, according to the UL listing standard, the conductors contained in SE cable aren't required to be marked as sunlight resistant.

(2) Covered with insulating material, such as tape or sleeving materials that are listed as being sunlight resistant or marked as being sunlight resistant.

Conductors Exposed
to Direct Sunlight
310.10(D)(1)

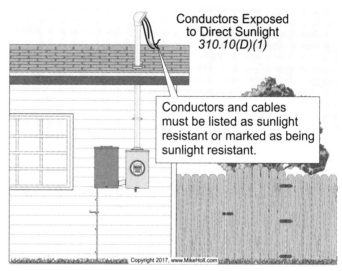

Conductors and cables must be listed as sunlight resistant or marked as being sunlight resistant.

Copyright 2017, www.MikeHolt.com

▶Figure 310–2

(G) Corrosive Conditions. Conductor insulation must be suitable for any substance to which it may be exposed that may have a detrimental effect on the conductor's insulation, such as oil, grease, vapor, gases, fumes, liquids, or other substances. See 110.11.

(H) Conductors in Parallel.

(1) General. Ungrounded and neutral conductors can be connected in parallel only in sizes 1/0 AWG and larger where installed in accordance with (H)(2) through (H)(6). ▶Figure 310–3

Conductors in Parallel
310.10(H)(1)

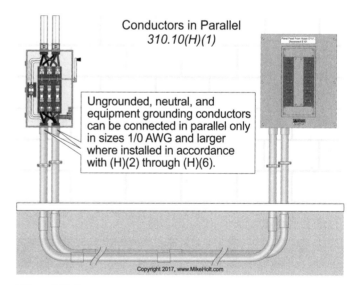

Ungrounded, neutral, and equipment grounding conductors can be connected in parallel only in sizes 1/0 AWG and larger where installed in accordance with (H)(2) through (H)(6).

Copyright 2017, www.MikeHolt.com

▶Figure 310–3

(2) Conductor and Installation Characteristics. When circuit conductors are installed in parallel, the conductors must be connected so the current will be evenly distributed between the individual parallel conductors by requiring all circuit conductors within each parallel set to: ▶Figure 310–4

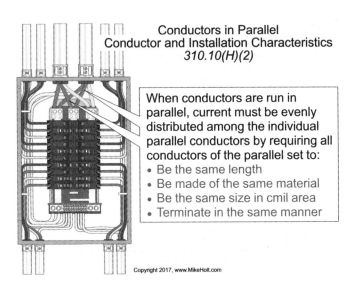

Conductors in Parallel
Conductor and Installation Characteristics
310.10(H)(2)

When conductors are run in parallel, current must be evenly distributed among the individual parallel conductors by requiring all conductors of the parallel set to:
• Be the same length
• Be made of the same material
• Be the same size in cmil area
• Terminate in the same manner

Copyright 2017, www.MikeHolt.com

▶Figure 310–4

(1) Be the same length.

(2) Consist of the same conductor material (copper/aluminum).

(3) Be the same size in circular mil area (minimum 1/0 AWG).

(4) Have the same type of insulation (like THHN).

(5) Terminate using the same method (set screw fitting versus compression fitting).

Author's Comment:

■ When installed in raceways or enclosures, paralleled conductors must be grouped to prevent inductive heating. ▶Figure 310–5

(3) Separate Raceways or Cables. Raceways or cables containing parallel conductors must have the same electrical characteristics. ▶Figure 310–6

Conductors of one phase, neutral, or equipment grounding conductor are not required to have the same physical characteristics as those of another phase, neutral, or equipment grounding conductor.

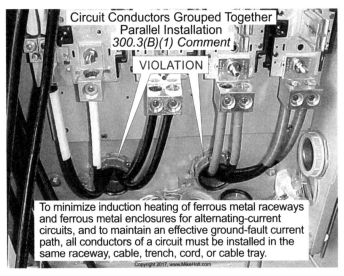

Circuit Conductors Grouped Together
Parallel Installation
300.3(B)(1) Comment

VIOLATION

To minimize induction heating of ferrous metal raceways and ferrous metal enclosures for alternating-current circuits, and to maintain an effective ground-fault current path, all conductors of a circuit must be installed in the same raceway, cable, trench, cord, or cable tray.

Copyright 2017, www.MikeHolt.com

▶Figure 310–5

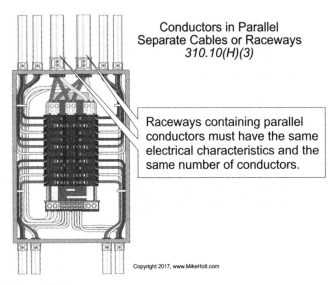

Conductors in Parallel
Separate Cables or Raceways
310.10(H)(3)

Raceways containing parallel conductors must have the same electrical characteristics and the same number of conductors.

Copyright 2017, www.MikeHolt.com

▶Figure 310–6

Author's Comment:

■ If one set of parallel conductors is installed in a metal raceway and the other conductors are installed in PVC conduit, the conductors in the metal raceway will have an increased opposition to current flow (impedance) as compared to the conductors in the nonmetallic raceway. This results in an unbalanced distribution of current between the parallel conductors.

■ Parallel conductor sets must have all circuit conductors within the same raceway [300.3(B)(1)]. ▶Figure 310–7

Parallel sets of conductors aren't required to have the same physical characteristics as those of another set to achieve balance.

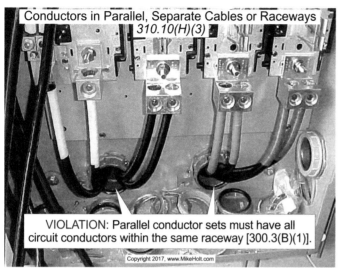

VIOLATION: Parallel conductor sets must have all circuit conductors within the same raceway [300.3(B)(1)].

Copyright 2017, www.MikeHolt.com

▶Figure 310–7

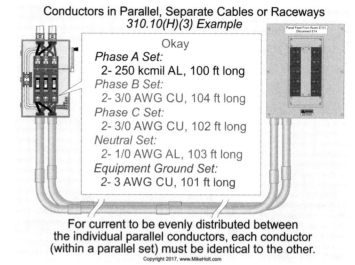

Conductors in Parallel, Separate Cables or Raceways
310.10(H)(3) Example

Okay
Phase A Set:
2- 250 kcmil AL, 100 ft long
Phase B Set:
2- 3/0 AWG CU, 104 ft long
Phase C Set:
2- 3/0 AWG CU, 102 ft long
Neutral Set:
2- 1/0 AWG AL, 103 ft long
Equipment Ground Set:
2- 3 AWG CU, 101 ft long

For current to be evenly distributed between the individual parallel conductors, each conductor (within a parallel set) must be identical to the other.

Copyright 2017, www.MikeHolt.com

▶Figure 310–8

Author's Comment:

■ For example, a 400A feeder with a neutral load of 240A can be paralleled as follows: ▶Figure 310–8

◆ Phase A, Two—250 kcmil THHN aluminum, 100 ft

◆ Phase B, Two—3/0 THHN copper, 104 ft

◆ Phase C, Two—3/0 THHN copper, 102 ft

◆ Neutral, Two—1/0 THHN aluminum, 103 ft

◆ Equipment Grounding Conductor, Two—3 AWG copper, 101 ft*

*The minimum 1/0 AWG requirement doesn't apply to equipment grounding conductors [310.10(H)(5)].

(4) Conductor Ampacity Adjustment. Each current-carrying conductor of a paralleled set of conductors must be counted as a current-carrying conductor for the purpose of conductor ampacity adjustment, in accordance with 310.15(B)(3)(a). ▶Figure 310–9

(5) Equipment Grounding Conductors. The equipment grounding conductors for circuits in parallel must be sized in accordance with 250.122(F). Sectioned equipment grounding conductors smaller than 1/0 AWG are permitted in multiconductor cables, if the combined circular mil area of the sectioned equipment grounding conductor in each cable complies with 250.122. ▶Figure 310–10

Author's Comment:

■ The minimum 1/0 AWG parallel conductor size rule of 310.10(H) doesn't apply to equipment grounding conductors.

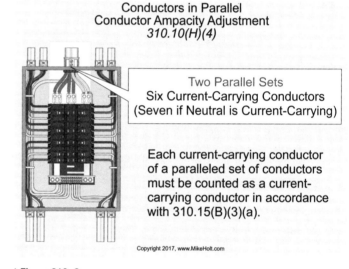

Conductors in Parallel
Conductor Ampacity Adjustment
310.10(H)(4)

Two Parallel Sets
Six Current-Carrying Conductors
(Seven if Neutral is Current-Carrying)

Each current-carrying conductor of a paralleled set of conductors must be counted as a current-carrying conductor in accordance with 310.15(B)(3)(a).

Copyright 2017, www.MikeHolt.com

▶Figure 310–9

(6) Bonding Jumpers. Equipment bonding jumpers and supply-side bonding jumpers are sized in accordance with 250.102.

Author's Comment:

■ The equipment bonding jumper isn't required to be larger than the largest ungrounded circuit conductors supplying the equipment.

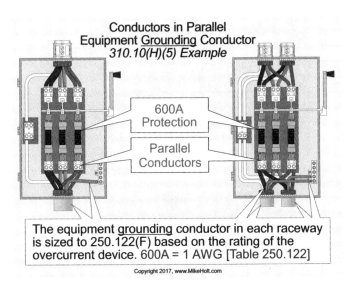

The equipment grounding conductor in each raceway is sized to 250.122(F) based on the rating of the overcurrent device. 600A = 1 AWG [Table 250.122]

Copyright 2017, www.MikeHolt.com

▶Figure 310–10

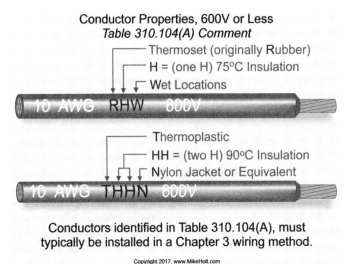

Conductors identified in Table 310.104(A), must typically be installed in a Chapter 3 wiring method.

Copyright 2017, www.MikeHolt.com

▶Figure 310–11

Part III. Construction Specifications

310.104 Conductor Construction and Application

Only conductors in Tables 310.104(A) though 310.104(G) can be installed, and only for the application identified in the tables.

Author's Comment:

- The following explains the lettering on conductor insulation:
  ▶Figure 310–11

  - F   Fixture wires (solid or 7 strands) [Table 402.3]
  - FF   Flexible fixture wire (19 strands) [Table 402.3]
  - No H   60°C insulation rating [Table 310.104(A)]
  - H   75°C insulation rating [Table 310.104(A)]
  - HH   90°C insulation rating [Table 310.104(A)]
  - N   Nylon outer cover [Table 310.104(A)]
  - R   Thermoset insulation [Table 310.104(A)]
  - T   Thermoplastic insulation [Table 310.104(A)]
  - U   Underground [Table 310.104(A)]
  - W   Wet or damp locations [Table 310.104(A)]
  - X   Cross-linked polyethylene insulation [Table 310.104(A)]
  - -2   90°C in dry and wet locations [Table 310.104(A)]

310.106 Conductors

(A) Minimum Size Conductors. The smallest conductor permitted for branch circuits for residential, commercial, and industrial locations is 14 AWG copper, except as permitted elsewhere in this *Code*. ▶Figure 310–12

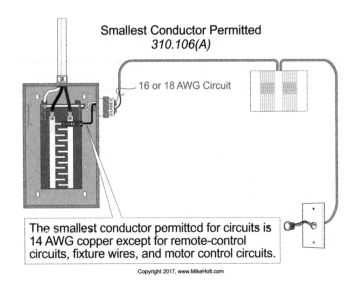

The smallest conductor permittcd for circuits is 14 AWG copper except for remote-control circuits, fixture wires, and motor control circuits.

Copyright 2017, www.MikeHolt.com

▶Figure 310–12

Author's Comment:

- There's a misconception that 12 AWG copper is the smallest conductor permitted for commercial or industrial facilities. Although this isn't true based on *NEC* rules, it may be a local code requirement.

(C) Stranded Conductors. Conductors 8 AWG and larger must be stranded when installed within a raceway. ▶Figure 310–13

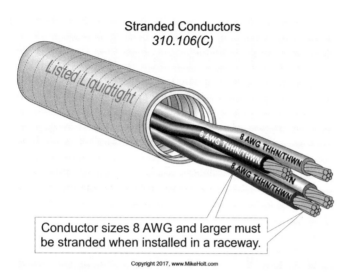

Stranded Conductors
310.106(C)

Conductor sizes 8 AWG and larger must be stranded when installed in a raceway.

Copyright 2017, www.MikeHolt.com

▶Figure 310–13

Author's Comment:

■ Solid conductors are often used for the grounding electrode conductor [250.62] and for the bonding of pools, spas, and outdoor hot tubs [680.26(C)].

(D) Insulated. Conductors must be insulated except where specific permission allows them to be covered or bare.

Author's Comment:

■ Equipment grounding conductors are permitted to be bare, see 250.118(1).

310.110 Conductor Identification

(A) Grounded [Neutral] Conductor. Grounded [neutral] conductors must be identified in accordance with 200.6.

(B) Equipment Grounding Conductor. Equipment grounding conductors must be identified in accordance with 250.119.

(C) Ungrounded Conductors. Ungrounded conductors must be clearly distinguishable from neutral and equipment grounding conductors.
▶Figure 310–14

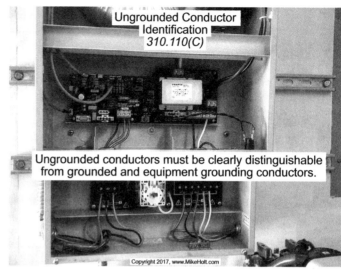

Ungrounded Conductor
Identification
310.110(C)

Ungrounded conductors must be clearly distinguishable from grounded and equipment grounding conductors.

Copyright 2017, www.MikeHolt.com

▶Figure 310–14

Author's Comment:

■ If the premises wiring system has branch circuits or feeders supplied from more than one nominal voltage system, each ungrounded conductor of the branch circuit or feeder, if accessible, must be identified by system. The means of identification can be by separate color coding, marking tape, tagging, or other means approved by the authority having jurisdiction. Such identification must be permanently posted at each panelboard [210.5(C) and 215.12].

■ The *NEC* doesn't require color coding of ungrounded conductors, except for the high-leg conductor when a neutral conductor is present [110.15 and 230.56]. Although not required, electricians often use the following color system for power and lighting conductor identification: ▶Figure 310–15

◆ 120/240V, single-phase—black, red, and white

◆ 120/208V, three-phase—black, red, blue, and white

◆ 120/240V, three-phase, delta-connected system—black, orange, blue, and white

◆ 277/480V, three-phase, wye-connected system—brown, orange, yellow, and gray; or, brown, purple, yellow, and gray

Conductor Identification
210.5, 215.12, 310.110 Comment

Although the *NEC* doesn't require a specific color code for ungrounded conductors, electricians often use the following color system for power and lighting conductor identification:
- 120/240V, single-phase–black, red, and white
- 120/208V, three-phase–black, red, blue, and white
- 120/240V, three-phase–black, orange, blue, and white
- 277/480V, three-phase–brown, orange, yellow, and gray; or, brown, purple, yellow, and gray

Copyright 2017, www.MikeHolt.com

▶Figure 310–15

PRACTICE QUESTIONS

Please use the 2017 *Code* book to answer the following questions.

1. Conductors shall be permitted for use in any of the wiring methods recognized in Chapter 3 and as permitted in the *NEC*.

    (a) True
    (b) False

2. In general, the minimum size conductor permitted for use in parallel installations is _____ AWG.

    (a) 10
    (b) 4
    (c) 1
    (d) 1/0

3. Parallel conductors shall have the same _____.

    (a) length
    (b) material
    (c) size in circular mil area
    (d) all of these

4. Where conductors in parallel are run in separate raceways, the raceways shall have the same electrical characteristics.

    (a) True
    (b) False

5. Sectioned equipment grounding conductors smaller than _____ AWG shall be permitted in multiconductor cables, if the combined circular mil area of the sectioned equipment grounding conductors in each cable complies with 250.122.

    (a) 3
    (b) 2
    (c) 1
    (d) 1/0

6. The minimum size copper conductor permitted for branch circuits under 600V is _____ AWG.

    (a) 14
    (b) 12
    (c) 10
    (d) 8

7. Where installed in raceways, conductors _____ AWG and larger shall be stranded, unless specifically permitted or required elsewhere in the *NEC*.

    (a) 10
    (b) 8
    (c) 6
    (d) 4

OUTLET, DEVICE, PULL, AND JUNCTION BOXES; CONDUIT BODIES; AND HANDHOLE ENCLOSURES

ARTICLE 314

Introduction to Article 314—Outlet, Device, Pull, and Junction Boxes; Conduit Bodies; and Handhole Enclosures

Article 314 contains installation requirements for outlet boxes, pull and junction boxes, conduit bodies, and handhole enclosures. As with the cabinets covered in Article 312, the conditions of use have a bearing on the type of material and equipment selected for a particular installation. If a raceway is installed in a wet location, for example, the correct fittings and the proper installation methods must be used.

The information here will help you size an outlet box using the proper cubic-inch capacity as well as calculating the minimum dimensions for larger pull boxes. There are limits on the amount of weight that can be supported by an outlet box and rules on how to support a device or outlet box to various surfaces. Article 314 will help you understand these types of rules so that your installation will be compliant with the *NEC*. As always, the clear illustrations in this article will help you visualize the finished installation.

Part I. Scope and General

314.1 Scope

Article 314 contains the installation requirements for outlet boxes, conduit bodies, pull and junction boxes, and handhole enclosures. ▶Figure 314–1

314.3 Nonmetallic Boxes

Nonmetallic boxes can only be used with nonmetallic cables and raceways.

Ex 1: Metal raceways and metal cables can be used with nonmetallic boxes if all raceways are bonded together in the nonmetallic box.
▶Figure 314–2

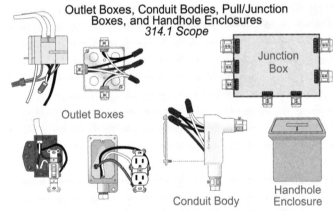

Outlet Boxes, Conduit Bodies, Pull/Junction Boxes, and Handhole Enclosures
314.1 Scope

Junction Box

Outlet Boxes

Conduit Body

Handhole Enclosure

Article 314 contains the installation requirements for outlet boxes, conduit bodies, pull and junction boxes, and handhole enclosures.
Copyright 2017, www.MikeHolt.com

▶Figure 314–1

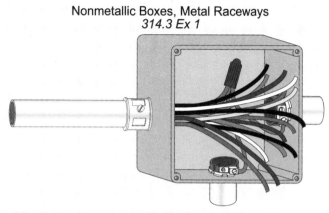

Nonmetallic Boxes, Metal Raceways
314.3 Ex 1

Metal raceways can terminate to a nonmetallic box where an internal bonding means is provided between all entries.

Copyright 2017, www.MikeHolt.com

▸Figure 314–2

314.4 Metal Boxes

Metal boxes containing circuits that operate at 50V or more must be connected to an equipment grounding conductor of a type listed in 250.118 [250.112(I) and 250.148]. ▸Figure 314–3

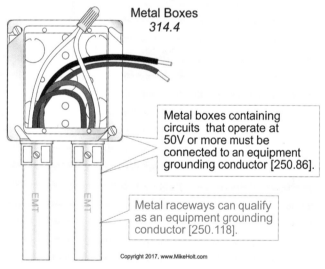

Metal Boxes
314.4

Metal boxes containing circuits that operate at 50V or more must be connected to an equipment grounding conductor [250.86].

Metal raceways can qualify as an equipment grounding conductor [250.118].

Copyright 2017, www.MikeHolt.com

▸Figure 314–3

Part II. Installation

314.15 Damp or Wet Locations

Boxes, conduit bodies, and fittings in damp or wet locations must be listed for wet locations and prevent moisture or water from entering or accumulating within the enclosure. ▸Figure 314–4 and ▸Figure 314–5

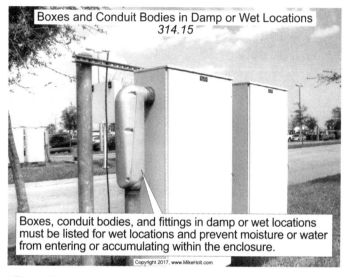

Boxes and Conduit Bodies in Damp or Wet Locations
314.15

Boxes, conduit bodies, and fittings in damp or wet locations must be listed for wet locations and prevent moisture or water from entering or accumulating within the enclosure.

Copyright 2017, www.MikeHolt.com

▸Figure 314–4

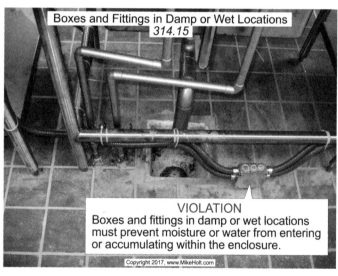

Boxes and Fittings in Damp or Wet Locations
314.15

VIOLATION
Boxes and fittings in damp or wet locations must prevent moisture or water from entering or accumulating within the enclosure.

Copyright 2017, www.MikeHolt.com

▸Figure 314–5

Approved drainage openings can be created in the field if they aren't smaller than ⅛ in. in diameter and not larger than ¼ in. in diameter.

314.16 Number of Conductors in Boxes and Conduit Bodies

Boxes containing 6 AWG and smaller conductors must be sized in an approved manner to provide free space for all conductors, devices, and fittings. In no case can the volume of the box, as calculated in 314.16(A), be less than the volume requirement as calculated in 314.16(B). ▶Figure 314–6

Conduit bodies must be sized in accordance with 314.16(C).

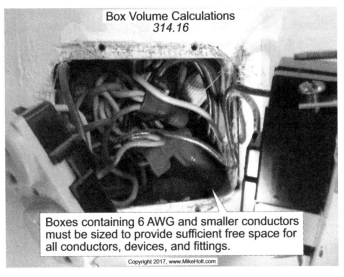

Box Volume Calculations
314.16

Boxes containing 6 AWG and smaller conductors must be sized to provide sufficient free space for all conductors, devices, and fittings.

Copyright 2017, www.MikeHolt.com

▶Figure 314–6

(A) Box Volume Calculations. The volume of a box includes plaster rings, extension rings, and domed covers that are either marked with their volume in cubic inches (cu in.), or are made from boxes listed in Table 314.16(A). ▶Figure 314–7 and ▶Figure 314–8

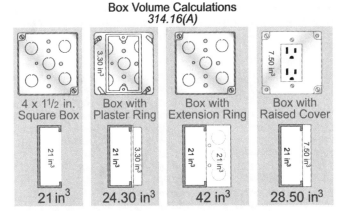

Box Volume Calculations
314.16(A)

4 x 1½ in. Square Box	Box with Plaster Ring	Box with Extension Ring	Box with Raised Cover
21 in³	24.30 in³	42 in³	28.50 in³

The volume of a box includes the volume of its assembled parts that are marked with their cu in. or are made from boxes listed in Table 314.16(A).

Copyright 2017, www.MikeHolt.com

▶Figure 314–7

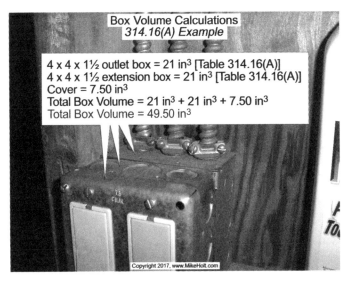

Box Volume Calculations
314.16(A) Example

4 x 4 x 1½ outlet box = 21 in³ [Table 314.16(A)]
4 x 4 x 1½ extension box = 21 in³ [Table 314.16(A)]
Cover = 7.50 in³
Total Box Volume = 21 in³ + 21 in³ + 7.50 in³
Total Box Volume = 49.50 in³

Copyright 2017, www.MikeHolt.com

▶Figure 314–8

Where a box is provided with barriers, the volume is apportioned to each of the resulting spaces. Each barrier, if not marked with its volume, is considered to take up ½ cu in. if metal and 1 cu in. if nonmetallic. ▶Figure 314–9

(B) Box Fill Calculations. The calculated conductor volume as determined by 314.16(B)(1) through (5) and Table 314.16(B) determine the total volume of the conductors, devices, and fittings. Raceway and cable fittings, including locknuts and bushings, aren't counted for box fill calculations. ▶Figure 314–10

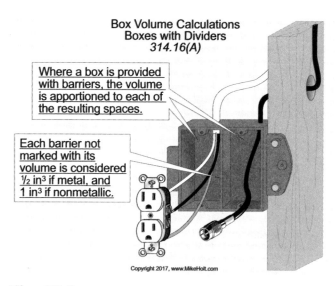

Box Volume Calculations
Boxes with Dividers
314.16(A)

Where a box is provided with barriers, the volume is apportioned to each of the resulting spaces.

Each barrier not marked with its volume is considered ½ in³ if metal, and 1 in³ if nonmetallic.

Copyright 2017, www.MikeHolt.com

▶Figure 314–9

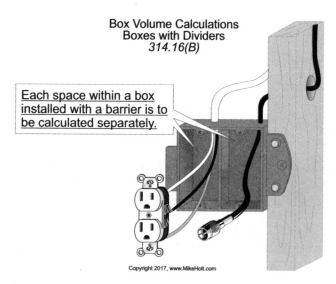

Box Volume Calculations
Boxes with Dividers
314.16(B)

Each space within a box installed with a barrier is to be calculated separately.

Copyright 2017, www.MikeHolt.com

▶Figure 314–11

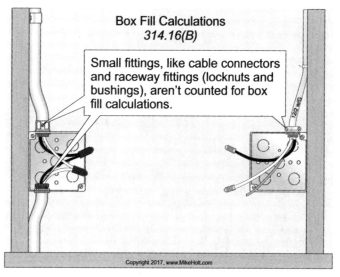

Box Fill Calculations
314.16(B)

Small fittings, like cable connectors and raceway fittings (locknuts and bushings), aren't counted for box fill calculations.

Copyright 2017, www.MikeHolt.com

▶Figure 314–10

The volume of a box that's provided with barriers, is apportioned to each of the resulting spaces. ▶Figure 314–11

Table 314.16(B) Volume Allowance Required per Conductor

Conductor AWG	Volume cu in.
18	1.50
16	1.75
14	2.00
12	2.25
10	2.50
8	3.00
6	5.00

(1) Conductor Volume. Each unbroken conductor that runs through a box, and each conductor that terminates in a box, is counted as a single conductor volume in accordance with Table 314.16(B). ▶Figure 314–12 and ▶Figure 314–13

Box Fill Calculations, Conductor Fill
314.16(B)(1)

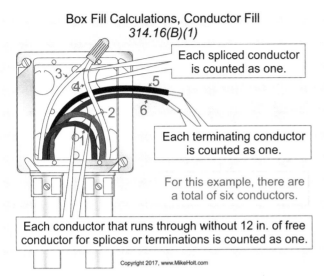

Each spliced conductor is counted as one.

Each terminating conductor is counted as one.

For this example, there are a total of six conductors.

Each conductor that runs through without 12 in. of free conductor for splices or terminations is counted as one.

Copyright 2017, www.MikeHolt.com

▶Figure 314–12

Box Fill Calculations, Conductor Volume
Conductors Passing Through With Loop
314.16(B)(1)

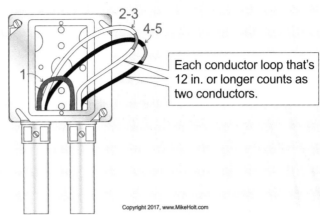

Each conductor loop that's 12 in. or longer counts as two conductors.

Copyright 2017, www.MikeHolt.com

▶Figure 314–14

Box Fill Calculations
Conductors That Originate and Terminate Inside an Outlet Box
314.16(B)(1)

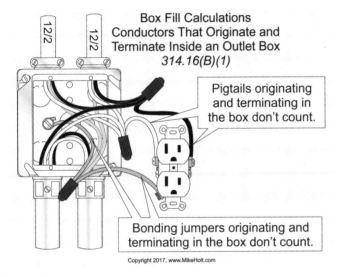

Pigtails originating and terminating in the box don't count.

Bonding jumpers originating and terminating in the box don't count.

Copyright 2017, www.MikeHolt.com

▶Figure 314–13

Box Fill Calculations, Fixture Wires
314.16(B)(1) Ex

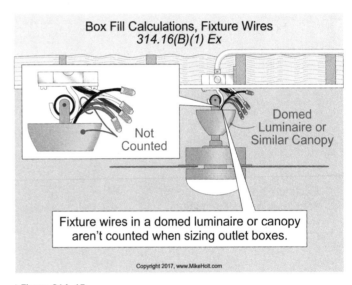

Not Counted

Domed Luminaire or Similar Canopy

Fixture wires in a domed luminaire or canopy aren't counted when sizing outlet boxes.

Copyright 2017, www.MikeHolt.com

▶Figure 314–15

Each loop or coil of unbroken conductor having a length of at least twice the minimum length required for free conductors in 300.14 must be counted as two conductor volumes. Conductors that originate and terminate within the box, such as pigtails, aren't counted at all. ▶Figure 314–14

Ex: Equipment grounding conductors, and up to four 16 AWG and smaller fixture wires, can be omitted from box fill calculations if they enter the box from a domed luminaire or similar canopy, such as a ceiling paddle fan canopy. ▶Figure 314–15

(2) Cable Clamp Volume. One or more internal cable clamps count as a single conductor volume in accordance with Table 314.16(B), based on the largest conductor that enters the box. Cable connectors that have their clamping mechanism outside the box aren't counted. ▶Figure 314–16

(3) Support Fitting Volume. Each luminaire stud or luminaire hickey counts as a single conductor volume in accordance with Table 314.16(B), based on the largest conductor that enters the box. ▶Figure 314–17

Box Fill Calculations
Internal Cable Clamps
314.16(B)(2)

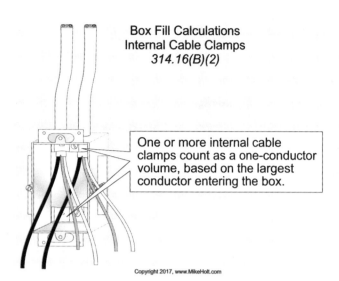

One or more internal cable clamps count as a one-conductor volume, based on the largest conductor entering the box.

Copyright 2017, www.MikeHolt.com

▶Figure 314–16

Box Fill Calculations, Device Yoke
314.16(B)(4)

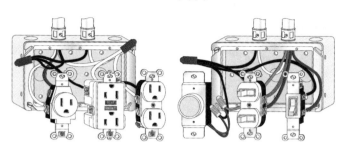

Each device yoke counts as a two-conductor volume, based on the largest conductor terminating on the device.

Copyright 2017, www.MikeHolt.com

▶Figure 314–18

Box Fill Calculations, Supporting Fittings
314.16(B)(3)

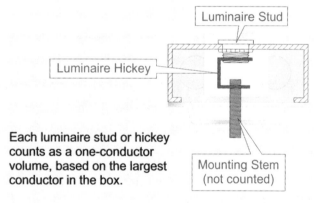

Luminaire Stud

Luminaire Hickey

Each luminaire stud or hickey counts as a one-conductor volume, based on the largest conductor in the box.

Mounting Stem (not counted)

Copyright 2017, www.MikeHolt.com

▶Figure 314–17

Box Fill Calculations, Device Yoke Wider Than Two Inches
314.16(B)(4)

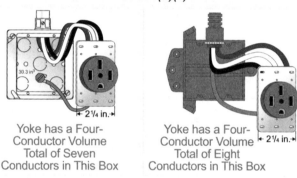

Yoke has a Four-Conductor Volume Total of Seven Conductors in This Box

Yoke has a Four-Conductor Volume Total of Eight Conductors in This Box

Each multigang device yoke counts as two conductor volumes for each gang, based on the largest conductor that terminates on the device.

Copyright 2017, www.MikeHolt.com

▶Figure 314–19

Author's Comment:

■ Luminaire stems don't need to be counted as a conductor volume.

(4) Device Yoke Volume. Each single-gang device yoke (regardless of the ampere rating of the device) counts as two conductor volumes, based on the largest conductor that terminates on the device in accordance with Table 314.16(B). ▶Figure 314–18

Each multigang device yoke counts as two conductor volumes for each gang, based on the largest conductor that terminates on the device in accordance with Table 314.16(B). ▶Figure 314–19

Author's Comment:

■ A device that's too wide for mounting in a single-gang box, as described in Table 314.16(A), is counted based on the number of gangs required for the device.

(5) Equipment Grounding Conductor Volume. Equipment grounding conductors in a box count as a single conductor volume in accordance with Table 314.16(B), based on the largest equipment grounding conductor that enters the box. Insulated equipment grounding conductors for receptacles having insulated grounding terminals (isolated ground receptacles) [250.146(D)], count as a single conductor volume in accordance with Table 314.16(B). ▶Figure 314–20

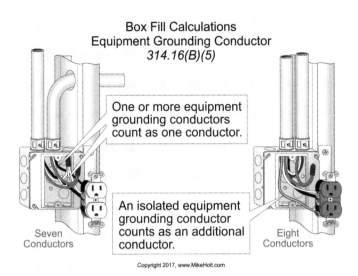

Box Fill Calculations
Equipment Grounding Conductor
314.16(B)(5)

One or more equipment grounding conductors count as one conductor.

An isolated equipment grounding conductor counts as an additional conductor.

Seven Conductors

Eight Conductors

Copyright 2017, www.MikeHolt.com

▶Figure 314–20

Author's Comment:

■ Conductor insulation isn't a factor that's considered when determining box volume calculations.

Example: *How many 14 AWG conductors can be pulled through a 4 in. square × 2⅛ in. deep box with a plaster ring with a marking of 3.60 cu in.? The box contains two receptacles, five 12 AWG conductors, and two 12 AWG equipment grounding conductors.* ▶Figure 314–21

Box Fill Calculations
314.16(B) Example

Existing Conductor and Device Volume: Ten 12 AWG

How many 14 AWG conductors can be added?

Step 1. Volume of box/ring: 30.3 + 3.6 cu in. = 33.9 cu in.
Step 2. Volume of existing conductors/devices = 22.5 cu in.
Step 3. Space remaining: 33.9 - 22.5 = 11.4 cu in.
Step 4. Number of 14 AWG added: 11.4/2.0 cu in. = 5

Copyright 2017, www.MikeHolt.com

▶Figure 314–21

Solution:

Step 1: *Determine the volume of the box assembly [314.16(A)]:*

Box 30.30 cu in. + 3.60 cu in. plaster ring = 33.90 cu in.

A 4 × 4 × 2⅛ in. box has a volume of 30.30 cu in., as listed in Table 314.16(A).

Step 2: *Determine the volume of the devices and conductors in the box:*

Two—receptacles	*4—12 AWG*
Five—12 AWG	*5—12 AWG*
Two—12 AWG Grounds	*1—12 AWG*

Total Ten—12 AWG × 2.25 cu in. = 22.50 cu in.

Step 3: *Determine the remaining volume permitted for the 14 AWG conductors (volume of box less volume of conductors):*

33.90 cu in. − 22.50 cu in. = 11.40 cu in.

Step 4: *Determine the number of 14 AWG conductors (at 2.00 cu in. each) permitted in the remaining volume of 11.40 cu in:*

14 AWG = 2.00 cu in. each [Table 314.16(B)]
11.40 cu in./2.00 cu in. = 5 conductors

Answer: *Five 14 AWG conductors can be pulled through.*

(C) Conduit Bodies.

(2) Splices. Splices are permitted in conduit bodies that are legibly marked by the manufacturer with their volume, and the maximum number of conductors permitted in a conduit body is limited in accordance with 314.16(B).

Example: *How many 12 AWG conductors can be spliced in an 11.80 cu in. conduit body?* ▶Figure 314–22

Solution:

12 AWG = 2.25 cu in. [Table 314.16(B)]
11.80 cu in./2.25 cu in. = 5.40 conductors

Answer: *A maximum of five 12 AWG conductors (round down) can be spliced in this conduit body.*

• • •

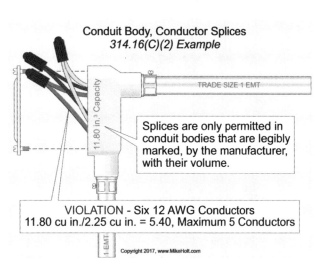

Conduit Body, Conductor Splices
314.16(C)(2) Example

11.80 in.³ Capacity

TRADE SIZE 1 EMT

Splices are only permitted in conduit bodies that are legibly marked, by the manufacturer, with their volume.

VIOLATION - Six 12 AWG Conductors
11.80 cu in./2.25 cu in. = 5.40, Maximum 5 Conductors

Copyright 2017, www.MikeHolt.com

▶Figure 314–22

(3) Short-Radius Conduit Bodies. Capped elbows, handy ells, and service-entrance elbows aren't permitted to contain any splices. ▶Figure 314–23

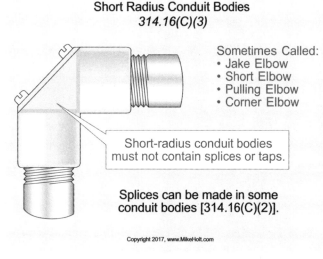

Short Radius Conduit Bodies
314.16(C)(3)

Sometimes Called:
• Jake Elbow
• Short Elbow
• Pulling Elbow
• Corner Elbow

Short-radius conduit bodies must not contain splices or taps.

Splices can be made in some conduit bodies [314.16(C)(2)].

Copyright 2017, www.MikeHolt.com

▶Figure 314–23

314.17 Conductors That Enter Boxes or Conduit Bodies

(A) Openings to be Closed. Unused openings through which cables or raceways enter must be closed in an approved manner. ▶**Figure 314–24**

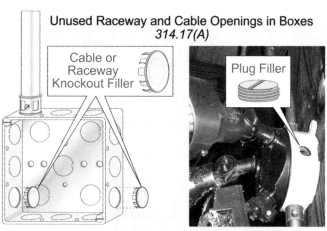

Unused Raceway and Cable Openings in Boxes
314.17(A)

Cable or Raceway Knockout Filler

Plug Filler

Unused cable or raceway openings must be closed in an approved manner [110.12(A)].

Copyright 2017, www.MikeHolt.com

▶Figure 314–24

Author's Comment:

■ Unused cable or raceway openings in electrical equipment must be effectively closed by fittings that provide protection substantially equivalent to the wall of the equipment [110.12(A)].

(B) Metal Boxes. Nonmetallic-sheathed cable and multiconductor Type UF cable must extend at least ¼ in. inside the box. ▶**Figure 314–25**

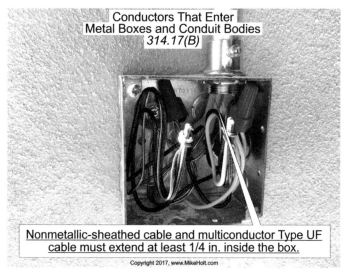

Conductors That Enter Metal Boxes and Conduit Bodies
314.17(B)

Nonmetallic-sheathed cable and multiconductor Type UF cable must extend at least 1/4 in. inside the box.

Copyright 2017, www.MikeHolt.com

▶Figure 314–25

(C) Nonmetallic Boxes and Conduit Bodies. Raceways and cables must be securely fastened to nonmetallic boxes or conduit bodies by fittings designed for the wiring method [300.12 and 300.15]. ▶**Figure 314–26**

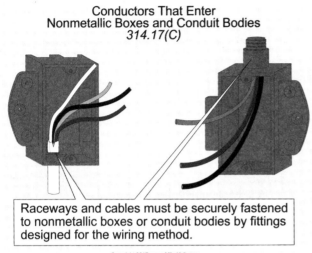

**Conductors That Enter
Nonmetallic Boxes and Conduit Bodies
314.17(C)**

Raceways and cables must be securely fastened
to nonmetallic boxes or conduit bodies by fittings
designed for the wiring method.

Copyright 2017, www.MikeHolt.com

▶Figure 314–26

The sheath of type NM cable must extend not less than ¼ in. into the nonmetallic box.

Author's Comment:

- Two Type NM cables can terminate in a single cable clamp, if the clamp is listed for this purpose.

Ex: Type NM cable terminating to a single-gang (2¼ in. × 4 in.) device box isn't required to be secured to the box if the cable is securely fastened within 8 in. of the box. ▶Figure 314–27

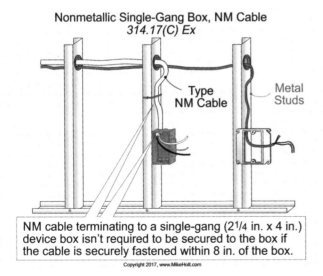

**Nonmetallic Single-Gang Box, NM Cable
314.17(C) Ex**

Type
NM Cable

Metal
Studs

NM cable terminating to a single-gang (2¼ in. x 4 in.)
device box isn't required to be secured to the box if
the cable is securely fastened within 8 in. of the box.

Copyright 2017, www.MikeHolt.com

▶Figure 314–27

314.20 Flush-Mounted Box Installations

Installation within or behind walls or ceilings that are constructed of noncombustible material must have the front edge of the flush-mounted box, plaster ring, extension ring, or listed extender set back no more than ¼ in. from the finished surface. ▶Figure 314–28

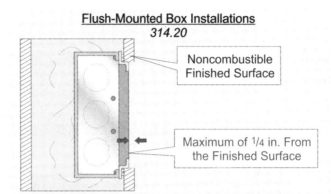

**Flush-Mounted Box Installations
314.20**

Noncombustible
Finished Surface

Maximum of ¼ in. From
the Finished Surface

Flush-mounted boxes installed within or behind walls or
ceilings that are constructed of noncombustible material
must have the front edge of the flush-mounted box,
plaster ring, extension ring, or listed extender set back
no more than ¼ in. from the finished surface.

Copyright 2017, www.MikeHolt.com

▶Figure 314–28

Installation within or behind walls or ceilings constructed of wood or other combustible material must have the front edge of the flush-mounted box, plaster ring, extension ring, or listed extender extend to the finished surface or project out from the finished surface. ▶Figure 314–29

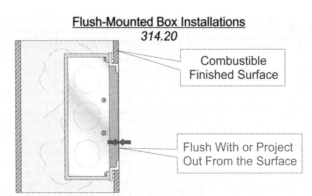

**Flush-Mounted Box Installations
314.20**

Combustible
Finished Surface

Flush With or Project
Out From the Surface

Flush-mounted boxes installed within walls or ceilings
constructed of wood or other combustible material must
have the front edge of the flush-mounted box, plaster
ring, extension ring, or listed extender extend to the
finished surface or project out from the finished surface.

Copyright 2017, www.MikeHolt.com

▶Figure 314–29

Author's Comment:

- Plaster rings and extension rings are available in a variety of depths to meet the above requirements.

314.21 Repairing Noncombustible Surfaces

Gaps around boxes with flush-type covers that are recessed in noncombustible surfaces (such as plaster, drywall, or plasterboard) must be repaired so there will be no gap more than ⅛ in. at the edge of the box. ▶Figure 314–30

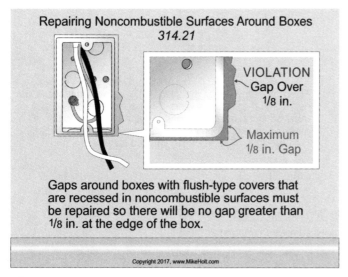

▶Figure 314–30

314.22 Surface Extensions

Surface extensions can only be made from an extension ring mounted over a flush-mounted box. ▶Figure 314–31

Ex: A surface extension can be made from the cover of a flush-mounted box if the cover is designed so it's unlikely to fall off if the mounting screws become loose. The surface extension wiring method must be flexible to permit the removal of the cover and provide access to the box interior, and equipment grounding continuity must be independent of the connection between the box and the cover. ▶Figure 314–32

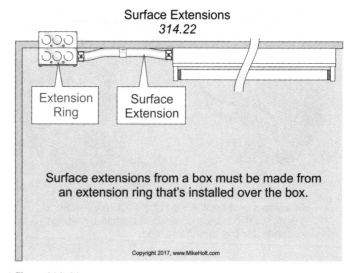

▶Figure 314–31

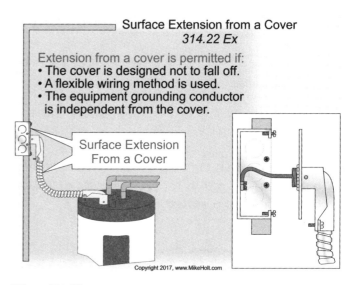

▶Figure 314–32

314.23 Support of Boxes and Conduit Bodies

(A) Surface. Boxes can be fastened to any surface that provides adequate support.

(B) Structural Mounting. Boxes can be supported from any structural member, or they can be supported from grade by a metal, plastic, or wood brace. ▶Figure 314–33

(1) Nails and Screws. Nails or screws used as a fastening means, must secure boxes by using outside brackets or by using mounting holes in the back or in a single side of the box, or pass through the interior within ¼ in. of the back or ends of the box. Screws aren't permitted to pass through the box unless the exposed threads in the box are protected

Support of Boxes and Conduit Bodies
314.23(B)

Boxes can be supported by metal, plastic, or wood braces.

▶Figure 314–33

using approved means to avoid abrasion of conductor insulation. Mounting holes made in the field to support boxes must be approved by the authority having jurisdiction.

(2) Braces. Metal braces no less than 0.02 in. thick and wood braces not less than a nominal 1 in. × 2 in. can support a box.

(C) Finished Surface Support. Boxes can be secured to a finished surface (drywall or plaster walls, or ceilings) by clamps, anchors, or fittings identified for the purpose. ▶Figure 314–34

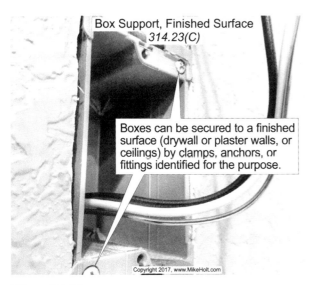

Box Support, Finished Surface
314.23(C)

Boxes can be secured to a finished surface (drywall or plaster walls, or ceilings) by clamps, anchors, or fittings identified for the purpose.

▶Figure 314–34

(D) Suspended-Ceiling Support. Outlet boxes can be supported to the structural or supporting elements of a suspended ceiling, if securely fastened by any of the following methods:

(1) Ceiling-Framing Members. An outlet box can be secured to suspended-ceiling framing members by bolts, screws, rivets, clips, or other means identified for the suspended-ceiling framing member(s). ▶Figure 314–35

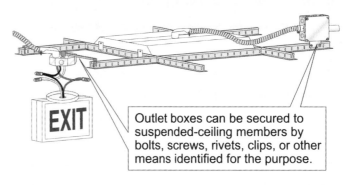

Box Support, Ceiling Framing Members
314.23(D)(1)

EXIT

Outlet boxes can be secured to suspended-ceiling members by bolts, screws, rivets, clips, or other means identified for the purpose.

Copyright 2017, www.MikeHolt.com

▶Figure 314–35

Author's Comment:

- If framing members of suspended-ceiling systems are used to support luminaires, they must be securely fastened to each other and must be securely attached to the building structure at appropriate intervals. In addition, luminaires must be attached to the suspended-ceiling framing members with screws, bolts, rivets, or clips listed and identified for such use [410.36(B)].

(2) Independent Support Wires. Outlet boxes can be secured with identified fittings to the ceiling-support wires. If independent support wires are used for outlet box support, they must be taunt and secured at both ends [300.11(B)]. ▶Figure 314–36

Author's Comment:

- See 300.11(B) on the use of independent support wires to support raceways and cables.

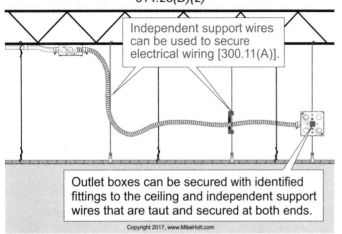

Box Support, Independent Support Wires
314.23(D)(2)

Independent support wires can be used to secure electrical wiring [300.11(A)].

Outlet boxes can be secured with identified fittings to the ceiling and independent support wires that are taut and secured at both ends.

Copyright 2017, www.MikeHolt.com

▶Figure 314–36

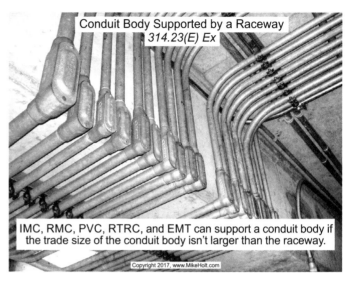

Conduit Body Supported by a Raceway
314.23(E) Ex

IMC, RMC, PVC, RTRC, and EMT can support a conduit body if the trade size of the conduit body isn't larger than the raceway.

Copyright 2017, www.MikeHolt.com

▶Figure 314–38

(E) Raceways—Boxes and Conduit Bodies Without Devices or Luminaires. Two intermediate metal or rigid metal conduits, threaded wrenchtight into the enclosure, can be used to support an outlet box that doesn't contain a device or luminaire, if each raceway is supported within 36 in. of the box or within 18 in. of the box if all conduit entries are on the same side. ▶**Figure 314–37**

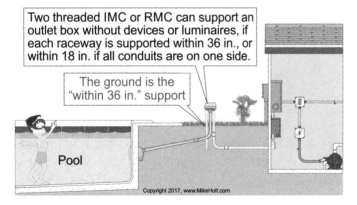

Box Support, Threaded Raceways
No Devices or Luminaires
314.23(E)

Two threaded IMC or RMC can support an outlet box without devices or luminaires, if each raceway is supported within 36 in., or within 18 in. if all conduits are on one side.

The ground is the "within 36 in." support

Pool

Copyright 2017, www.MikeHolt.com

▶Figure 314–37

Ex: Conduit bodies are permitted to be supported by any of the following wiring methods: ▶**Figure 314–38**

(1) Intermediate metal conduit, Type IMC

(2) Rigid metal conduit, Type RMC

(3) Rigid polyvinyl chloride conduit, Type PVC

(4) Reinforced thermosetting resin conduit, Type RTRC

(5) Electrical metallic tubing, Type EMT

(F) Raceways—Boxes and Conduit Bodies with Devices or Luminaires. Two intermediate metal or rigid metal conduits, threaded wrenchtight into the enclosure, can be used to support an outlet box containing devices or luminaires, if each raceway is supported within 18 in. of the box. ▶**Figure 314–39** and ▶**Figure 314–40**

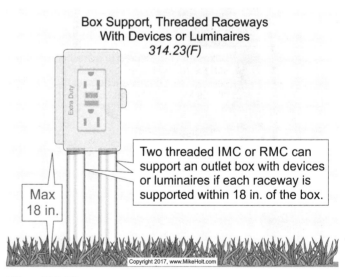

Box Support, Threaded Raceways
With Devices or Luminaires
314.23(F)

Extra Duty

Two threaded IMC or RMC can support an outlet box with devices or luminaires if each raceway is supported within 18 in. of the box.

Max 18 in.

Copyright 2017, www.MikeHolt.com

▶Figure 314–39

▶Figure 314–40

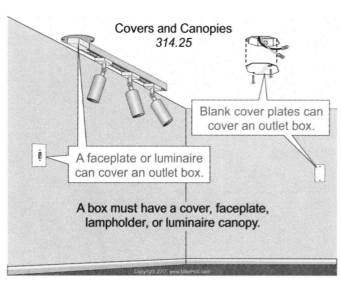

▶Figure 314–42

(H) Pendant Boxes.

(1) Flexible Cord. Boxes containing a hub can be supported from a flexible cord connected to fittings that prevent tension from being transmitted to joints or terminals [400.10]. ▶**Figure 314–41**

Screws used for attaching covers or other equipment to the box must be machine screws that match the thread gage or size of the screw holes in the box or they must be in accordance with the manufacturer's instructions. ▶**Figure 314–43**

▶Figure 314–41

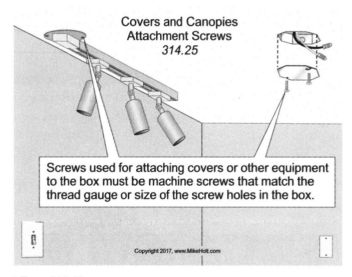

▶Figure 314–43

314.25 Covers and Canopies

When the installation is complete, each outlet box must be provided with a cover or faceplate, unless covered by a fixture canopy, lampholder, or similar device. ▶Figure 314–42

(A) Metal Covers. Metal covers are only permitted if they can be connected to an equipment grounding conductor of a type recognized in 250.118 [250.110]. ▶Figure 314–44

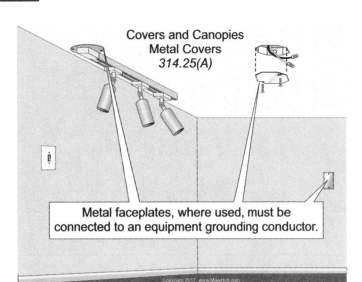

Covers and Canopies
Metal Covers
314.25(A)

Metal faceplates, where used, must be connected to an equipment grounding conductor.

▶Figure 314–44

Author's Comment:

- Metal switch faceplates [404.9(B)] and metal receptacle faceplates [406.6(A)] must be connected to an equipment grounding conductor.

314.27 Outlet Box

(A) Boxes at Luminaire Outlets.

(1) Luminaire Outlets in or on Vertical Surfaces. Boxes or fittings designed for the support of luminaires in or on a wall or other vertical surface must be identified and marked on the interior of the box to indicate the maximum weight of the luminaire if other than 50 lb. ▶Figure 314–45

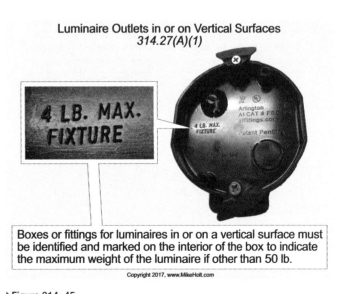

Luminaire Outlets in or on Vertical Surfaces
314.27(A)(1)

4 LB. MAX. FIXTURE

Boxes or fittings for luminaires in or on a vertical surface must be identified and marked on the interior of the box to indicate the maximum weight of the luminaire if other than 50 lb.

Copyright 2017, www.MikeHolt.com

▶Figure 314–45

Ex: A vertically mounted luminaire weighing no more than 6 lb can be supported to a device box or plaster ring secured to a device box, provided the luminaire or its supporting yoke, or the lampholder, is secured to the box with no fewer than two No. 6 or larger screws. ▶Figure 314–46

Luminaire Outlets in or on Vertical Surfaces
314.27(A)(1) Ex

Device Box or Plaster Ring

6 lb
or Less

A luminaire mounted in or on a vertical surface weighing no more than 6 lb can be supported to a device box or plaster ring.
Copyright 2017, www.MikeHolt.com

▶Figure 314–46

(2) Luminaire Outlets in the Ceiling. Boxes for ceiling luminaires must be listed and marked to support a luminaire weighing a minimum of 50 lb. Luminaires weighing more than 50 lb must be supported independently of the outlet box unless the outlet box is listed and marked on the interior of the box by the manufacturer for the maximum weight the box can support. ▶Figure 314–47

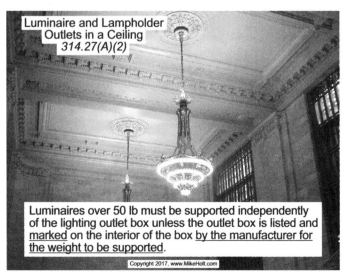

Luminaire and Lampholder
Outlets in a Ceiling
314.27(A)(2)

Luminaires over 50 lb must be supported independently of the lighting outlet box unless the outlet box is listed and marked on the interior of the box by the manufacturer for the weight to be supported.

Copyright 2017, www.MikeHolt.com

▶Figure 314–47

(B) Floor Box. Floor boxes must be specifically listed for the purpose. ▶Figure 314–48

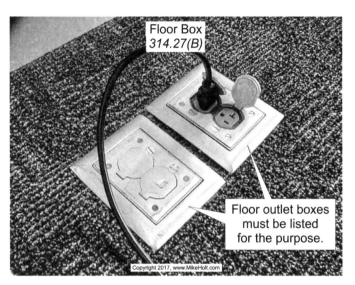

▶Figure 314–48

(C) Ceiling Paddle Fan Box. Outlet boxes for a ceiling paddle fan must be listed and marked as suitable for the purpose, and must not support a fan weighing more than 70 lb. Outlet boxes for a ceiling paddle fan that weighs more than 35 lb must include the maximum weight to be supported in the required marking. ▶Figure 314–49

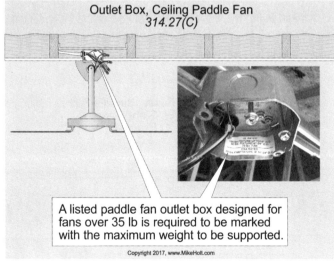

▶Figure 314–49

Author's Comment:

■ If the maximum weight isn't marked on the box, and the fan weighs over 35 lb, it must be supported independently of the outlet box. Ceiling paddle fans over 70 lb must be supported independently of the outlet box. ▶Figure 314–50

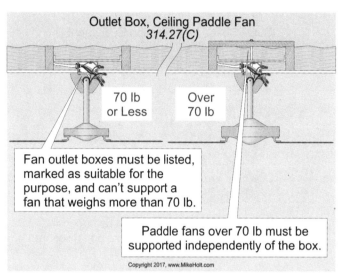

▶Figure 314–50

Where spare, separately switched, ungrounded conductors are provided to a ceiling-mounted outlet box, in a location acceptable for a ceiling-suspended (paddle) fan in one-family, two-family, or multifamily dwellings, the outlet box or outlet box system must be listed for the support of a ceiling-suspended (paddle) fan. ▶Figure 314–51

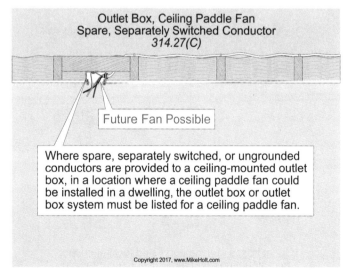

▶Figure 314–51

(D) Utilization Equipment. Boxes used for the support of utilization equipment must be designed to support equipment that weighs a minimum of 50 lb [314.27(A)].

Ex: Utilization equipment weighing 6 lb or less can be supported by any box or plaster ring secured to a box, provided the equipment is secured with no fewer than two No. 6 or larger screws. ▶Figure 314–52

Outlet Boxes for Utilization Equipment
314.27(D) Ex

Device Box or
Plaster Ring

Utilization equipment 6 lb or less can be supported
by any box or plaster ring secured to a box if secured
by at least two No. 6 or larger screws.

Copyright 2017, www.MikeHolt.com

▶Figure 314–52

(E) Separable Attachment Fittings. Outlet boxes are permitted to support listed locking support and mounting receptacles (SQL receptacles) used in combination with compatible attachment fittings. The combination must be identified for the support of equipment within the weight and mounting orientation limits of the listing. ▶Figure 314–53

Separable Attachment Fittings (SQL Receptacles)
314.27(E)

Outlet boxes can support listed locking support
and mounting receptacles (SQL receptacles).

Copyright 2017, www.MikeHolt.com

▶Figure 314–53

Author's Comment:

- See the Article 100 definition of "Receptacle" and visit http://www.safetyquicklight.com/ for additional information on SQL receptacles.

314.28 Sizing Conductors 4 AWG and Larger

 Scan this QR code to watch Mike explain this topic; it's a sample video clip from Mike's *Understanding the NEC Volume 1* DVDs.

Boxes containing conductors 4 AWG and larger that are required to be insulated must be sized so the conductor insulation won't be damaged.

Author's Comment:

- The requirements for sizing boxes containing conductors 6 AWG and smaller are contained in 314.16.

- If conductors 4 AWG and larger enter a box or other enclosure, a fitting that provides a smooth, rounded, insulating surface, such as a bushing or adapter, is required to protect the conductors from abrasion during and after installation [300.4(G)].

(A) Minimum Size. For raceways containing conductors 4 AWG and larger, the minimum dimensions of boxes must comply with the following:

(1) Straight Pulls. The minimum distance from where the conductors enter the box to the opposite wall isn't permitted to be less than eight times the trade size of the largest raceway. ▶Figure 314–54

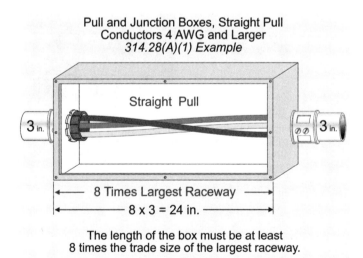

Pull and Junction Boxes, Straight Pull
Conductors 4 AWG and Larger
314.28(A)(1) Example

Straight Pull

3 in.   3 in.

◀— 8 Times Largest Raceway —▶
◀——— 8 x 3 = 24 in. ———▶

The length of the box must be at least
8 times the trade size of the largest raceway.

Copyright 2017, www.MikeHolt.com

▶Figure 314–54

(2) Angle Pulls, U Pulls, or Splices.

Angle Pulls. The distance from the raceway entry of the box to the opposite wall isn't permitted to be less than six times the trade size of the largest raceway, plus the sum of the trade sizes of the remaining raceways on the same wall and row. ▶Figure 314–55

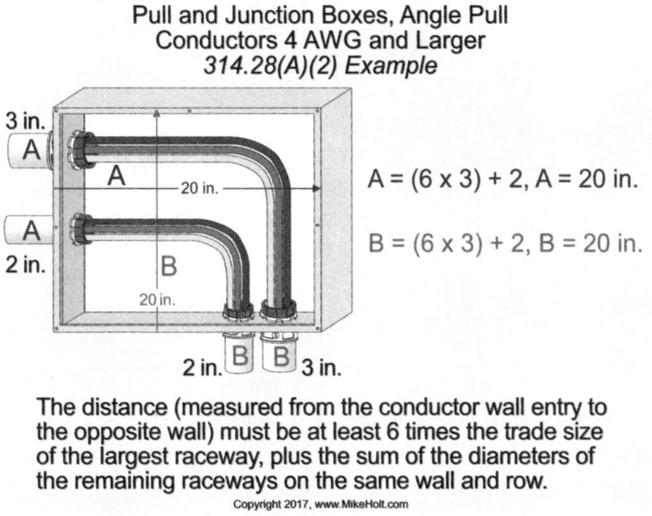

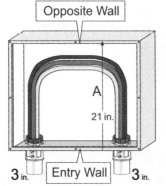

Pull and Junction Boxes, Angle Pull
Conductors 4 AWG and Larger
314.28(A)(2) Example

3 in.
A
A   20 in.
A
2 in.
B
20 in.
2 in. B B 3 in.

A = (6 x 3) + 2, A = 20 in.

B = (6 x 3) + 2, B = 20 in.

The distance (measured from the conductor wall entry to the opposite wall) must be at least 6 times the trade size of the largest raceway, plus the sum of the diameters of the remaining raceways on the same wall and row.
Copyright 2017, www.MikeHolt.com

▶Figure 314–55

U Pulls. When a conductor enters and leaves from the same wall of the box, the distance from where the raceways enter to the opposite wall isn't permitted to be less than six times the trade size of the largest raceway, plus the sum of the trade sizes of the remaining raceways on the same wall and row. ▶Figure 314–56

Pull and Junction Boxes, U Pull
Conductors 4 AWG and Larger
314.28(A)(2) Example

Opposite Wall

A
21 in.

3 in. Entry Wall 3 in.

A: U Pull Sizing:
The distance must be at least 6 times the largest raceway, plus the sum of the other raceways on the same wall and row.
A = (6 x 3) + 3 = 21 in.

Copyright 2017, www.MikeHolt.com

▶Figure 314–56

Splices. When conductors are spliced, the distance from where the raceways enter to the opposite wall isn't permitted to be less than six times the trade size of the largest raceway, plus the sum of the trade sizes of the remaining raceways on the same wall and row. ▶Figure 314–57

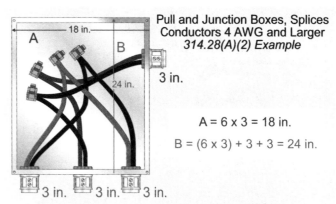

Pull and Junction Boxes, Splices
Conductors 4 AWG and Larger
314.28(A)(2) Example

A 18 in. B
24 in.
3 in.

3 in. 3 in. 3 in.

A = 6 x 3 = 18 in.

B = (6 x 3) + 3 + 3 = 24 in.

When conductors are spliced, the distance from where the raceways enter to the opposite wall must be at least 6 times the trade size of the largest raceway plus the sum of all other raceways on the same wall and row.
Copyright 2017, www.MikeHolt.com

▶Figure 314–57

Rows. If there are multiple rows of raceway entries, each row is calculated individually and the row with the largest distance must be used. ▶Figure 314–58

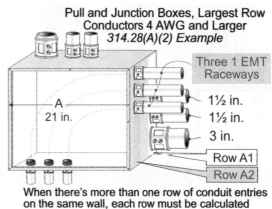

Pull and Junction Boxes, Largest Row
Conductors 4 AWG and Larger
314.28(A)(2) Example

Three 1 EMT Raceways

A
21 in.

1½ in.
1½ in.
3 in.

Row A1
Row A2

When there's more than one row of conduit entries on the same wall, each row must be calculated separately and the larger answer used.
Row A1 = (6 x 3) + 1½ + 1½ = 21 in.
Row A2 = (6 x 1) + 1 + 1 = 8 in. (omit)
Dimension A = 21 in.
Copyright 2017, www.MikeHolt.com

▶Figure 314–58

Distance Between Raceways. The distance between raceways enclosing the same conductor isn't permitted to be less than six times the trade size of the largest raceway, measured from the raceways' nearest edge-to-nearest edge. ▶Figure 314–59 and ▶Figure 314–60

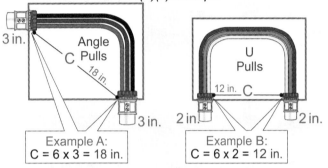

Pull and Junction Boxes, Distance Between Raceways
Conductors 4 AWG and Larger
314.28(A)(2) Example

Angle Pulls
C
18 in.

Example A:
C = 6 x 3 = 18 in.

U Pulls
12 in. C

Example B:
C = 6 x 2 = 12 in.

The distance between raceway entries containing the same conductor must be at least 6 times the trade size of the larger raceway entry.

Copyright 2017, www.MikeHolt.com

▶Figure 314–59

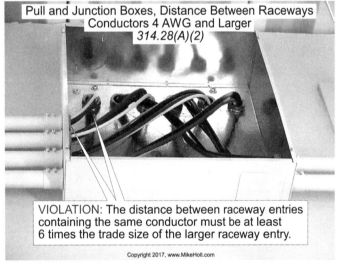

Pull and Junction Boxes, Distance Between Raceways
Conductors 4 AWG and Larger
314.28(A)(2)

VIOLATION: The distance between raceway entries containing the same conductor must be at least 6 times the trade size of the larger raceway entry.

Copyright 2017, www.MikeHolt.com

▶Figure 314–60

Ex: When conductors enter an enclosure with a removable cover, the distance from where the conductors enter to the removable cover isn't permitted to be less than the bending distance as listed in Table 312.6(A) for one conductor per terminal. ▶Figure 314–61

(B) Conductors in Pull or Junction Boxes. Pull boxes or junction boxes with any dimension over 6 ft must have all conductors cabled or racked in an approved manner.

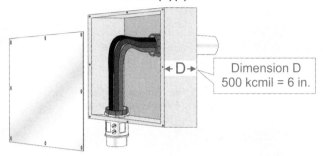

Pull and Junction Boxes, Depth
Conductors 4 AWG and Larger
314.28(A)(2) Ex

◀D▶
Dimension D
500 kcmil = 6 in.

The distance from where the conductors enter to the removable cover can't be less than the bending distance listed in Table 312.6(A) for one wire per terminal.

Copyright 2017, www.MikeHolt.com

▶Figure 314–61

(C) Covers. Pull boxes and junction boxes must have a cover suitable for the conditions. Metal covers must be connected to an equipment grounding conductor of a type recognized in 250.118, in accordance with 250.110 [250.4(A)(3)]. ▶Figure 314–62

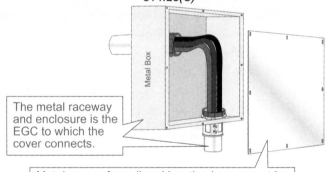

Pull and Junction Boxes, Depth
Conductors 4 AWG and Larger
314.28(C)

Metal Box

The metal raceway and enclosure is the EGC to which the cover connects.

Metal covers for pull and junction boxes must be connected to an equipment grounding conductor in accordance with 250.110.

Copyright 2017, www.MikeHolt.com

▶Figure 314–62

(E) Power Distribution Block. Power distribution blocks must comply with the following: ▶Figure 314–63

(1) Installation. Power distribution blocks must be listed; if installed on the line side of the service equipment, power distribution blocks must be listed and marked "suitable for use on the line side of service equipment" or equivalent. ▶Figure 314–64

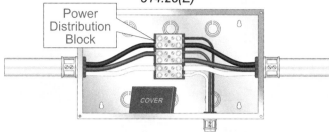

Power Distribution Blocks in Pull/Junction Boxes
314.28(E)

Power distribution blocks in pull and junction boxes must:
(1) Be listed as a power distribution block.
(2) Be installed in a box with dimensions not smaller than specified in the installation instructions of the block.
(3) Comply with 312.6 for wire-bending space at terminals.
(4) Have no uninsulated exposed live parts, whether the junction/pull box cover is on or off.

Copyright 2017, www.MikeHolt.com

▶Figure 314–63

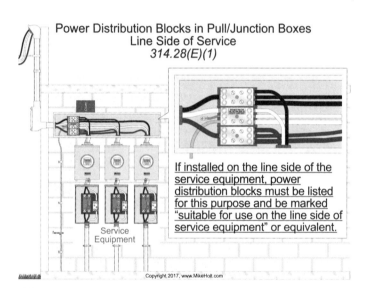

Power Distribution Blocks in Pull/Junction Boxes
Line Side of Service
314.28(E)(1)

If installed on the line side of the service equipment, power distribution blocks must be listed for this purpose and be marked "suitable for use on the line side of service equipment" or equivalent.

Copyright 2017, www.MikeHolt.com

▶Figure 314–64

(2) Size. Be installed in a box not smaller than required by the installation instructions of the power distribution block.

(3) Wire-Bending Space. The junction box is sized so the wire-bending space requirements of 312.6 can be met.

(4) Live Parts. Exposed live parts on the power distribution block aren't present when the junction box cover is removed.

(5) Through Conductors. Where the junction box has conductors that don't terminate on the power distribution block(s), the through conductors must be arranged so the power distribution block terminals are unobstructed following installation.

314.29 Wiring to be Accessible

Boxes, conduit bodies, and handhole enclosures must be installed so the wiring is accessible without removing any part of the building or structure, sidewalks, paving, or earth. ▶Figure 314–65 and ▶Figure 314–66

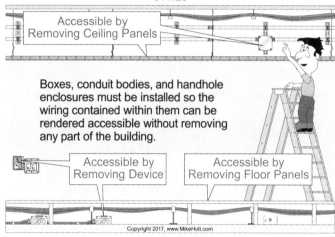

Wiring Must be Accessible
314.29

Accessible by Removing Ceiling Panels

Boxes, conduit bodies, and handhole enclosures must be installed so the wiring contained within them can be rendered accessible without removing any part of the building.

Accessible by Removing Device

Accessible by Removing Floor Panels

Copyright 2017, www.MikeHolt.com

▶Figure 314–65

Wiring Must be Accessible
314.29

VIOLATION
A box or conduit body must be installed so that the wiring can be rendered accessible without removing any part of the building or structure, or excavating sidewalks, paving, or the earth.

Copyright 2017, www.MikeHolt.com

▶Figure 314–66

Ex: Listed boxes and handhole enclosures can be buried if covered by gravel, light aggregate, or noncohesive granulated soil, and their location is effectively identified and accessible for excavation.

314.30 Handhole Enclosures

Handhole enclosures must be identified for underground use, and be designed and installed to withstand all loads likely to be imposed on them. ▶Figure 314–67

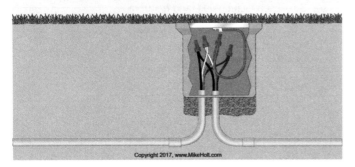

Handhole Enclosure
314.30

Handhole enclosures must be identified for underground use, and be designed and installed to withstand all loads likely to be imposed.

▶Figure 314–67

(A) Size. Handhole enclosures must be sized in accordance with 314.28(A). For handhole enclosures without bottoms, the measurement to the removable cover is taken from the end of the raceway or cable assembly. When the measurement is taken from the end of the raceway or cable assembly, the values in Table 312.6(A) for one wire to terminal can be used [314.28(A)(2) Ex].

(B) Mechanical Raceway and Cable Connection. Underground raceways and cables entering a handhole enclosure aren't required to be mechanically connected to the handhole enclosure. ▶Figure 314–68

(C) Enclosure Wiring. Splices or terminations within a handhole must be listed as suitable for wet locations [110.14(B)].

(D) Covers. Handhole enclosure covers must have an identifying mark or logo that prominently identifies the function of the enclosure, such as "electric." Handhole enclosure covers must require the use of tools to open, or they must weigh over 100 lb. ▶Figure 314–69 and ▶Figure 314–70

Metal covers and exposed conductive surfaces of handhole enclosures containing branch-circuit or feeder conductors must be connected to an equipment grounding conductor sized in accordance with 250.122, based on the rating of the overcurrent protection device [250.102(D)]. ▶Figure 314–71

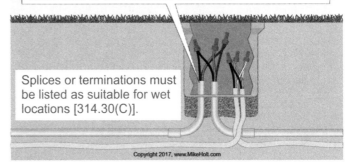

Handhole Enclosure
Mechanical Raceway and Cable Connection
314.30(B)

Underground raceways and cables entering a handhole enclosure aren't required to be mechanically connected to the handhole enclosure.

Splices or terminations must be listed as suitable for wet locations [314.30(C)].

▶Figure 314–68

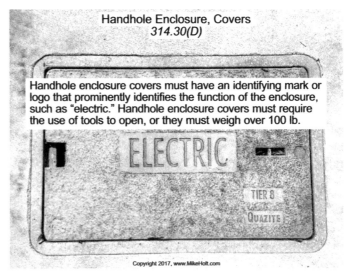

Handhole Enclosure, Covers
314.30(D)

Handhole enclosure covers must have an identifying mark or logo that prominently identifies the function of the enclosure, such as "electric." Handhole enclosure covers must require the use of tools to open, or they must weigh over 100 lb.

ELECTRIC

▶Figure 314–69

Metal covers and exposed conductive surfaces of handhole enclosures containing service conductors must be connected to a supply-side bonding jumper sized in accordance with Table 250.102(C)(1), based on the size of service conductors [250.92 and 250.102(C)].

Handhole Enclosure, Covers
314.30(D)

Handhole enclosure covers must require the use of tools to open, or they must weigh over 100 lbs.

Copyright 2017, www.MikeHolt.com

▶Figure 314–70

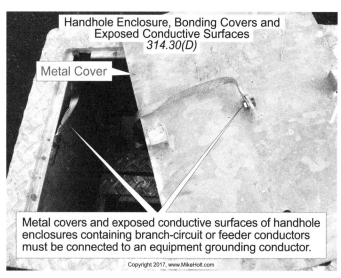

Handhole Enclosure, Bonding Covers and Exposed Conductive Surfaces
314.30(D)

Metal Cover

Metal covers and exposed conductive surfaces of handhole enclosures containing branch-circuit or feeder conductors must be connected to an equipment grounding conductor.

Copyright 2017, www.MikeHolt.com

▶Figure 314–71

ARTICLE 314 PRACTICE QUESTIONS

Please use the 2017 *Code* book to answer the following questions.

1. Nonmetallic boxes can be used with _____.

    (a) nonmetallic sheaths
    (b) nonmetallic raceways
    (c) flexible cords
    (d) all of these

2. Metal boxes shall be _____ in accordance with Article 250.

    (a) grounded
    (b) bonded
    (c) a and b
    (d) none of these

3. Boxes, conduit bodies, and fittings installed in wet locations shall be listed for use in wet locations.

    (a) True
    (b) False

4. _____ drainage openings not smaller than ⅛ in. and not larger than ¼ in. in diameter shall be permitted to be installed in the field in boxes or conduit bodies listed for use in damp or wet locations.

    (a) Listed
    (b) Approved
    (c) Labeled
    (d) Identified

5. Where a box is provided with _____ or more securely installed barriers, the volume shall be apportioned to each of the resulting spaces; each barrier, if not marked with its volume, shall be considered to take up ½ cu in. if metal, and 1 cu in. if nonmetallic.

    (a) one
    (b) two
    (c) three
    (d) four

6. According to the *NEC*, the volume of a 3 in. x 2 in. x 2 in. device box is _____ cu in.

    (a) 8
    (b) 10
    (c) 12
    (d) 14

7. When calculating box fill, each space within a box installed with a barrier shall be calculated separately.

    (a) True
    (b) False

8. The total volume occupied by two internal cable clamps, six 12 AWG conductors, and a single-pole switch is _____ cu in.

    (a) 2.00
    (b) 4.50
    (c) 14.50
    (d) 20.25

9. When counting the number of conductors in a box, a conductor running through the box with an unbroken loop or coil not less than twice the minimum length required for free conductors shall be counted as _____ conductor(s).

(a) one
(b) two
(c) three
(d) four

10. Equipment grounding conductor(s), and not more than _____ fixture wires smaller than 14 AWG shall be permitted to be omitted from the calculations where they enter the box from a domed luminaire or similar canopy and terminate within that box.

(a) one
(b) two
(c) three
(d) four

11. Where one or more internal cable clamps are present in the box, a single volume allowance in accordance with Table 314.16(B) shall be made based on the largest conductor present in the box.

(a) True
(b) False

12. Where a luminaire stud or hickey is present in the box, a _____ volume allowance in accordance with Table 314.16(B) shall be made for each type of fitting, based on the largest conductor present in the box.

(a) single
(b) double
(c) single allowance for each gang
(d) none of these

13. For the purposes of determining box fill, each device or utilization equipment in the box which is wider than a single device box counts as two conductors for each _____ required for the mounting.

(a) inch
(b) kilometer
(c) gang
(d) box

14. Each strap containing one or more devices shall count as a _____ volume allowance in accordance with Table 314.16(B), based on the largest conductor connected to a device(s) or equipment supported by the strap.

(a) single
(b) double
(c) triple
(d) none of these

15. A device or utilization equipment wider than a single 2 in. device box shall have _____ volume allowances provided for each gang required for mounting.

(a) single
(b) double
(c) triple
(d) none of these

16. Where one or more equipment grounding conductors enter a box, a _____ volume allowance in accordance with Table 314.16(B) shall be made based on the largest equipment grounding conductor.

(a) single
(b) double
(c) triple
(d) none of these

17. Conduit bodies that are durably and legibly marked by the manufacturer with their volume can contain splices, taps, or devices.

(a) True
(b) False

18. Short-radius conduit bodies such as capped elbows and service-entrance elbows that enclose conductors 6 AWG or smaller shall not contain _____.

(a) splices
(b) taps
(c) devices
(d) any of these

19. Where nonmetallic-sheathed cable or multiconductor Type UF cable is used, the sheath shall extend not less than _____ in. inside the box and beyond any cable clamp.

    (a) ¼
    (b) ⅜
    (c) ½
    (d) ¾

20. When Type NM cable is used with nonmetallic boxes not larger than 2¼ x 4 in., securing the cable to the box shall not be required if the cable is fastened within _____ in. of that box.

    (a) 6
    (b) 8
    (c) 10
    (d) 12

21. In installations within or behind noncombustible walls or ceilings, the front edge of a box, plaster ring, extension ring, or listed extender employing a flush-type cover, shall be set back not more than _____ in. from the finished surface.

    (a) ⅛
    (b) ¼
    (c) ⅜
    (d) ½

22. In installations within walls or ceilings constructed of wood or other combustible surface material, boxes, plaster rings, extension rings, or listed extenders shall _____.

    (a) extend to the finished surface
    (b) project from the finished surface
    (c) a or b
    (d) be set back no more than ¼ in.

23. Noncombustible surfaces that are broken or incomplete around boxes employing a flush-type cover or faceplate shall be repaired so there will be no gaps or open spaces larger than _____ in. at the edge of the box.

    (a) ¹⁄₁₆
    (b) ⅛
    (c) ¼
    (d) ½

24. Surface extensions shall be made by mounting and mechanically securing an extension ring over the box, unless otherwise permitted.

    (a) True
    (b) False

25. A surface extension can be made from the cover of a box where the cover is designed so it is unlikely to fall off or be removed if its securing means becomes loose. The wiring method shall be _____ for an approved length that permits removal of the cover and provides access to the box interior, and arranged so that any grounding continuity is independent of the connection between the box and cover.

    (a) solid
    (b) flexible
    (c) rigid
    (d) cord

26. Surface-mounted outlet boxes shall be _____.

    (a) rigidly and securely fastened in place
    (b) supported by cables that protrude from the box
    (c) supported by cable entries from the top and permitted to rest against the supporting surface
    (d) none of these

27. _____ can be used to secure boxes to a structural member using brackets on the outside of the enclosure.

    (a) Nails
    (b) Screws
    (c) Bolts
    (d) a and b

28. Mounting holes for screws used to secure boxes to a structural member using brackets on the outside of the enclosure shall be _____.

    (a) identified
    (b) approved
    (c) listed
    (d) labeled

29. A wood brace used for supporting a box for structural mounting shall have a cross-section not less than nominal _____.

    (a) 1 in. x 2 in.
    (b) 2 in. x 2 in.
    (c) 2 in. x 3 in.
    (d) 2 in. x 4 in.

30. When mounting an enclosure in a finished surface, the enclosure shall be _____ secured to the surface by clamps, anchors, or fittings identified for the application.

    (a) temporarily
    (b) partially
    (c) never
    (d) rigidly

31. Outlet boxes can be secured to suspended-ceiling framing members by mechanical means such as _____, or by other means identified for use with the suspended-ceiling framing member(s).

    (a) bolts
    (b) screws
    (c) rivets
    (d) any of these

32. Enclosures not over 100 cu in. having threaded entries and not containing a device shall be considered to be adequately supported where _____ or more conduits are threaded wrenchtight into the enclosure and each conduit is secured within 3 ft of the enclosure.

    (a) one
    (b) two
    (c) three
    (d) four

33. Two intermediate metal or rigid metal conduits threaded wrenchtight into an enclosure can be used to support an outlet box containing devices or luminaires, if each raceway is supported within _____ in. of the box.

    (a) 12
    (b) 18
    (c) 24
    (d) 36

34. In completed installations, each outlet box shall have a _____.

    (a) cover
    (b) faceplate
    (c) canopy
    (d) any of these

35. A vertically mounted luminaire weighing not more than _____ lb can be supported to a device box or plaster ring with no fewer than two No. 6 or larger screws.

    (a) 4
    (b) 6
    (c) 8
    (d) 10

36. Boxes used at luminaire or lampholder outlets in a ceiling shall be designed so that a luminaire or lampholder can be attached and the boxes shall be required to support a luminaire weighing a minimum of _____ lb.

    (a) 20
    (b) 30
    (c) 40
    (d) 50

37. A luminaire that weighs more than _____ lb can be supported by an outlet box that is listed for the weight of the luminaire to be supported.

    (a) 20
    (b) 30
    (c) 40
    (d) 50

38. Floor boxes _____ specifically for the application shall be used for receptacles located in the floor.

    (a) identified
    (b) listed
    (c) approved
    (d) none of these

39. Listed outlet boxes to support ceiling-suspended fans that weigh more than _____ lb shall have the maximum allowable weight marked on the box.

    (a) 35
    (b) 50
    (c) 60
    (d) 70

40. Utilization equipment weighing not more than 6 lb can be supported to any box or plaster ring secured to a box, provided the equipment is secured with at least two _____ or larger screws.

    (a) No. 6
    (b) No. 8
    (c) No. 10
    (d) any of these

41. Outlet boxes required in 314.27 shall be permitted to support _____ locking support and mounting receptacles used in combination with compatible attachment fittings.

    (a) identified
    (b) listed
    (c) approved
    (d) labeled

42. In straight pulls, the length of the box or conduit body shall not be less than _____ times the trade size of the largest raceway.

    (a) six
    (b) eight
    (c) twelve
    (d) none of these

43. Where angle or U pulls are made, the distance between each raceway entry inside the box or conduit body and the opposite wall of the box or conduit body shall not be less than _____ times the trade size of the largest raceway in a row plus the sum of the trade sizes of the remaining raceways in the same wall and row.

    (a) six
    (b) eight
    (c) twelve
    (d) none of these

44. Pull boxes or junction boxes with any dimension over _____ft shall have all conductors cabled or racked in an approved manner.

    (a) 3
    (b) 6
    (c) 9
    (d) 12

45. Power distribution blocks shall be permitted in pull and junction boxes over 100 cu in. when they comply with the provisions of 314.28(E)(1) through (5).

    (a) True
    (b) False

46. Power distribution blocks installed on the line side of the service equipment shall be _____ "suitable for use on the line side of service equipment" or equivalent.

    (a) marked
    (b) listed
    (c) a and b
    (d) none of these

47. Power distribution blocks shall be permitted in pull and junction boxes over 100 cu in. when _____.

    (a) they are listed as a power distribution block
    (b) they are installed in a box not smaller than required by the installation instructions of the power distribution block
    (c) the junction box is sized so that the wire-bending space requirements of 312.6 can be met
    (d) all of these

48. Exposed live parts on the power distribution block are allowed when the junction box cover is removed.

    (a) True
    (b) False

49. Where the junction box contains a power distribution block, and it has conductors that do not terminate on the power distribution block(s), the through conductors shall be arranged so the power distribution block terminals are _____ following installation.

    (a) unobstructed
    (b) above the through conductors
    (c) visible
    (d) labeled

50. _____ shall be installed so that the wiring contained in them can be rendered accessible without removing any part of the building or structure or, in underground circuits, without excavating sidewalks, paving, or earth.

    (a) Boxes
    (b) Conduit bodies
    (c) Handhole enclosures
    (d) all of these

51. Listed boxes and handhole enclosures designed for underground installation can be directly buried when covered by _____, if their location is effectively identified and accessible.

    (a) concrete
    (b) gravel
    (c) noncohesive granulated soil
    (d) b or c

52. Handhole enclosures shall be designed and installed to withstand _____.

    (a) 600 lb
    (b) 3,000 lb
    (c) 6,000 lb
    (d) all loads likely to be imposed on them

53. Underground raceways and cable assemblies entering a handhole enclosure shall extend into the enclosure, but they are not required to be _____.

    (a) bonded
    (b) insulated
    (c) mechanically connected to the handhole enclosure
    (d) below minimum cover requirements after leaving the handhole

54. Conductors, splices, or terminations in a handhole enclosure shall be listed as suitable for _____.

    (a) wet locations
    (b) damp locations
    (c) direct burial in the earth
    (d) none of these

55. Handhole enclosure covers shall have an identifying _____ that prominently identifies the function of the enclosure, such as "electric."

    (a) mark
    (b) logo
    (c) manual
    (d) a or b

56. Handhole enclosure covers shall require the use of tools to open, or they shall weigh over _____ lb.

    (a) 45
    (b) 70
    (c) 100
    (d) 200

Notes

ARTICLE 320

ARMORED CABLE (TYPE AC)

Introduction to Article 320—Armored Cable (Type AC)

Armored cable is an assembly of insulated conductors, 14 AWG through 1 AWG, individually wrapped within waxed paper and contained within a flexible spiral metal sheath. The outside appearance of armored cable looks like flexible metal conduit as well as metal-clad cable to the casual observer. This cable has been referred to as "BX®" cable over the years and used in residential wiring in some areas of the country.

Part I. General

320.1 Scope

This article covers the use, installation, and construction specifications of armored cable, Type AC. ▶Figure 320–1

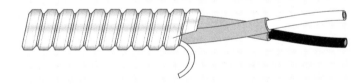

Armored Cable (Type AC)
320.1 Scope

This article covers the use, installation, and construction specifications of armored cable, Type AC.

Copyright 2017, www.MikeHolt.com

▶Figure 320–1

320.2 Definition

Armored Cable (Type AC). A fabricated assembly of conductors in a flexible interlocked metal armor with an internal bonding strip in intimate contact with the armor for its entire length. ▶Figure 320–2

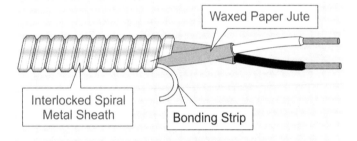

Armored Cable, (Type AC)
320.2 Definition

Waxed Paper Jute

Interlocked Spiral Metal Sheath

Bonding Strip

A fabricated assembly of conductors in a flexible interlocked metal armor with an internal bonding strip in intimate contact with the armor for its entire length.

Copyright 2017, www.MikeHolt.com

▶Figure 320–2

Author's Comment:

■ The conductors are contained within a flexible metal sheath that interlocks at the edges with an internal aluminum bonding strip, giving the cable an outside appearance similar to that of flexible metal conduit. Many electricians call this metal cable "BX®." The advantages the use of any flexible cables, as compared to raceway wiring methods, are that there's no limit to the number of bends between terminations and the cable can be quickly installed.

Part II. Installation

320.10 Uses Permitted

Type AC cable can be used or installed as follows:

(1) Feeders and branch circuits in both exposed and concealed installations.

(2) Cable trays.

(3) Dry locations.

(4) Embedded in plaster or brick, except in damp or wet locations.

(5) In air voids where not exposed to excessive moisture or dampness.

Note: The "Uses Permitted" isn't an all-inclusive list, which indicates that other suitable uses are permitted if approved by the authority having jurisdiction.

Author's Comment:

■ Type AC cable is also permitted to be installed in a plenum space [300.22(C)(1)].

320.12 Uses Not Permitted

Type AC cable isn't permitted to be installed:

(1) Where subject to physical damage.

(2) In damp or wet locations.

(3) In air voids of masonry block or tile walls where such walls are exposed or subject to excessive moisture or dampness.

(4) Where exposed to corrosive conditions.

ARTICLE 320

PRACTICE QUESTIONS

Please use the 2017 *Code* book to answer the following questions.

1. Type _____ cable is a fabricated assembly of insulated conductors in a flexible interlocked metallic armor.

   (a) AC
   (b) MC
   (c) NM
   (d) b and c

2. Type AC cable is permitted in _____.

   (a) wet locations
   (b) cable trays
   (c) exposed installations
   (d) b and c

3. Armored cable shall not be installed _____.

   (a) in damp or wet locations
   (b) where subject to physical damage
   (c) where exposed to corrosive conditions
   (d) all of these

Mike Holt's Electrical Apprenticeship Year 1 Supplement, Based on the 2017 NEC

ARTICLE
330

METAL-CLAD CABLE (TYPE MC)

Introduction to Article 330—Metal-Clad Cable (Type MC)

Metal-clad cable encloses insulated conductors in a metal sheath of either corrugated or smooth copper or aluminum tubing, or spiral interlocked steel or aluminum. The physical characteristics of Type MC cable make it a versatile wiring method that you can use in almost any location, and for almost any application. The most commonly used Type MC cable is the interlocking kind, which looks similar to armored cable or flexible metal conduit. Traditional interlocked Type MC cable isn't permitted to serve as an equipment grounding conductor, therefore this cable must contain an equipment grounding conductor in accordance with 250.118(1). There's a fairly new product available called interlocked Type MC^AP® cable that contains a bare aluminum grounding/bonding conductor running just below the metal armor, which allows the sheath to serve as an equipment grounding conductor [250.118(10)(b)].

Part I. General

330.1 Scope

Scan this QR code to watch Mike explain this topic; it's a sample video clip from Mike's *Understanding the NEC Volume 1* DVDs.

Article 330 covers the use, installation, and construction specifications of metal-clad cable. ▶Figure 330–1

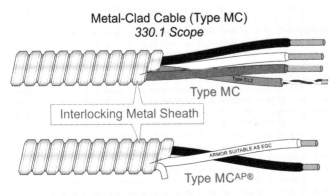

Metal-Clad Cable (Type MC)
330.1 Scope

Type MC

Interlocking Metal Sheath

Type MC^AP®

Article 330 covers the use, installation, and construction specifications of metal-clad cable, Type MC.

Copyright 2017, www.MikeHolt.com

▶Figure 330–1

330.2 Definition

Metal-Clad Cable (Type MC). A factory assembly of insulated circuit conductors, with or without optical fiber members, enclosed in an armor of interlocking metal tape; or a smooth or corrugated metallic sheath. ▶Figure 330–2

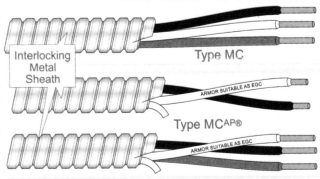

Metal-Clad Cable (Type MC Cable)
330.2 Definition

Interlocking Metal Sheath

Type MC

ARMOR SUITABLE AS EGC

Type MC^AP®

ARMOR SUITABLE AS EGC

A factory assembly of one or more insulated circuit conductors enclosed in an armor of interlocking metal tape, or a smooth or corrugated metallic sheath.

Copyright 2017, www.MikeHolt.com

▶Figure 330–2

Author's Comment:

- Because the outer sheath of interlocked Type MC cable isn't listed as an equipment grounding conductor, it contains an equipment grounding conductor [330.108].

Part II. Installation

330.10 Uses Permitted

(A) General Uses.

(1) In branch circuits, feeders, and services

(2) In power, lighting, control, and signal circuits

(3) Indoors or outdoors

(4) Exposed or concealed

(5) Directly buried (if identified for the purpose)

(6) In a cable tray

(7) In a raceway

(8) As aerial cable on a messenger

(9) In hazardous locations as permitted in 501.10(B), 502.10(B), and 503.10

(10) Embedded in plaster or brick in dry locations

(11) In wet locations, where a corrosion-resistant jacket is provided over the metal sheath and any of the following are met:

    a. The metallic covering is impervious to moisture.

    b. A jacket is provided under the metal covering that's moisture resistant. ▶Figure 330–3

    c. The insulated conductors under the metallic covering are listed for use in wet locations.

(12) If single-conductor cables are used, all circuit conductors must be grouped together to minimize induced voltage on the sheath [300.3(B)].

(B) Specific Uses.

(1) Cable Tray. Type MC cable installed in a cable tray in accordance with Article 392.

(2) Direct Buried. Direct-buried cables must be protected in accordance with 300.5.

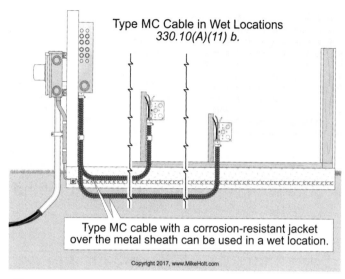

Type MC Cable in Wet Locations
330.10(A)(11) b.

Type MC cable with a corrosion-resistant jacket over the metal sheath can be used in a wet location.

Copyright 2017, www.MikeHolt.com

▶Figure 330–3

(3) Installed as Service-Entrance Cable. Type MC cable is permitted for service entrances when installed in accordance with 230.43.

(4) Installed Outside of Buildings. Type MC cable installed outside of buildings must comply with 225.10, 396.10, and 396.12.

Note: The "Uses Permitted" isn't an all-inclusive list, which indicates that other suitable uses are permitted if approved by the authority having jurisdiction.

330.12 Uses Not Permitted

Type MC cable isn't permitted to be used where:

(1) Subject to physical damage.

(2) Exposed to the destructive corrosive conditions in (a) or (b), unless the metallic sheath or armor is resistant to the conditions, or protected by material resistant to the conditions:

    a. Direct burial in the earth or embedded in concrete unless identified for the application.

    b. Exposed to cinder fills, strong chlorides, caustic alkalis, or vapors of chlorine or of hydrochloric acids.

ARTICLE
330
PRACTICE QUESTIONS

Please use the 2017 *Code* book to answer the following questions.

1. Type _____ cable is a factory assembly of insulated circuit conductors within an armor of interlocking metal tape, or a smooth or corrugated metallic sheath.

   (a) AC
   (b) MC
   (c) NM
   (d) b and c

2. Type MC cable shall not be used under which of the following conditions?

   (a) Where subject to physical damage.
   (b) Direct buried in the earth or embedded in concrete unless identified for direct burial.
   (c) Exposed to cinder fills, strong chlorides, caustic alkalis, or vapors of chlorine or of hydrochloric acids.
   (d) all of these

ARTICLE 334

NONMETALLIC-SHEATHED CABLE (TYPES NM AND NMC)

Introduction to Article 334—Nonmetallic-Sheathed Cable (Types NM and NMC)

Nonmetallic-sheathed cable is flexible, inexpensive, and easily installed. It provides very limited physical protection for the conductors, so the installation restrictions are stringent. Its low cost and relative ease of installation make it a common wiring method for residential and commercial branch circuits. In the field, Type NM cable is typically referred to as "Romex®."

Part I. General

334.1 Scope

Article 334 covers the use, installation, and construction specifications of nonmetallic-sheathed cable. ▶Figure 334–1

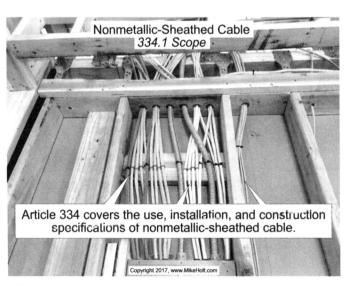

Nonmetallic-Sheathed Cable
334.1 Scope

Article 334 covers the use, installation, and construction specifications of nonmetallic-sheathed cable.

Copyright 2017, www.MikeHolt.com

▶Figure 334–1

334.2 Definition

Nonmetallic-Sheathed Cable (Types NM and NMC). A wiring method that encloses two or more insulated conductors, 14 AWG through 2 AWG, within a nonmetallic jacket. ▶Figure 334–2

Nonmetallic-Sheathed Cable
(Types NM and NMC Cable)
334.2 Definition

14/2 w/G   NM-B   600V

A wiring method that encloses two, three, or four insulated conductors (14 AWG to 2 AWG) within an outer nonmetallic jacket.

Copyright 2017, www.MikeHolt.com

▶Figure 334–2

- NM cable has insulated conductors enclosed within an overall nonmetallic jacket.
- NMC cable has insulated conductors enclosed within an overall, corrosion-resistant, nonmetallic jacket.

Author's Comment:

- It's the generally accepted practice in the electrical industry to call Type NM cable "Romex®," a registered trademark of the Southwire Company.

Part II. Installation

334.10 Uses Permitted

Type NM and Type NMC cables can be used in the following, except as prohibited in 334.12:

(1) One- and two-family dwellings of any height, and their attached/detached garages or storage buildings. ▶ Figure 334–3 and ▶ Figure 334–4

NM Cable, One- and Two-Family Dwelling Units
334.10(1)

NM cable can be installed in one- and two-family dwelling units of any height.

Copyright 2017, www.MikeHolt.com

▶ Figure 334–3

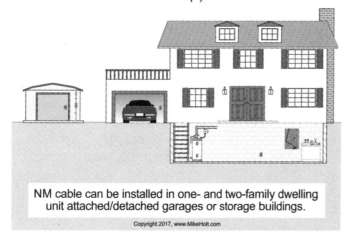

NM Cable, One- and Two-Family Dwelling Units
334.10(1)

NM cable can be installed in one- and two-family dwelling unit attached/detached garages or storage buildings.

Copyright 2017, www.MikeHolt.com

▶ Figure 334–4

(2) Multifamily dwellings permitted to be of Types III, IV, and V construction. ▶ Figure 334–5

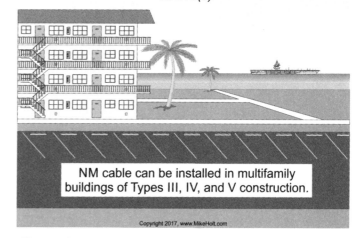

NM Cable, Multifamily Dwellings
334.10(2)

NM cable can be installed in multifamily buildings of Types III, IV, and V construction.

Copyright 2017, www.MikeHolt.com

▶ Figure 334–5

(3) Other structures permitted to be of Types III, IV, and V construction. Cables must be concealed within walls, floors, or ceilings that provide a thermal barrier of material with at least a 15-minute finish rating, as identified in listings of fire-rated assemblies. ▶ Figure 334–6

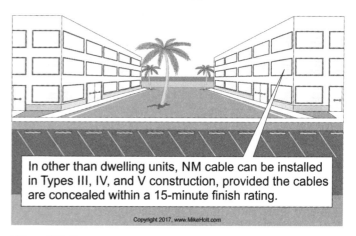

NM Cable, Other Structures
334.10(3)

In other than dwelling units, NM cable can be installed in Types III, IV, and V construction, provided the cables are concealed within a 15-minute finish rating.

Copyright 2017, www.MikeHolt.com

▶ Figure 334–6

Author's Comment:

- See the definition of "Concealed" in Article 100.

Note 1: Building constructions are defined in NFPA 220-2006, *Standard on Types of Building Construction*, the applicable building code, or both.

Note 2: See Annex E for the determination of building types [NFPA 220, Table 3-1].

334.12 Uses Not Permitted

(A) Types NM and NMC. Types NM and NMC cables aren't permitted.

(1) In any dwelling or structure not specifically permitted in 334.10(1), (2), (3), and (5).

(2) Exposed within a dropped or suspended ceiling cavity in other than one- and two-family, and multifamily dwellings. ▶Figure 334–7

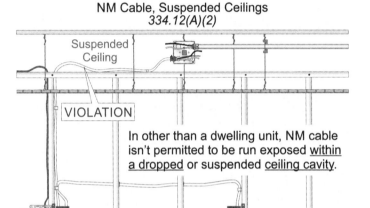

NM Cable, Suspended Ceilings
334.12(A)(2)

Suspended Ceiling

VIOLATION

In other than a dwelling unit, NM cable isn't permitted to be run exposed within a dropped or suspended ceiling cavity.

Copyright 2017, www.MikeHolt.com

▶Figure 334–7

(3) As service-entrance cable.

(4) In commercial garages having hazardous locations, as defined in 511.3.

(5) In theaters and similar locations, except where permitted in 518.4(B).

(6) In motion picture studios.

(7) In storage battery rooms.

(8) In hoistways, or on elevators or escalators.

(9) Embedded in poured cement, concrete, or aggregate.

(10) In any hazardous location, except where permitted by other sections in the *Code*.

(B) Type NM. Type NM cables aren't permitted to be used under the following conditions, or in the following locations:

(1) If exposed to corrosive fumes or vapors.

(2) If embedded in masonry, concrete, adobe, fill, or plaster.

(3) In a shallow chase in masonry, concrete, or adobe and covered with plaster, adobe, or similar finish.

(4) In wet or damp locations. ▶Figure 334–8

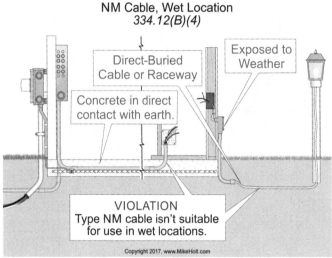

NM Cable, Wet Location
334.12(B)(4)

Direct-Buried Cable or Raceway

Exposed to Weather

Concrete in direct contact with earth.

VIOLATION
Type NM cable isn't suitable for use in wet locations.

Copyright 2017, www.MikeHolt.com

▶Figure 334–8

Author's Comment:

■ A raceway in a ground floor slab is considered a wet location. ▶Figure 334–9

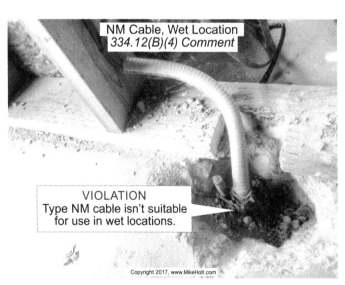

NM Cable, Wet Location
334.12(B)(4) Comment

VIOLATION
Type NM cable isn't suitable for use in wet locations.

Copyright 2017, www.MikeHolt.com

▶Figure 334–9

ARTICLE
334 PRACTICE QUESTIONS

Please use the 2017 *Code* book to answer the following questions.

1. Type _____ cable is a factory assembly that encloses two or more insulated conductors within a nonmetallic jacket.

    (a) AC
    (b) MC
    (c) NM
    (d) b and c

2. Type NM cables shall not be used in one- and two-family dwellings exceeding three floors above grade.

    (a) True
    (b) False

3. Type NM and Type NMC cables shall be permitted in _____, except as prohibited in 334.12.

    (a) one- and two-family dwellings and their attached/detached garages and storage buildings
    (b) multifamily dwellings permitted to be of Types III, IV, and V construction
    (c) other structures permitted to be of Types III, IV, and V construction
    (d) any of these

ARTICLE 336

POWER AND CONTROL TRAY CABLE (TYPE TC)

Introduction to Article 336—Power and Control Tray Cable (Type TC)

Power and control tray cable is flexible, inexpensive, and easily installed. It provides very limited physical protection for the conductors, so the installation restrictions are stringent. Its low cost and relative ease of installation make it a common wiring method for industrial applications.

Part I. General

336.1 Scope

This article covers the use and installation for power and control tray cable, Type TC.

336.2 Definition

Power and Control Tray Cable, Type TC. A factory assembly of two or more insulated conductors under a nonmetallic jacket.

336.6 Listing Requirements

Type TC cable and associated fittings must be listed. ▶Figure 336–1

Part II. Installation

336.10 Uses Permitted

 Scan this QR code to watch Mike explain this topic; it's a sample video clip from Mike's *Understanding the NEC Volume 1* DVDs.

(1) Power, lighting, control, and signal circuits.

(2) In cable trays <u>including those with mechanically discontinuous segments up to 1 ft.</u>

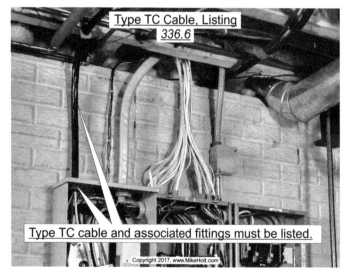

Type TC Cable, Listing
336.6

Type TC cable and associated fittings must be listed.

Copyright 2017, www.MikeHolt.com

▶Figure 336–1

(3) In raceways.

(4) Outdoor locations supported by a messenger wire.

(5) Class 1 circuits as permitted in Parts II and III of Article 725.

(6) Nonpower-limited fire alarm circuits in accordance with if 760.49.

(7) Industrial establishments where the conditions of maintenance and supervision ensure that only qualified persons service the installation.

(8) In wet locations where the cable is resistant to moisture and corrosive agents.

(9) In one- and two-family dwellings, Type TC-ER cable is permitted in accordance with Part II of Article 334. ▶Figure 336–2

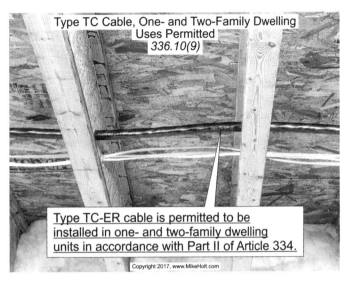

▶Figure 336–2

Author's Comment:

■ The "ER" marking on Type TC-ER cable identifies the cable as suitable for exposed run use in accordance with UL 1277.

Ex: Where Type TC cable is used to connect a generator and its associated equipment, the cable ampacity limitations of 334.80 don't apply.

Note 1: Type TC cable that's suitable for pulling through structural members of a dwelling unit will be marked "TC-ER-JP." ▶Figure 336–3

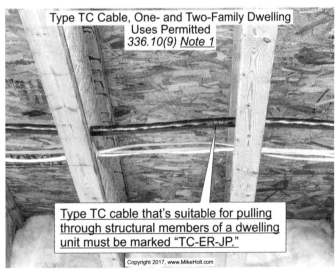

▶Figure 336–3

Author's Comment:

■ The "JP" marking on Type TC-ER-JP cable identifies the cable as suitable to be pulled through wood framing members because the cable has met the joist pull testing requirements of UL 1277.

Note 2: Control and Class 1 power conductors within the same Type TC cable are only permitted where the conductors are functionally associated with each other in accordance with 725.136.

(10) Direct buried where identified for direct burial.

336.12 Uses Not Permitted

Type TC tray cables aren't permitted:

(1) Where exposed to physical damage

(2) Outside a raceway or cable tray system, except as permitted in 336.10(4), 336.10(7), 336.10(9), and 336.10(10)

(3) Exposed to direct rays of the sun, unless identified as sunlight resistant

336.24 Bending Radius

Bends in Type TC cable must be made so as not to damage the cable. Type TC cable without metal shielding must have a minimum bending radius as follows:

(1) Four times the overall diameter for cables 1 in. or less in diameter

(2) Five times the overall diameter for cables larger than 1 in. but not more than 2 in. in diameter

336.80 Ampacity

The ampacity of Type TC tray cable is in accordance with 310.15(B)(16) as limited by 110.14(C)(1).

ARTICLE
336 PRACTICE QUESTIONS

Please use the 2017 *Code* book to answer the following questions.

1. Type _____ cable is a factory assembly of two or more insulated conductors, with or without associated bare of covered grounding conductors, under a nonmetallic jacket.

   (a) NM
   (b) TC
   (c) SE
   (d) UF

2. Type TC cable can be used _____.

   (a) for power, lighting, control, and signal circuits
   (b) in cable trays including those with mechanically discontinuous segments up to 1 ft
   (c) for Class 1 control circuits as permitted in Parts II and III of Article 725
   (d) all of these

3. Type TC cable can be used in one- and two-family dwelling units.

   (a) True
   (b) False

4. Where Type TC-ER cable is used to connect a generator and associated equipment having terminals rated _____ or higher, the cable shall not be limited in ampacity by 334.80 or 340.80.

   (a) 60°C
   (b) 75°C
   (c) 90°C
   (d) 100°C

5. Type TC-ER cable used for interior wiring in one- and two-family dwelling units that is suitable for pulling through structural members is marked "TC-ER-JP."

   (a) True
   (b) False

6. Where Type TC cable is installed in one- and two-family dwelling units, 725.136 provides rules for limitations on Class 2 or 3 circuits contained within the same cable with conductors of electric light, power, or Class 1 circuits.

   (a) True
   (b) False

7. Type TC cable shall be permitted to be direct buried, where _____ for such use.

   (a) identified
   (b) approved
   (c) listed
   (d) labeled

8. Type TC cable shall not be _____.

   (a) installed where it will be exposed to physical damage
   (b) installed outside of a raceway or cable tray system, unless permitted in 336.10(4), 336.10(7), 336.10(9), and 336.10(10)
   (c) used where exposed to direct rays of the sun, unless identified as sunlight resistant
   (d) all of these

Notes

ARTICLE
338

SERVICE-ENTRANCE CABLE (TYPES SE AND USE)

Introduction to Article 338—Service-Entrance Cable (Types SE and USE)

Service-entrance cable is a single conductor or multiconductor assembly with or without an overall moisture-resistant covering. This cable is used primarily for services, but can also be used for feeders and branch circuits when the limitations of this article are observed.

Part I. General

Article 338 covers the use, installation, and construction specifications of service-entrance cable, Types SE and USE. ▶Figure 338–1

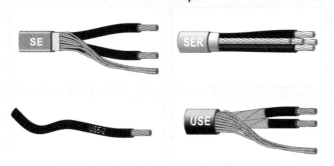

Service-Entrance Cable (Types SE and USE)
338.1 Scope

Article 338 covers the use, installation, and construction specifications of service-entrance cable, Types SE and USE.

Copyright 2017, www.MikeHolt.com

▶Figure 338–1

338.2 Definitions

Service-Entrance Cable. Service-entrance cable is a single or multi-conductor assembly, with or without an overall covering, used primarily for services. ▶Figure 338–2

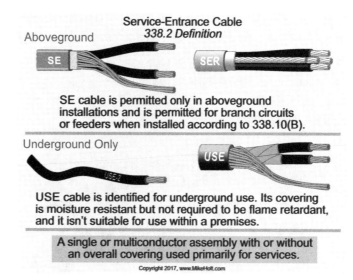

Service-Entrance Cable
338.2 Definition

Aboveground

SE cable is permitted only in aboveground installations and is permitted for branch circuits or feeders when installed according to 338.10(B).

Underground Only

USE cable is identified for underground use. Its covering is moisture resistant but not required to be flame retardant, and it isn't suitable for use within a premises.

A single or multiconductor assembly with or without an overall covering used primarily for services.

Copyright 2017, www.MikeHolt.com

▶Figure 338–2

Type SE. SE and SER cables have a flame-retardant, moisture-resistant covering and are permitted only in aboveground installations. These cables are permitted for branch circuits or feeders when installed in accordance with 338.10(B).

Author's Comment:

- SER cable is SE cable with an insulated neutral, resulting in three insulated conductors with an uninsulated equipment grounding conductor. SER cable is round, while 2-wire SE cable is flat.

Type USE. USE cable is identified as a wiring method permitted for underground use; its covering is moisture resistant, but not flame retardant.

Author's Comment:

- USE cable isn't permitted to be installed indoors [338.10(B)], except single-conductor USE dual rated as RHH/RHW.

Part II. Installation

338.10 Uses Permitted

(A) Service-Entrance Conductors. Service-entrance cable used as service-entrance conductors must be installed in accordance with Article 230.

(B) Branch Circuits or Feeders.

(1) Insulated Conductor. Type SE service-entrance cable is permitted for branch circuits and feeders where the circuit conductors are insulated.

(2) Uninsulated Conductor. SE cable is permitted for branch circuits and feeders if the insulated conductors are used for circuit wiring, and the uninsulated conductor is only used for equipment grounding purposes. ▶Figure 338–3

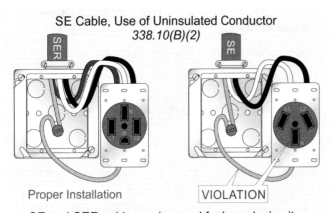

SE Cable, Use of Uninsulated Conductor
338.10(B)(2)

Proper Installation   VIOLATION

SE and SER cable can be used for branch circuits and feeders, but the uninsulated conductor can only be used for equipment grounding.

Copyright 2017, www.MikeHolt.com

▶Figure 338–3

Ex: In existing installations, uninsulated conductors may be used for the neutral conductor if the uninsulated neutral conductor of the cable originates in service equipment.

(3) Temperature Limitations. SE cable isn't permitted to be subjected to conductor temperatures exceeding its insulation rating.

(4) Installation Methods for Branch Circuits and Feeders. SE cable used for branch circuits or feeders must comply with (a) and (b).

(a) Interior Installations. SE cable used for interior branch-circuit or feeder wiring must be installed in accordance with the same requirements as Type NM Cable—Article 334, excluding 334.80.

Where installed in thermal insulation, the ampacity of conductors 10 AWG and smaller, must be sized in accordance with 60°C (140°F) conductor temperature rating. For conductor ampacity correction and/or adjustment, the conductor temperature rating ampacity is to be used.

⚠ **CAUTION:** *Underground service-entrance cable (USE) isn't permitted for interior wiring because it doesn't have a flame-retardant insulation. It's only permitted in interior wiring when listed as both a cable (USE) and a conductor, such as RHH, in accordance with Table 310.104.*

(b) Exterior Installations. The cable must be supported in accordance with 334.30 and where run underground, the cable must comply with Part II of Article 340.

338.12 Uses Not Permitted

(A) Service-Entrance Cable. SE cable isn't permitted under the following conditions or locations:

(1) If subject to physical damage unless protected in accordance with 230.50(A).

(2) Underground with or without a raceway.

(B) Underground Service-Entrance Cable. USE cable isn't permitted:

(1) For interior wiring.

(2) Above ground, except where protected against physical damage in accordance with 300.5(D).

ARTICLE
338 PRACTICE QUESTIONS

Please use the 2017 *Code* book to answer the following questions.

1. Type _____ cable is an assembly primarily used for services.

   (a) NM
   (b) TC
   (c) SE
   (d) none of these

2. Type _____ cable is a multiconductor assembly identified for use as underground service-entrance cable.

   (a) SE
   (b) NM
   (c) UF
   (d) USE

3. Type SE cable shall be permitted to be used as _____ in wiring systems where all of the circuit conductors of the cable are of the thermoset or thermoplastic type.

   (a) branch circuits
   (b) feeders
   (c) a or b
   (d) none of these

4. Type SE cables shall be permitted to be used for branch circuits or feeders where the insulated conductors are used for circuit wiring and the uninsulated conductor is used only for _____ purposes.

   (a) grounded connection
   (b) equipment grounding
   (c) remote control and signaling
   (d) none of these

5. Type SE cable can be used for interior wiring as long as it complies with the installation requirements of Part II of Article 334, excluding 334.80.

   (a) True
   (b) False

6. For interior installations of Type SE cable with ungrounded conductor sizes _____ AWG and smaller, where installed in thermal insulation, the ampacity shall be in accordance with 60°C (140°F) conductor temperature rating.

   (a) 14
   (b) 12
   (c) 10
   (d) 8

7. Type USE cable is not permitted for _____ wiring.

   (a) underground
   (b) interior
   (c) a or b
   (d) a and b

8. Type USE cable used for service laterals shall be permitted to emerge from the ground if terminated in an enclosure at an outside location and protected in accordance with 300.5(D).

   (a) True
   (b) False

Notes

Mike Holt's Electrical Apprenticeship Year 1 Supplement, Based on the 2017 NEC

UNDERGROUND FEEDER AND BRANCH-CIRCUIT CABLE (TYPE UF)

Introduction to Article 340—Underground Feeder and Branch-Circuit Cable (Type UF)

UF cable is a moisture-, fungus-, and corrosion-resistant cable suitable for direct burial in the earth.

Part I. General

340.1 Scope

Article 340 covers the use, installation, and construction specifications of underground feeder and branch-circuit cable, Type UF. ▶Figure 340–1

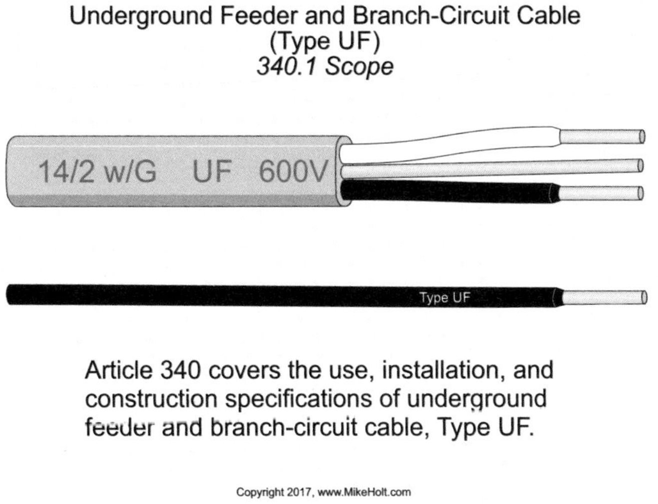

Underground Feeder and Branch-Circuit Cable
(Type UF)
340.1 Scope

Article 340 covers the use, installation, and construction specifications of underground feeder and branch-circuit cable, Type UF.

Copyright 2017, www.MikeHolt.com

▶Figure 340–1

340.2 Definition

Underground Feeder and Branch-Circuit Cable (Type UF). A factory assembly of insulated conductors with an integral or an overall covering of nonmetallic material suitable for direct burial in the earth. Notice that Type UF isn't allowed as a service cable. ▶Figure 340–2

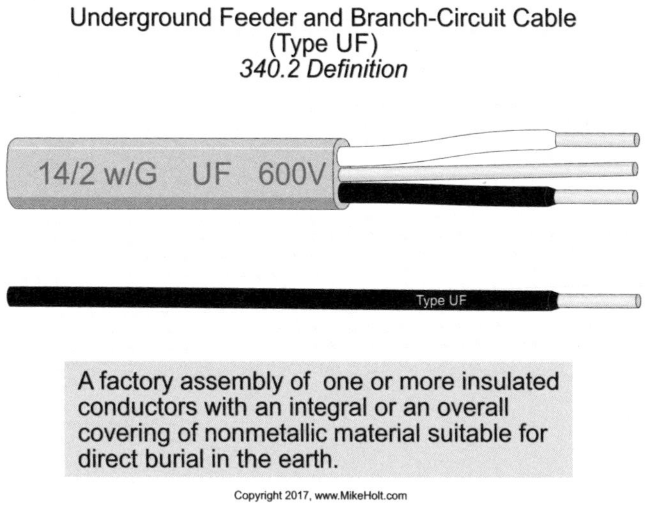

Underground Feeder and Branch-Circuit Cable
(Type UF)
340.2 Definition

A factory assembly of one or more insulated conductors with an integral or an overall covering of nonmetallic material suitable for direct burial in the earth.

Copyright 2017, www.MikeHolt.com

▶Figure 340–2

Author's Comment:

■ UF cable is a moisture-, fungus-, and corrosion-resistant cable suitable for direct burial in the earth. It comes in sizes 14 AWG through 4/0 AWG [340.104]. The covering of multiconductor Type UF cable is molded plastic that encases the insulated conductors.

■ Because the covering of Type UF cable encapsulates the insulated conductors, it's difficult to strip off the outer jacket to gain access to the conductors, but this covering provides excellent corrosion protection. Be careful not to damage the conductor insulation or cut yourself when you remove the outer cover.

Part II. Installation

340.10 Uses Permitted

(1) Underground, in accordance with 300.5.

(2) As a single conductor in the same trench or raceway with circuit conductors.

(3) As interior or exterior wiring in wet, dry, or corrosive locations.

(4) As Type NM cable, when installed in accordance with Article 334.

(5) For solar PV systems, in accordance with 690.31.

(6) As single-conductor cables for nonheating leads for heating cables, as provided in 424.43.

(7) Supported by cable trays.

340.12 Uses Not Permitted

(1) As services [230.43].

(2) In commercial garages [511.3].

(3) In theaters [520.5].

(4) In motion picture studios [530.11].

(5) In storage battery rooms [Article 480].

(6) In hoistways [Article 620].

(7) In hazardous locations, except as specifically permitted by other articles in the *Code*.

(8) Embedded in concrete.

(9) Exposed to direct sunlight unless identified.

(10) If subject to physical damage. ▶Figure 340–3

(11) As overhead messenger-supported wiring.

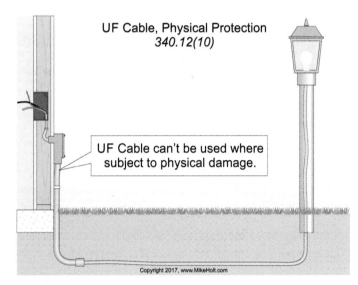

UF Cable, Physical Protection
340.12(10)

UF Cable can't be used where subject to physical damage.

Copyright 2017, www.MikeHolt.com

▶Figure 340–3

Author's Comment:

■ UF cable isn't permitted in ducts or plenum spaces [300.22], or in patient care spaces [517.13].

ARTICLE 340 PRACTICE QUESTIONS

Please use the 2017 *Code* book to answer the following questions.

1. Type _____ cable is a factory assembly of conductors with an overall covering of nonmetallic material suitable for direct burial in the earth.

   (a) NM
   (b) UF
   (c) SE
   (d) TC

2. Type UF cable is permitted to be used for inside wiring.

   (a) True
   (b) False

3. Type UF cable can be used for service conductors.

   (a) True
   (b) False

4. Type UF cable can be used in commercial garages.

   (a) True
   (b) False

5. Type UF cable shall not be used in _____.

   (a) motion picture studios
   (b) storage battery rooms
   (c) hoistways
   (d) all of these

6. Type UF cable shall not be used _____.

   (a) in any hazardous (classified) location except as otherwise permitted in this *Code*
   (b) embedded in poured cement, concrete, or aggregate
   (c) where exposed to direct rays of the sun, unless identified as sunlight resistant
   (d) all of these

7. Type UF cable shall not be used where subject to physical damage.

   (a) True
   (b) False

ARTICLE 342

INTERMEDIATE METAL CONDUIT (TYPE IMC)

Introduction to Article 342—Intermediate Metal Conduit (Type IMC)

Intermediate metal conduit is a circular metal raceway with an outside diameter equal to that of rigid metal conduit. The wall thickness of intermediate metal conduit is less than that of rigid metal conduit, so it has a greater interior cross-sectional area for containing conductors. Intermediate metal conduit is lighter and less expensive than rigid metal conduit, and it can be used in all of the same locations as rigid metal conduit. Intermediate metal conduit also uses a different steel alloy that makes it stronger than rigid metal conduit, even though the walls are thinner. Intermediate metal conduit is manufactured in both galvanized steel and aluminum; the steel type is much more common.

Part I. General

342.1 Scope

Article 342 covers the use, installation, and construction specifications of intermediate metal conduit and associated fittings. ▶Figure 342–1

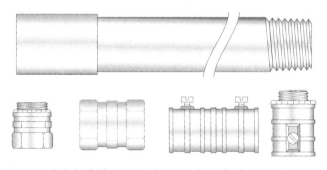

Intermediate Metal Conduit (Type IMC)
342.1 Scope

Article 342 covers the use, installation, and construction specifications of intermediate metal conduit and associated fittings.

Copyright 2017, www.MikeHolt.com

▶Figure 342–1

342.2 Definition

Intermediate Metal Conduit (Type IMC). A listed steel raceway of circular cross section that can be threaded with integral or associated couplings. It's listed for the installation of electrical conductors, and is used with listed fittings to provide electrical continuity. ▶Figure 342–2

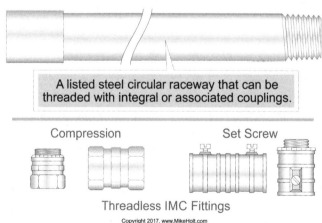

Intermediate Metal Conduit (Type IMC)
342.2 Definition

A listed steel circular raceway that can be threaded with integral or associated couplings.

Compression   Set Screw

Threadless IMC Fittings

Copyright 2017, www.MikeHolt.com

▶Figure 342–2

Author's Comment:

■ The type of steel from which intermediate metal conduit is manufactured, the process by which it's made, and the corrosion protection applied are all equal, or superior, to that of rigid metal conduit.

Part II. Installation

342.10 Uses Permitted

(A) Atmospheric Conditions and Occupancies. Intermediate metal conduit is permitted in all atmospheric conditions and occupancies.

(B) Corrosive Environments. Intermediate metal conduit, elbows, couplings, and fittings can be installed in concrete, in direct contact with the earth, or in areas subject to severe corrosive influences if provided with supplementary corrosion protection approved for the condition.

Author's Comment:

■ See 300.6 for additional details.

(D) Wet Locations. Support fittings, such as screws, straps, and so forth, installed in a wet location must be made of corrosion-resistant material, or be protected by corrosion-resistant coatings in accordance with 300.6.

CAUTION: *Supplementary coatings for corrosion protection haven't been investigated by a product testing and listing agency, and these coatings are known to cause cancer in laboratory animals. There's a documented case where an electrician was taken to the hospital for lead poisoning after using a supplemental coating product (asphalted paint) in a poorly ventilated area. As with all products, be sure to read and follow all product instructions, including material data safety sheets, particularly when petroleum-based chemicals (volatile organic compounds) may be in the material.*

PRACTICE QUESTIONS

Please use the 2017 *Code* book to answer the following questions.

1. IMC, elbows, couplings, and fittings shall be permitted to be installed in concrete, in direct contact with the earth, or in areas subject to severe corrosive influences where protected by corrosion protection _____ for the condition.

    (a) identified
    (b) approved
    (c) listed
    (d) none of these

2. Materials such as straps, bolts, screws, and so forth, which are associated with the installation of IMC in wet locations shall be _____.

    (a) weatherproof
    (b) protected against corrosion by corrosion-resistant materials
    (c) corrosion resistant
    (d) b or c

ARTICLE 344

RIGID METAL CONDUIT (TYPE RMC)

Introduction to Article 344—Rigid Metal Conduit (Type RMC)

Rigid metal conduit, commonly called "rigid," has long been the standard raceway for providing protection from physical impact and from difficult environments. The outside diameter of rigid metal conduit is the same as intermediate metal conduit. However, the wall thickness of rigid metal conduit is greater than intermediate metal conduit; therefore the interior cross-sectional area is smaller. Rigid metal conduit is heavier and more expensive than intermediate metal conduit, and it can be used in any location. It's manufactured in both galvanized steel and aluminum; the steel type is much more common.

Part I. General

344.1 Scope

Article 344 covers the use, installation, and construction specifications of rigid metal conduit and associated fittings. ▶Figure 344–1

Article 344 covers the use, installation, and construction specifications of rigid metal conduit and associated fittings.

▶Figure 344–1

344.2 Definition

Rigid Metal Conduit (Type RMC). A listed metal raceway of circular cross section with integral or associated couplings, listed for the installation of electrical conductors, and used with listed fittings to provide electrical continuity. ▶Figure 344–2

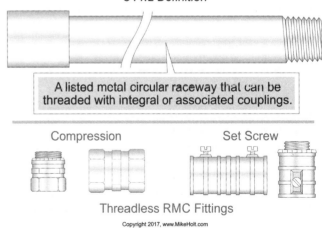

▶Figure 344–2

Author's Comment:

■ When the mechanical and physical characteristics of rigid metal conduit are desired and a corrosive environment is anticipated, a PVC-coated raceway system is commonly used. This type of raceway is frequently used in the petro-chemical industry. The common trade name of this coated raceway is "Plasti-Bond®," and it's commonly referred to as "Rob Roy conduit." The benefits of the improved corrosion protection can be achieved only when the system is properly installed. Joints must be sealed in accordance with the manufacturer's instructions, and coated to prevent corrosion where damaged with tools such as benders, pliers, and pipe wrenches. Couplings are available with an extended skirt that can be properly sealed after installation.

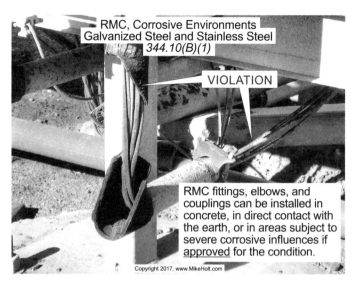

▶Figure 344–3

Part II. Installation

344.10 Uses Permitted

(A) Atmospheric Conditions and Occupancies.

(1) Galvanized Steel and Stainless Steel. Galvanized steel and stainless steel rigid metal conduit is permitted in all atmospheric conditions and occupancies.

(2) Red Brass. Red brass rigid metal conduit is permitted for direct burial and swimming pool applications.

(3) Aluminum. Rigid aluminum conduit is permitted if approved for the environment.

(B) Corrosive Environments.

(1) Galvanized Steel and Stainless Steel. Rigid metal conduit fittings, elbows, and couplings can be installed in concrete, in direct contact with the earth, or in areas subject to severe corrosive influences if approved for the condition. ▶Figure 344–3

(2) Aluminum. Rigid aluminum conduit must be provided with supplementary corrosion protection approved by the authority having jurisdiction if encased in concrete or in direct contact with the earth.

(D) Wet Locations. Support fittings, such as screws, straps, and so forth, installed in a wet location must be made of corrosion-resistant material or protected by corrosion-resistant coatings in accordance with 300.6.

⚡ **CAUTION:** *Supplementary coatings (asphalted paint) for corrosion protection haven't been investigated by a product testing and listing agency, and these coatings are known to cause cancer in laboratory animals.*

ARTICLE 344 PRACTICE QUESTIONS

Please use the 2017 *Code* book to answer the following questions.

1. Aluminum RMC shall be permitted to be installed where approved for the environment.

    (a) True
    (b) False

2. Galvanized steel, stainless steel, and red brass RMC elbows, couplings, and fittings shall be permitted to be installed in concrete, in direct contact with the earth, or in areas subject to severe corrosive influences when protected by _____ approved for the condition.

    (a) ceramic
    (b) corrosion protection
    (c) backfill
    (d) a natural barrier

3. Materials such as straps, bolts, and so forth, associated with the installation of RMC in wet locations shall be _____.

    (a) weatherproof
    (b) protected against corrosion by corrosion-resistant materials
    (c) corrosion resistant
    (d) b or c

ARTICLE 348

FLEXIBLE METAL CONDUIT (TYPE FMC)

Introduction to Article 348—Flexible Metal Conduit (Type FMC)

Flexible metal conduit (FMC), commonly called "Greenfield" or "flex," is a raceway of an interlocked metal strip of either steel or aluminum. It's primarily used for the final 6 ft or less of raceways between a more rigid raceway system and equipment that moves, shakes, or vibrates. Examples of such equipment include pump motors and industrial machinery.

Part I. General

348.1 Scope

Article 348 covers the use, installation, and construction specifications for flexible metal conduit and associated fittings. ▶Figure 348–1

Flexible Metal Conduit (Type FMC)
348.1 Scope

Article 348 covers the use, installation, and construction specifications for flexible metal conduit and associated fittings.

Copyright 2017, www.MikeHolt.com

▶Figure 348–1

348.2 Definition

Flexible Metal Conduit (Type FMC). A raceway of circular cross section made of a helically wound, formed, interlocked metal strip. ▶Figure 348–2

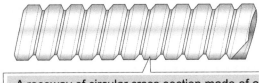

Flexible Metal Conduit (Type FMC)
348.2 Definition

A raceway of circular cross section made of a helically wound, formed, interlocked metal strip.

Straight Connector   Angle Connector

Copyright 2017, www.MikeHolt.com

▶Figure 348–2

Part II. Installation

348.10 Uses Permitted

Flexible metal conduit is permitted exposed or concealed.

348.12 Uses Not Permitted

(1) In wet locations. ▶Figure 348–3

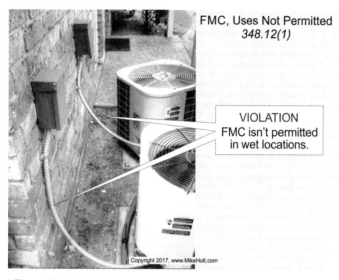

FMC, Uses Not Permitted
348.12(1)

VIOLATION
FMC isn't permitted
in wet locations.

Copyright 2017, www.MikeHolt.com

▶Figure 348–3

(2) In hoistways, other than as permitted in 620.21(A)(1).

(3) In storage battery rooms.

(4) In any hazardous location, except as permitted by 501.10(B).

(5) Exposed to material having a deteriorating effect on the installed conductors.

(6) Underground or embedded in poured concrete.

(7) If subject to physical damage.

ARTICLE 348 PRACTICE QUESTIONS

Please use the 2017 *Code* book to answer the following questions.

1. _____ is a raceway of circular cross section made of a helically wound, formed, interlocked metal strip.

   (a) Type MC cable
   (b) Type AC cable
   (c) LFMC
   (d) FMC

2. FMC can be installed exposed or concealed where not subject to physical damage.

   (a) True
   (b) False

3. FMC shall not be installed _____.

   (a) in wet locations
   (b) embedded in poured concrete
   (c) where subject to physical damage
   (d) all of these

Notes

Mike Holt's Electrical Apprenticeship Year 1 Supplement, Based on the 2017 NEC

ARTICLE 350

LIQUIDTIGHT FLEXIBLE METAL CONDUIT (TYPE LFMC)

Introduction to Article 350—Liquidtight Flexible Metal Conduit (Type LFMC)

Liquidtight flexible metal conduit (LFMC), with its associated connectors and fittings, is a flexible raceway commonly used for connections to equipment that vibrates or is required to move occasionally. Liquidtight flexible metal conduit is commonly called "Sealtight®" or "liquidtight." Liquidtight flexible metal conduit is of similar construction to flexible metal conduit, but it also has an outer liquidtight thermoplastic covering. It has the same primary purpose as flexible metal conduit, but it also provides protection from moisture and some corrosive effects.

Part I. General

350.1 Scope

Article 350 covers the use, installation, and construction specifications of liquidtight flexible metal conduit and associated fittings. ▶Figure 350–1

Liquidtight Flexible Metal Conduit (Type LFMC)
350.1 Scope

Article 350 covers the use, installation, and construction specifications of liquidtight flexible metal conduit and associated fittings.

Copyright 2017, www.MikeHolt.com

▶Figure 350–1

350.2 Definition

Liquidtight Flexible Metal Conduit (Type LFMC). A raceway of circular cross section, having an outer liquidtight, nonmetallic, sunlight-resistant jacket over an inner flexible metal core, with associated connectors and fittings for the installation of electric conductors. ▶Figure 350–2

Liquidtight Flexible Metal Conduit (Type LFMC)
350.2 Definition

A circular raceway having an outer liquidtight, nonmetallic, sunlight-resistant jacket over an inner flexible metal core.

Copyright 2017, www.MikeHolt.com

▶Figure 350–2

Part II. Installation

350.10 Uses Permitted

Listed liquidtight flexible metal conduit is permitted, either exposed or concealed, at any of the following locations: ▶Figure 350–3

▶Figure 350–3

(1) If flexibility or protection from liquids, vapors, or solids is required.

(2) In hazardous locations as permitted in Chapter 5.

(3) For direct burial, if listed and marked for this purpose. ▶Figure 350–4

▶Figure 350–4

350.12 Uses Not Permitted

Liquidtight flexible metal conduit is not to be used as follows:

(1) If subject to physical damage. ▶Figure 350–5

▶Figure 350–5

(2) If the combination of the ambient and conductor operating temperatures exceeds the rating of the raceway.

ARTICLE
350

PRACTICE QUESTIONS

Please use the 2017 *Code* book to answer the following questions.

1. _____ is a raceway of circular cross section having an outer liquid-tight, nonmetallic, sunlight-resistant jacket over an inner flexible metal core.

    (a) FMC
    (b) LFNMC
    (c) LFMC
    (d) none of these

2. The use of LFMC shall be permitted for _____.

    (a) direct burial where listed and marked for the purpose
    (b) exposed work
    (c) concealed work
    (d) all of these

Notes

ARTICLE 352

RIGID POLYVINYL CHLORIDE CONDUIT (TYPE PVC)

Introduction to Article 352—Rigid Polyvinyl Chloride Conduit (Type PVC)

Rigid polyvinyl chloride conduit is a rigid nonmetallic conduit that provides many of the advantages of rigid metal conduit, while allowing installation in areas that are wet or corrosive. It's an inexpensive raceway, and easily installed. It's lightweight, easily cut and glued together, and relatively strong. However, conduits manufactured from polyvinyl chloride (PVC) are brittle when cold, and they sage when hot. This type of conduit is commonly used as an underground raceway because of its low cost, ease of installation, and resistance to corrosion and decay.

Part I. General

352.1 Scope

Article 352 covers the use, installation, and construction specifications of PVC conduit and associated fittings. ▶Figure 352–1

352.2 Definition

Rigid Polyvinyl Chloride Conduit (PVC). A rigid nonmetallic raceway of circular cross section with integral or associated couplings, listed for the installation of electrical conductors and cables. ▶Figure 352–2

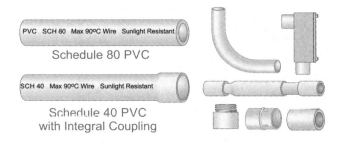

Rigid Polyvinyl Chloride Conduit (Type PVC)
352.1 Scope

Schedule 80 PVC

Schedule 40 PVC
with Integral Coupling

Article 352 covers the use, installation, and construction specifications for rigid polyvinyl chloride conduit and associated fittings.

Copyright 2017, www.MikeHolt.com

▶Figure 352–1

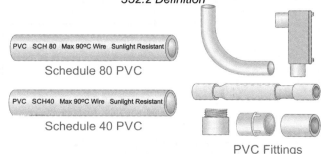

Rigid Polyvinyl Chloride Conduit (Type PVC)
352.2 Definition

Schedule 80 PVC

Schedule 40 PVC

PVC Fittings

A rigid nonmetallic raceway with a circular cross section with integral or associated couplings, connectors, and fittings.

Copyright 2017, www.MikeHolt.com

▶Figure 352–2

Part II. Installation

352.10 Uses Permitted

Note: In extreme cold, PVC conduit can become brittle, and is more susceptible to physical damage.

(A) Concealed. PVC conduit can be concealed within walls, floors, or ceilings, directly buried or embedded in concrete in buildings of any height. ▶Figure 352–3

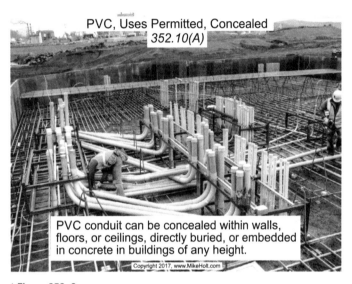

PVC, Uses Permitted, Concealed
352.10(A)

PVC conduit can be concealed within walls, floors, or ceilings, directly buried, or embedded in concrete in buildings of any height.

▶Figure 352–3

(B) Corrosive Influences. PVC conduit is permitted in areas subject to severe corrosion for which the material is specifically approved by the authority having jurisdiction.

Author's Comment:

- If subject to exposure to chemical solvents, vapors, splashing, or immersion, materials or coatings must either be inherently resistant to chemicals based upon their listing, or be identified for the specific chemical reagent [300.6(C)(2)].

(D) Wet Locations. PVC conduit is permitted in wet locations such as dairies, laundries, canneries, car washes, and other areas frequently washed or in outdoor locations. Support fittings such as straps, screws, and bolts must be made of corrosion-resistant materials, or must be protected with a corrosion-resistant coating, in accordance with 300.6(A).

(E) Dry and Damp Locations. PVC conduit is permitted in dry and damp locations, except where limited in 352.12.

(F) Exposed. Schedule 40 PVC conduit is permitted for exposed locations where not subject to physical damage. If PVC conduit is exposed to physical damage, the raceway must be identified for the application. ▶Figure 352–4

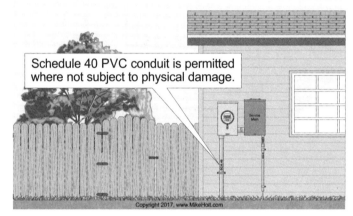

PVC, Exposed Locations
352.10(F)

Schedule 40 PVC conduit is permitted where not subject to physical damage.

▶Figure 352–4

Note: PVC Schedule 80 conduit is identified for use in areas subject to physical damage. ▶Figure 352–5

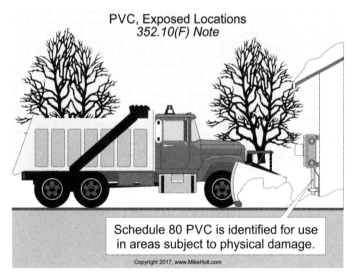

PVC, Exposed Locations
352.10(F) Note

Schedule 80 PVC is identified for use in areas subject to physical damage.

▶Figure 352–5

(G) Underground. PVC conduit installed underground must comply with the burial requirements of 300.5.

(H) Support of Conduit Bodies. PVC conduit can support nonmetallic conduit bodies that aren't larger than the largest trade size of an entering raceway. These conduit bodies can't support luminaires or other equipment, and aren't permitted to contain devices other than splicing devices permitted by 110.14(B) and 314.16(C)(2).

352.12 Uses Not Permitted

(A) Hazardous Locations. PVC conduit isn't permitted to be used in hazardous locations except as permitted by 501.10(A)(1)(a) Ex, 503.10(A), 504.20, 514.8 Ex 2, and 515.8.

(2) In Class I, Division 2 locations, except as permitted in 501.10(B)(7).

(B) Support of Luminaires. PVC conduit isn't permitted to be used for the support of luminaires or other equipment not described in 352.10(H).

Author's Comment:

■ PVC conduit can support conduit bodies in accordance with 314.23(E) Ex.

(C) Physical Damage. Schedule 40 PVC conduit isn't permitted to be installed if subject to physical damage, unless identified for the application. ▶Figure 352–6

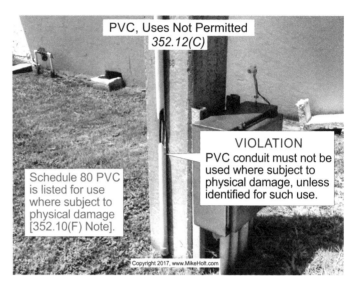

PVC, Uses Not Permitted
352.12(C)

Schedule 80 PVC is listed for use where subject to physical damage [352.10(F) Note].

VIOLATION
PVC conduit must not be used where subject to physical damage, unless identified for such use.

Copyright 2017, www.MikeHolt.com

▶Figure 352–6

Author's Comment:

■ PVC Schedule 80 conduit is identified for use in areas subject to physical damage [352.10(F) Note].

(D) Ambient Temperature. PVC conduit isn't permitted to be installed if the ambient temperature exceeds 50°C (122°F).

ARTICLE
352 PRACTICE QUESTIONS

Please use the 2017 *Code* book to answer the following questions.

1. Extreme _____ may cause PVC conduit to become brittle, and therefore more susceptible to damage from physical contact.

    (a) sunlight
    (b) corrosive conditions
    (c) heat
    (d) cold

2. PVC conduit shall be permitted for exposed work where subject to physical damage if identified for such use.

    (a) True
    (b) False

3. PVC conduit can support nonmetallic conduit bodies not larger than the largest trade size of an entering raceway, but the conduit bodies shall not contain devices, luminaires, or other equipment.

    (a) True
    (b) False

4. PVC conduit shall not be used _____, unless specifically permitted.

    (a) in hazardous (classified) locations
    (b) for the support of luminaires or other equipment
    (c) where subject to physical damage unless identified for such use
    (d) all of these

LIQUIDTIGHT FLEXIBLE NONMETALLIC CONDUIT (TYPE LFNC)

Introduction to Article 356—Liquidtight Flexible Nonmetallic Conduit (Type LFNC)

Liquidtight flexible nonmetallic conduit (LFNC) is a listed raceway of circular cross section having an outer liquidtight, nonmetallic, sunlight-resistant jacket over an inner flexible core with associated couplings, connectors, and fittings.

Part I. General

356.1 Scope

Article 356 covers the use, installation, and construction specifications of liquidtight flexible nonmetallic conduit and associated fittings. ▶Figure 356–1

Liquidtight Flexible Nonmetallic Conduit (Type LFNC)
356.1 Scope

Article 356 covers the use, installation, and construction specifications of liquidtight flexible nonmetallic conduit and associated fittings.

Copyright 2017, www.MikeHolt.com

▶Figure 356–1

356.2 Definition

Liquidtight Flexible Nonmetallic Conduit (Type LFNC). A listed raceway of circular cross section, having an outer liquidtight, nonmetallic, sunlight-resistant jacket over a flexible inner core, with associated couplings, connectors, and fittings, listed for the installation of electrical conductors. ▶Figure 356–2

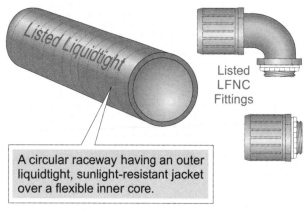

Liquidtight Flexible Nonmetallic Conduit (Type LFNC)
356.2 Definition

A circular raceway having an outer liquidtight, sunlight-resistant jacket over a flexible inner core.

Copyright 2017, www.MikeHolt.com

▶Figure 356–2

(1) Type LFNC-A (orange color). A smooth seamless inner core and cover having reinforcement layers between the core and cover.

(2) Type LFNC-B (gray color). A smooth inner surface with integral reinforcement within the raceway wall.

(3) Type LFNC-C (black color). A corrugated internal and external surface without integral reinforcement.

Part II. Installation

356.10 Uses Permitted

Listed liquidtight flexible nonmetallic conduit is permitted, either exposed or concealed, at any of the following locations:

Note: Extreme cold can cause nonmetallic conduits to become brittle and more susceptible to damage from physical contact.

(1) If flexibility is required.

(2) If protection from liquids, vapors, or solids is required.

(3) Outdoors, if listed and marked for this purpose.

(4) Directly buried in the earth, if listed and marked for this purpose.
▶Figure 356–3

(5) LFNC (gray color) is permitted in lengths over 6 ft if secured in accordance with 356.30.

(6) LFNC, Type B (black color) as a listed manufactured prewired assembly.

(7) Encasement in concrete if listed for direct burial.

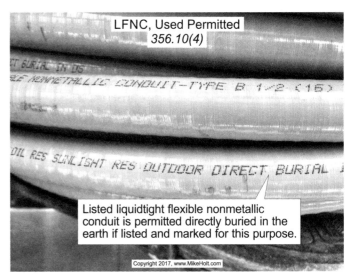

LFNC, Used Permitted
356.10(4)

Listed liquidtight flexible nonmetallic conduit is permitted directly buried in the earth if listed and marked for this purpose.

Copyright 2017, www.MikeHolt.com

▶Figure 356–3

356.12 Uses Not Permitted

(1) If subject to physical damage.

(2) If the ambient temperature and/or conductor temperature is in excess of its listing.

(3) Longer than 6 ft, except if approved by the authority having jurisdiction as essential for a required degree of flexibility.

(4) In any hazardous location, except as permitted by 501.10(B), 502.10(A) and (B), and 504.20.

ARTICLE 356 PRACTICE QUESTIONS

Please use the 2017 *Code* book to answer the following questions.

1. LFNC shall be permitted for _____.

    (a) direct burial where listed and marked for the purpose

    (b) exposed work

    (c) outdoors where listed and marked for this purpose

    (d) all of these

Notes

ARTICLE
358

ELECTRICAL METALLIC TUBING (TYPE EMT)

Introduction to Article 358—Electrical Metallic Tubing (Type EMT)

Electrical metallic tubing is a lightweight raceway that's relatively easy to bend, cut, and ream. Because it isn't threaded, all connectors and couplings are of the threadless type and provide quick, easy, and inexpensive installation when compared to other metallic conduit systems, which makes it very popular. Electrical metallic tubing is manufactured in both galvanized steel and aluminum; the steel type is used the most.

Part I. General

358.1 Scope

Article 358 covers the use, installation, and construction specifications of electrical metallic tubing and associated fittings. ▶Figure 358–1

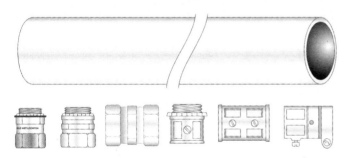

Electrical Metallic Tubing (Type EMT)
358.1 Scope

Article 358 covers the use, installation, and construction specifications of electrical metallic tubing and associated fittings.

Copyright 2017, www.MikeHolt.com

▶Figure 358–1

358.2 Definition

Electrical Metallic Tubing (Type EMT). A metallic tubing of circular cross section used for the installation and physical protection of electrical conductors when joined together with fittings. ▶Figure 358–2

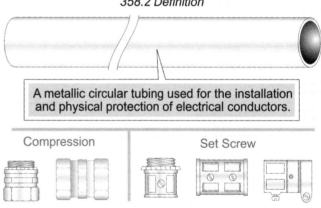

Electrical Metallic Tubing (Type EMT)
358.2 Definition

A metallic circular tubing used for the installation and physical protection of electrical conductors.

Compression | Set Screw

Threadless EMT Fittings
Copyright 2017, www.MikeHolt.com

▶Figure 358–2

Part II. Installation

358.10 Uses Permitted

(A) Exposed and Concealed. Electrical metallic tubing is permitted exposed or concealed for the following applications: ▶Figure 358–3

(1) In concrete in direct contact with the earth in accordance with 358.10(B).

(2) In wet, dry, or damp locations.

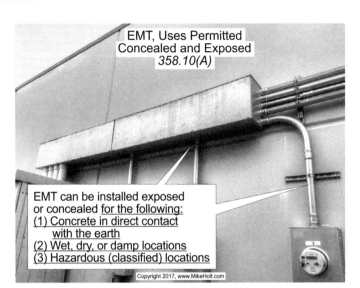

▶Figure 358–3

(3) In any hazardous (classified) location as permitted by other articles in this *Code*.

(B) Corrosive Environments.

(1) Galvanized Steel. Electrical metallic tubing, elbows, and fittings can be installed in concrete, in direct contact with the earth, or in areas subject to severe corrosive influences if protected by corrosion protection and approved as suitable for the condition [300.6(A)].

(D) Wet Locations. Support fittings, such as screws, straps, and so on, installed in a wet location must be made of corrosion-resistant material.

Author's Comment:

■ If installed in wet locations, fittings for EMT must be listed for use in wet locations and prevent moisture or water from entering or accumulating within the enclosure in accordance with 314.15 [358.42].

358.12 Uses Not Permitted

EMT isn't permitted to be used under the following conditions:

(1) Where subject to severe physical damage.

(2) For the support of luminaires or other equipment (like boxes), except conduit bodies no larger than the largest trade size of the tubing that can be supported by the raceway. ▶Figure 358–4

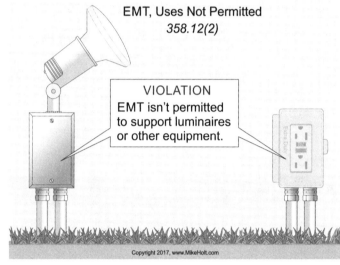

▶Figure 358–4

Please use the 2017 *Code* book to answer the following questions.

1. _____ is an unthreaded thinwall raceway of circular cross section designed for the routing and physical protection of electrical conductors and cables when joined together with listed fittings.

   (a) LFNC
   (b) EMT
   (c) NUCC
   (d) RTRC

2. The use of EMT shall be permitted for both exposed and concealed work in _____.

   (a) concrete, in direct contact with the earth, or in areas subject to severe corrosive influences where installed in accordance with 358.10(B)
   (b) dry, damp, and wet locations
   (c) any hazardous (classified) location as permitted by other articles in this *Code*
   (d) all of these

3. Galvanized steel and stainless steel EMT, elbows, couplings, and fittings can be installed in concrete, in direct contact with the earth, or in areas subject to severe corrosive influences where _____.

   (a) protected by corrosion protection
   (b) approved as suitable for the condition
   (c) a and b
   (d) listed for wet locations

4. When EMT is installed in wet locations, all supports, bolts, straps, and screws shall be _____.

   (a) of corrosion-resistant materials
   (b) protected against corrosion by corrosion-resistant materials
   (c) a or b
   (d) of nonmetallic materials only

5. EMT shall not be used where _____.

   (a) subject to severe physical damage
   (b) protected from corrosion only by enamel
   (c) used for the support of luminaires except conduit bodies no larger than the largest trade size of the tubing
   (d) a and c

ARTICLE
362

ELECTRICAL NONMETALLIC TUBING (TYPE ENT)

Introduction to Article 362—Electrical Nonmetallic Tubing (Type ENT)

Electrical nonmetallic tubing (ENT) is a pliable, corrugated, circular raceway made of polyvinyl chloride. In some parts of the country, the field name for electrical nonmetallic tubing is "Smurf Pipe" or "Smurf Tube," because it was only available in blue when it originally came out when the children's cartoon characters "The Smurfs" were most popular. Today, the raceway is available in many colors such as white, yellow, red, green, and orange, and is sold in both fixed lengths and on reels.

Part I. General

362.1 Scope

Article 362 covers the use, installation, and construction specifications of electrical nonmetallic tubing and associated fittings. ▶Figure 362–1

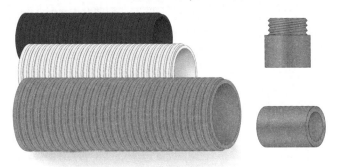

Electrical Nonmetallic Tubing (Type ENT)
362.1 Scope

Article 362 covers the use, installation, and construction specifications of electrical nonmetallic tubing and associated fittings.

Copyright 2017, www.MikeHolt.com

▶Figure 362–1

362.2 Definition

Electrical Nonmetallic Tubing (Type ENT). A pliable corrugated raceway of circular cross section, with integral or associated couplings, connectors, and fittings listed for the installation of electrical conductors. ENT is composed of a material that's resistant to moisture and chemical atmospheres and is flame retardant. ▶Figure 362–2

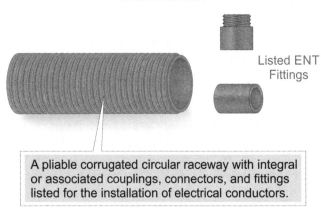

Electrical Nonmetallic Tubing (Type ENT)
362.2 Definition

Listed ENT Fittings

A pliable corrugated circular raceway with integral or associated couplings, connectors, and fittings listed for the installation of electrical conductors.

Copyright 2017, www.MikeHolt.com

▶Figure 362–2

Electrical nonmetallic tubing can be bent by hand with a reasonable force, but without other assistance.

Part II. Installation

362.10 Uses Permitted

Electrical nonmetallic tubing is permitted as follows:

(1) In buildings not exceeding three floors. ▶Figure 362–3

   a. Exposed, where not prohibited by 362.12.

   b. Concealed within walls, floors, and ceilings.

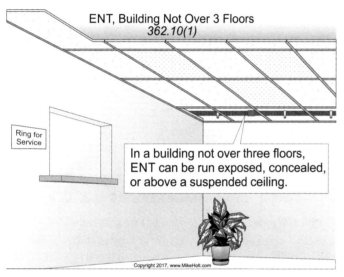

ENT, Building Not Over 3 Floors
362.10(1)

In a building not over three floors, ENT can be run exposed, concealed, or above a suspended ceiling.

▶Figure 362–3

(2) In buildings exceeding three floors, electrical nonmetallic tubing can be installed concealed in walls, floors, or ceilings that provide a thermal barrier having a 15-minute finish rating, as identified in listings of fire-rated assemblies. ▶Figure 362–4

Ex to (2): If a fire sprinkler system is installed on all floors, in accordance with NFPA 13, Standard for the Installation of Sprinkler Systems, electrical nonmetallic tubing is permitted exposed or concealed in buildings of any height. ▶Figure 362–5

(3) Electrical nonmetallic tubing is permitted in severe corrosive and chemical locations, when identified for this use.

(4) Electrical nonmetallic tubing is permitted in dry and damp concealed locations, if not prohibited by 362.12.

(5) Electrical nonmetallic tubing is permitted above a suspended ceiling, if the suspended ceiling provides a thermal barrier having a 15-minute finish rating, as identified in listings of fire-rated assemblies. ▶Figure 362–6

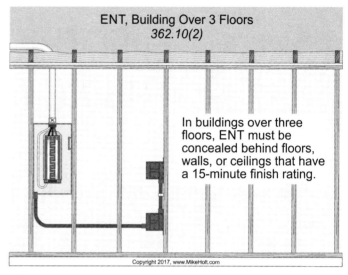

ENT, Building Over 3 Floors
362.10(2)

In buildings over three floors, ENT must be concealed behind floors, walls, or ceilings that have a 15-minute finish rating.

▶Figure 362–4

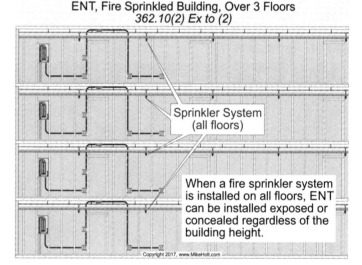

ENT, Fire Sprinkled Building, Over 3 Floors
362.10(2) Ex to (2)

Sprinkler System (all floors)

When a fire sprinkler system is installed on all floors, ENT can be installed exposed or concealed regardless of the building height.

▶Figure 362–5

Ex to (5): If a fire sprinkler system is installed on all floors, in accordance with NFPA 13, Standard for the Installation of Sprinkler Systems, electrical nonmetallic tubing is permitted above a suspended ceiling that doesn't have a 15-minute finish rated thermal barrier. ▶Figure 362–7

(6) Electrical nonmetallic tubing can be encased or embedded in a concrete slab provided fittings identified for the purpose are used.

Author's Comment:

■ Electrical nonmetallic tubing isn't permitted in the earth [362.12(5)].

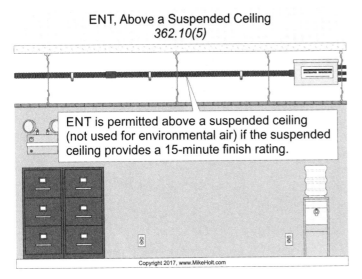

ENT, Above a Suspended Ceiling
362.10(5)

ENT is permitted above a suspended ceiling (not used for environmental air) if the suspended ceiling provides a 15-minute finish rating.

Copyright 2017, www.MikeHolt.com

▶Figure 362–6

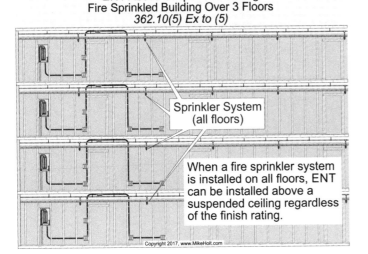

ENT Above Suspended Ceiling
Fire Sprinkled Building Over 3 Floors
362.10(5) Ex to (5)

Sprinkler System
(all floors)

When a fire sprinkler system is installed on all floors, ENT can be installed above a suspended ceiling regardless of the finish rating.

Copyright 2017, www.MikeHolt.com

▶Figure 362–7

(7) Electrical nonmetallic tubing is permitted in wet locations indoors, or in a concrete slab on or below grade, with fittings listed for the purpose.

(8) Listed prewired electrical nonmetallic tubing with conductors is permitted in trade sizes ½, ¾, and 1.

362.12 Uses Not Permitted

ENT isn't permitted to be used in the following:

(1) In any hazardous location, except as permitted by 504.20 and 505.15(A)(1).

(2) For the support of luminaires or equipment. See 314.2.

(3) If the ambient temperature exceeds 50°C (122°F).

(4) For direct earth burial.

Author's Comment:

■ Electrical nonmetallic tubing can be encased in concrete [362.10(6)].

(5) Exposed in buildings over three floors, except as permitted by 362.10(2) and (5) Ex.

(6) In assembly occupancies or theaters, except as permitted by 518.4 and 520.5.

(7) Exposed to the direct rays of the sun for an extended period, unless listed as sunlight resistant. ▶Figure 362–8

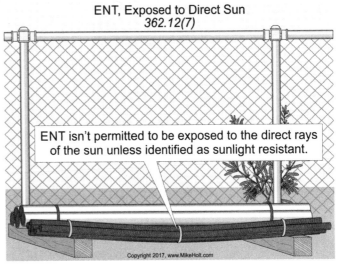

ENT, Exposed to Direct Sun
362.12(7)

ENT isn't permitted to be exposed to the direct rays of the sun unless identified as sunlight resistant.

Copyright 2017, www.MikeHolt.com

▶Figure 362–8

Author's Comment:

■ Exposing electrical nonmetallic tubing to the direct rays of the sun for an extended time may result in the product becoming brittle, unless it's listed to resist the effects of ultraviolet (UV) radiation.

(8) If subject to physical damage.

Author's Comment:

■ Electrical nonmetallic tubing is prohibited in ducts, plenum spaces [300.22(C)], and patient care space circuits in health care facilities [517.13(A)].

Please use the 2017 *Code* book to answer the following questions.

1. ENT is composed of a material resistant to moisture and chemical atmospheres, and is _____.

   (a) flexible
   (b) flame retardant
   (c) fireproof
   (d) flammable

2. When a building is supplied with a(n) _____ fire sprinkler system, ENT shall be permitted to be used within walls, floors, and ceilings, exposed or concealed, in buildings exceeding three floors above grade.

   (a) listed
   (b) identified
   (c) *NFPA 13-2013*
   (d) none of these

3. When a building is supplied with a fire sprinkler system, ENT can be installed above any suspended ceiling.

   (a) True
   (b) False

4. ENT and fittings can be _____, provided fittings identified for this purpose are used.

   (a) encased in poured concrete
   (b) embedded in a concrete slab on grade where the tubing is placed on sand or approved screenings
   (c) a or b
   (d) none of these

5. ENT is not permitted in hazardous (classified) locations, unless permitted in other articles of the *NEC*.

   (a) True
   (b) False

6. ENT shall be permitted for direct earth burial unless used with fittings listed for this purpose.

   (a) True
   (b) False

7. ENT shall not be used where exposed to the direct rays of the sun, unless identified as _____.

   (a) high-temperature rated
   (b) sunlight resistant
   (c) Schedule 80
   (d) none of these

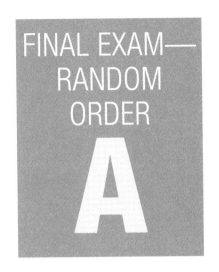

FINAL EXAM A— RANDOM ORDER

Please use the 2017 *Code* book to answer the following questions.

1. The minimum height of dedicated equipment space for motor control centers installed indoors is _____ ft above the enclosure, or to the structural ceiling, whichever is lower.

    (a) 3
    (b) 5
    (c) 6
    (d) 6½

2. Where nonmetallic wiring methods are subject to exposure to chemical solvents or vapors, they shall be inherently resistant to chemicals based upon their being _____ for the specific chemical reagent.

    (a) listed
    (b) identified
    (c) a and b
    (d) a or b

3. Unused openings other than those intended for the operation of equipment, intended for mounting purposes, or permitted as part of the design for listed equipment shall be _____.

    (a) filled with cable clamps or connectors only
    (b) taped over with electrical tape
    (c) repaired only by welding or brazing in a metal slug
    (d) closed to afford protection substantially equivalent to the wall of the equipment

4. Where Type TC cable is installed in one- and two-family dwelling units, 725.136 provides rules for limitations on Class 2 or 3 circuits contained within the same cable with conductors of electric light, power, or Class 1 circuits.

    (a) True
    (b) False

5. ENT is composed of a material resistant to moisture and chemical atmospheres, and is _____.

    (a) flexible
    (b) flame retardant
    (c) fireproof
    (d) flammable

6. The use of EMT shall be permitted for both exposed and concealed work in ___ .

    (a) concrete, in direct contact with the earth, or in areas subject to severe corrosive influences where installed in accordance with 358.10(B)
    (b) dry, damp, and wet locations
    (c) any hazardous (classified) location as permitted by other articles in this *Code*
    (d) all of these

7. Where a metal underground water pipe is used as a grounding electrode, the continuity of the grounding path or the bonding connection to interior piping shall not rely on _____ and similar equipment.

    (a) bonding jumpers
    (b) water meters or filtering devices
    (c) grounding clamps
    (d) all of these

8. Which of the following metal parts shall be protected from corrosion?

    (a) Ferrous metal raceways.
    (b) Ferrous metal elbows.
    (c) Ferrous boxes.
    (d) all of these

9. _____drainage openings not smaller than ⅛ in. and not larger than ¼ in. in diameter shall be permitted to be installed in the field in boxes or conduit bodies listed for use in damp or wet locations.

    (a) Listed
    (b) Approved
    (c) Labeled
    (d) Identified

10. Cable wiring methods shall not be used as a means of support for _____.

    (a) other cables
    (b) raceways
    (c) nonelectrical equipment
    (d) all of these

11. Type UF cable shall not be used in _____.

    (a) motion picture studios
    (b) storage battery rooms
    (c) hoistways
    (d) all of these

12. Grounding electrodes of bare or electrically conductive coated iron or steel plates shall be at least _____ in. thick.

    (a) ⅛
    (b) ¼
    (c) ½
    (d) ¾

13. Exposed normally noncurrent-carrying metal parts of fixed equipment likely to become energized shall be connected to the equipment grounding conductor where located _____.

    (a) within 8 ft vertically or 5 ft horizontally of ground or grounded metal objects and subject to contact by persons
    (b) in wet or damp locations and not isolated
    (c) in electrical contact with metal
    (d) any of these

14. Where a tightening torque is indicated as a numeric value on equipment or in installation instructions provided by the manufacturer, a(n) _____ torque tool shall be used to achieve the indicated torque value, unless the equipment manufacturer has provided installation instructions for an alternative method of achieving the required torque.

    (a) calibrated
    (b) identified
    (c) adjustable
    (d) listed

15. Type SE cable shall be permitted to be used as _____ in wiring systems where all of the circuit conductors of the cable are of the thermoset or thermoplastic type.

    (a) branch circuits
    (b) feeders
    (c) a or b
    (d) none of these

16. "_____" is defined as the shortest distance measured between a point on the top surface of direct-burial cable and the top surface of the finished grade.

    (a) Notch
    (b) Cover
    (c) Gap
    (d) none of these

17. What is the minimum cover requirement for direct burial Type UF cable installed outdoors that supplies a 120V, 30A circuit?

    (a) 6 in.
    (b) 12 in.
    (c) 18 in.
    (d) 24 in.

18. Aluminum raceways, cable trays, cablebus, auxiliary gutters, cable armor, boxes, cable sheathing, cabinets, elbows, couplings, nipples, fittings, supports, and support hardware _____ shall be provided with supplementary corrosion protection.

    (a) embedded or encased in concrete
    (b) in direct contact with the earth
    (c) likely to become energized
    (d) a or b

19. Type TC cable can be used in one- and two-family dwelling units.

    (a) True
    (b) False

20. The *NEC* does not apply to electric utility-owned wiring and equipment _____.

    (a) installed by an electrical contractor
    (b) installed on public property
    (c) consisting of service drops or service laterals
    (d) in a utility office building

21. NFPA 70E, *Standard for Electrical Safety in the Workplace*, provides guidance for working space about electrical equipment, such as determining severity of potential exposure, planning safe work practices, arc-flash labeling, and selecting personal protective equipment.

    (a) True
    (b) False

22. Parallel conductors shall have the same _____.

    (a) length
    (b) material
    (c) size in circular mil area
    (d) all of these

23. At least _____ support method(s) shall be provided for each conductor at the top of the vertical raceway or as close to the top as practical if the vertical rise exceeds the values in Table 300.19(A).

    (a) one
    (b) two
    (c) three
    (d) four

24. _____ shall not be used as grounding electrodes.

    (a) Metal underground gas piping systems
    (b) Aluminum
    (c) Metal well casings
    (d) a and b

25. Aluminum RMC shall be permitted to be installed where approved for the environment.

    (a) True
    (b) False

26. Where nonmetallic-sheathed cable or multiconductor Type UF cable is used, the sheath shall extend not less than _____ in. inside the box and beyond any cable clamp.

    (a) ¼
    (b) ⅜
    (c) ½
    (d) ¾

27. Type UF cable can be used for service conductors.

    (a) True
    (b) False

28. Nonmandatory Informative Annexes contained in the back of the *Code* book are _____.

    (a) for information only
    (b) not enforceable as a requirement of the *NEC*
    (c) enforceable as a requirement of the *NEC*
    (d) a and b

29. Where exposed to sunlight, nonmetallic raceways, cable trays, boxes, cables with a nonmetallic outer jacket, fittings, and support hardware shall be _____.

    (a) listed as sunlight resistant
    (b) identified as sunlight resistant
    (c) a and b
    (d) a or b

30. Raceways, cable trays, cablebus, auxiliary gutters, cable armor, boxes, cable sheathing, cabinets, elbows, couplings, fittings, supports, and support hardware shall be of materials suitable for ____.

    (a) corrosive locations
    (b) wet locations
    (c) the environment in which they are to be installed
    (d) none of these

31. For indoor installations, piping, ducts, leak protection apparatus, or other equipment foreign to the electrical installation shall not be installed in the dedicated space above a panelboard or switchboard.

    (a) True
    (b) False

32. Where installed in raceways, conductors ____ AWG and larger shall be stranded, unless specifically permitted or required elsewhere in the *NEC*.

    (a) 10
    (b) 8
    (c) 6
    (d) 4

33. The independent support wires for supporting electrical wiring methods in a fire-rated ceiling assembly shall be distinguishable from fire-rated suspended-ceiling framing support wires by ____.

    (a) color
    (b) tagging
    (c) other effective means
    (d) any of these

34. Independent support wires used for the support of electrical raceways and cables within nonfire-rated assemblies shall be distinguishable from the suspended-ceiling framing support wires.

    (a) True
    (b) False

35. The ____ has the responsibility for deciding on the approval of equipment and materials.

    (a) manufacturer
    (b) authority having jurisdiction
    (c) testing agency
    (d) none of these

36. Conduit bodies that are durably and legibly marked by the manufacturer with their volume can contain splices, taps, or devices.

    (a) True
    (b) False

37. A wire-type equipment grounding conductor is permitted to be used as a grounding electrode conductor if it meets all of the requirements of Parts II, III, and VI of Article 250.

    (a) True
    (b) False

38. LFNC shall be permitted for ____.

    (a) direct burial where listed and marked for the purpose
    (b) exposed work
    (c) outdoors where listed and marked for this purpose
    (d) all of these

39. A box or conduit body shall not be required where cables enter or exit from conduit or tubing that is used to provide cable support or protection against physical damage.

    (a) True
    (b) False

40. Soldered splices shall first be spliced or joined so as to be mechanically and electrically secure without solder and then be soldered.

    (a) True
    (b) False

41. Where circuit conductors are installed in parallel in multiple raceways or cables and include an EGC of the wire type, the equipment grounding conductor shall be installed in parallel in each raceway or cable, sized in compliance with 250.122 based on the overcurrent protective device for the feeder or branch circuit.

    (a) True
    (b) False

42. Access and ____ shall be provided and maintained about all electrical equipment to permit ready and safe operation and maintenance of such equipment.

    (a) ventilation
    (b) cleanliness
    (c) circulation
    (d) working space

43. Direct-buried conductors or cables can be spliced or tapped without the use of splice boxes when the splice or tap is made in accordance with 110.14(B).

    (a) True
    (b) False

44. A "_____" is an area that includes a basin with a toilet, urinal, tub, shower, bidet, or similar plumbing fixtures.

    (a) bath area
    (b) bathroom
    (c) rest area
    (d) none of these

45. The use of LFMC shall be permitted for _____.

    (a) direct burial where listed and marked for the purpose
    (b) exposed work
    (c) concealed work
    (d) all of these

46. All switchboards, switchgear, panelboards, and motor control centers shall be located in dedicated spaces and protected from damage, and outdoor installations shall be _____.

    (a) installed in identified enclosures
    (b) protected from accidental contact by unauthorized personnel or by vehicular traffic
    (c) protected from accidental spillage or leakage from piping systems
    (d) all of these

47. ENT shall be permitted for direct earth burial unless used with fittings listed for this purpose.

    (a) True
    (b) False

48. Listed FMC can be used as the equipment grounding conductor if the conduit does not exceed trade size _____.

    (a) $1\frac{1}{4}$
    (b) $1\frac{1}{2}$
    (c) 2
    (d) $2\frac{1}{4}$

49. Two or more grounding electrodes bonded together are considered a single grounding electrode system.

    (a) True
    (b) False

50. Working space shall not be used for _____.

    (a) storage
    (b) raceways
    (c) lighting
    (d) accessibility

Notes

Mike Holt's Electrical Apprenticeship Year 1 Supplement, Based on the 2017 NEC

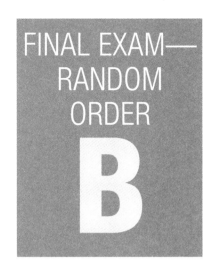

FINAL EXAM B— RANDOM ORDER

Please use the 2017 *Code* book to answer the following questions.

1. Chapters 5, 6, and 7 apply to special occupancies, special equipment, or other special conditions and may supplement or modify the requirements in Chapters 1 through 7.

   (a) True
   (b) False

2. The dedicated equipment space for electrical equipment that is required for panelboards installed indoors is measured from the floor to a height of _____ ft above the equipment, or to the structural ceiling, whichever is lower.

   (a) 3
   (b) 6
   (c) 12
   (d) 30

3. Where portions of a cable raceway or sleeve are subjected to different temperatures and condensation is known to be a problem, the _____ shall be filled with an approved material to prevent the circulation of warm air to a colder section of the raceway or sleeve.

   (a) raceway
   (b) sleeve
   (c) a or b
   (d) none of these

4. Surface extensions shall be made by mounting and mechanically securing an extension ring over the box, unless otherwise permitted.

   (a) True
   (b) False

5. The *NEC* requires tested series-rated installations of circuit breakers or fuses to be legibly marked in the field to indicate the equipment has been applied with a series combination rating.

   (a) True
   (b) False

6. In multiwire branch circuits, the continuity of the _____ conductor shall not be dependent upon the device connections.

   (a) ungrounded
   (b) grounded
   (c) grounding electrode
   (d) a and b

7. A device or utilization equipment wider than a single 2 in. device box shall have _____ volume allowances provided for each gang required for mounting.

   (a) single
   (b) double
   (c) triple
   (d) none of these

8. Metal boxes shall be _____ in accordance with Article 250.

   (a) grounded
   (b) bonded
   (c) a and b
   (d) none of these

9. Type TC cable shall be permitted to be direct buried, where _____ for such use.

   (a) identified
   (b) approved
   (c) listed
   (d) labeled

10. The *NEC* applies to the installation of _____.

    (a) electrical conductors and equipment within or on public and private buildings
    (b) outside conductors and equipment on the premises
    (c) optical fiber cables and raceways
    (d) all of these

11. Power distribution blocks shall be permitted in pull and junction boxes over 100 cu in. when _____.

    (a) they are listed as a power distribution block
    (b) they are installed in a box not smaller than required by the installation instructions of the power distribution block
    (c) the junction box is sized so that the wire-bending space requirements of 312.6 can be met
    (d) all of these

12. Hazards often occur because of _____.

    (a) overloading of wiring systems by methods or usage not in conformity with the *NEC*
    (b) initial wiring not providing for increases in the use of electricity
    (c) a and b
    (d) none of these

13. The *NEC* requires that electrical equipment be _____.

    (a) installed in a neat and workmanlike manner
    (b) installed under the supervision of a licensed person
    (c) completed before being inspected
    (d) all of these

14. Separately installed pressure connectors shall be used with conductors at the _____ not exceeding the ampacity at the listed and identified temperature rating of the connector.

    (a) voltages
    (b) temperatures
    (c) listings
    (d) ampacities

15. Conductors in raceways shall be _____ between outlets, boxes, devices, and so forth.

    (a) continuous
    (b) installed
    (c) copper
    (d) in conduit

16. A listed expansion/deflection fitting or other approved means shall be used where a raceway crosses a _____ intended for expansion, contraction or deflection used in buildings, bridges, parking garages, or other structures.

    (a) junction box
    (b) structural joint
    (c) cable tray
    (d) unistrut hanger

17. This *Code* covers the installation of _____ for public and private premises, including buildings, structures, mobile homes, recreational vehicles, and floating buildings.

    (a) optical fiber cables
    (b) electrical equipment
    (c) raceways
    (d) all of these

18. FMC shall not be installed _____.

    (a) in wet locations
    (b) embedded in poured concrete
    (c) where subject to physical damage
    (d) all of these

19. EMT shall not be used where _____.

    (a) subject to severe physical damage
    (b) protected from corrosion only by enamel
    (c) used for the support of luminaires except conduit bodies no larger than the largest trade size of the tubing
    (d) a and c

20. Extreme _____ may cause PVC conduit to become brittle, and therefore more susceptible to damage from physical contact.

    (a) sunlight
    (b) corrosive conditions
    (c) heat
    (d) cold

21. The armor of Type AC cable is recognized by the *NEC* as an equipment grounding conductor.

    (a) True
    (b) False

22. Electrical installations in hollow spaces, vertical shafts, and ventilation or air-handling ducts shall be made so that the possible spread of fire or products of combustion is not _____.

    (a) substantially increased
    (b) allowed
    (c) inherent
    (d) possible

23. Type TC cable can be used _____.

    (a) for power, lighting, control, and signal circuits
    (b) in cable trays including those with mechanically discontinuous segments up to 1 ft
    (c) for Class 1 control circuits as permitted in Parts II and III of Article 725
    (d) all of these

24. Raceways and cables installed into the _____ of open bottom equipment shall not be required to be mechanically secured to the equipment.

    (a) bottom
    (b) sides
    (c) top
    (d) any of these

25. A handhole enclosure is an enclosure for use in underground systems, provided with an open or closed bottom, and sized to allow personnel to _____.

    (a) enter and exit freely
    (b) reach into but not enter
    (c) have full working space
    (d) visually examine the interior

26. Conductors installed in nonmetallic raceways run underground shall be permitted to be arranged as _____ installations. The raceways shall be installed in close proximity, and the conductors shall comply with the provisions of 300.20(B).

    (a) neutral
    (b) grounded conductor
    (c) isolated phase
    (d) all of these

27. When the opening to an outlet, junction, or switch point is less than 8 in. in any dimension, each conductor shall be long enough to extend at least _____ in. outside the opening of the enclosure.

    (a) 1
    (b) 3
    (c) 6
    (d) 12

28. Where the resistance-to-ground of 25 ohms or less is not achieved for a single rod electrode, _____.

    (a) other means besides electrodes shall be used in order to provide grounding
    (b) the single rod electrode shall be supplemented by one additional electrode
    (c) no additional electrodes are required
    (d) none of these

29. Listed FMC can be used as the equipment grounding conductor if the length in any ground return path does not exceed 6 ft and the circuit conductors contained in the conduit are protected by overcurrent devices rated at _____ or less.

    (a) 15A
    (b) 20A
    (c) 30A
    (d) 60A

30. IMC, elbows, couplings, and fittings shall be permitted to be installed in concrete, in direct contact with the earth, or in areas subject to severe corrosive influences where protected by corrosion protection _____ for the condition.

    (a) identified
    (b) approved
    (c) listed
    (d) none of these

31. Utilization equipment weighing not more than 6 lb can be supported to any box or plaster ring secured to a box, provided the equipment is secured with at least two _____ or larger screws.

    (a) No. 6
    (b) No. 8
    (c) No. 10
    (d) any of these

32. Ferrous metal raceways, boxes, fittings, supports, and support hardware can be installed in concrete or in direct contact with the earth or other areas subject to severe corrosive influences, where _____ approved for the condition.

    (a) the soil is
    (b) made of material
    (c) the qualified installer is
    (d) none of these

33. The minimum working space on a circuit for equipment operating at 120 volts-to-ground, with exposed live parts on one side and no live or grounded parts on the other side of the working space, is _____ ft.

    (a) 1
    (b) 3
    (c) 4
    (d) 6

34. Type _____ cable is a factory assembly of two or more insulated conductors, with or without associated bare of covered grounding conductors, under a nonmetallic jacket.

    (a) NM
    (b) TC
    (c) SE
    (d) UF

35. A surface extension can be made from the cover of a box where the cover is designed so it is unlikely to fall off or be removed if its securing means becomes loose. The wiring method shall be _____ for an approved length that permits removal of the cover and provides access to the box interior, and arranged so that any grounding continuity is independent of the connection between the box and cover.

    (a) solid
    (b) flexible
    (c) rigid
    (d) cord

36. Raceways shall be _____ between outlet, junction, or splicing points prior to the installation of conductors.

    (a) installed complete
    (b) tested for ground faults
    (c) a minimum of 80 percent complete
    (d) none of these

37. The *NEC* is _____.

    (a) intended to be a design manual
    (b) meant to be used as an instruction guide for untrained persons
    (c) for the practical safeguarding of persons and property
    (d) published by the Bureau of Standards

38. In general, the minimum size conductor permitted for use in parallel installations is _____ AWG.

    (a) 10
    (b) 4
    (c) 1
    (d) 1/0

39. Galvanized steel and stainless steel EMT, elbows, couplings, and fittings can be installed in concrete, in direct contact with the earth, or in areas subject to severe corrosive influences where _____.

    (a) protected by corrosion protection
    (b) approved as suitable for the condition
    (c) a and b
    (d) listed for wet locations

40. Materials such as straps, bolts, and so forth, associated with the installation of RMC in wet locations shall be _____.

    (a) weatherproof
    (b) protected against corrosion by corrosion-resistant materials
    (c) corrosion resistant
    (d) b or c

41. Type _____ cable is a factory assembly that encloses two or more insulated conductors within a nonmetallic jacket.

    (a) AC
    (b) MC
    (c) NM
    (d) b and c

42. Floor boxes _____ specifically for the application shall be used for receptacles located in the floor.

    (a) identified
    (b) listed
    (c) approved
    (d) none of these

43. An exposed wiring system for indoor wet locations where walls are frequently washed shall be mounted so that there is at least a _____ between the mounting surface and the electrical equipment.

    (a) ¼-in. airspace
    (b) separation by insulated bushings
    (c) separation by noncombustible tubing
    (d) none of these

44. Type SE cable can be used for interior wiring as long as it complies with the installation requirements of Part II of Article 334, excluding 334.80.

    (a) True
    (b) False

45. Listed FMC and LFMC shall contain an equipment grounding conductor if the raceway is installed for the reason of _____.

    (a) physical protection
    (b) flexibility after installation
    (c) minimizing transmission of vibration from equipment
    (d) b or c

46. Outlet boxes required in 314.27 shall be permitted to support _____ locking support and mounting receptacles used in combination with compatible attachment fittings.

    (a) identified
    (b) listed
    (c) approved
    (d) labeled

47. Each direct-buried single conductor cable shall be located _____ in the trench to the other single conductor cables in the same parallel set of conductors, including equipment grounding conductors.

    (a) perpendicular
    (b) bundled together
    (c) in close proximity
    (d) spaced apart

48. Premises wiring includes _____ wiring from the service point or power source to the outlets.

    (a) interior
    (b) exterior
    (c) underground
    (d) a and b

49. When a building is supplied with a(n) _____ fire sprinkler system, ENT shall be permitted to be used within walls, floors, and ceilings, exposed or concealed, in buildings exceeding three floors above grade.

    (a) listed
    (b) identified
    (c) NFPA 13-2013
    (d) none of these

50. Where Type NM cable passes through factory or field openings in metal members, it shall be protected by _____ bushings or _____ grommets that cover metal edges.

    (a) approved
    (b) identified
    (c) listed
    (d) none of these

Mike Holt's Electrical Apprenticeship Year 1 Supplement, Based on the 2017 NEC

ABOUT THE AUTHOR

Mike Holt—Author

Founder and President
Mike Holt Enterprises
Groveland, Florida

Mike Holt's electrical career has spanned all aspects of the trade, from being an apprentice to becoming a contractor and inspector. His teaching career began in 1974 when he became an exam preparation instructor at a local community school. He was so effective that his students encouraged him to open his own training school, dedicated to helping the electrical industry. In 1975, while also running a full-service electrical contracting firm, Mike opened his school. It became so successful that by 1980 he stopped electrical contracting to completely devote his time to electrical training at a national level. Today, Mike Holt Enterprises is a leading training and publishing company for the industry, specializing in helping electrical professionals take their careers to the next level.

Mike's own educational journey impacts the way he designs training programs. As a young man he was unable to complete the requirements for his high school diploma due to life circumstances. Realizing that success depends on one's education, he immediately attained his GED. Then ten years later, he attended the University of Miami's Graduate School for a Master's degree in Business Administration. He understands the needs of his students, and because of his own experience, strongly encourages and motivates them to continue their own education. He's never lost sight of how hard it can be for students who are intimidated by the complexity of the *NEC*, by school, or by their own feelings about learning. His ultimate goal has always been about increasing electrical safety and improving lives—this commitment and vision continue to guide him to this day.

Mike has written hundreds of books, and created DVDs, online programs, MP3s, and other training materials that have made a huge impact on the industry. He's mastered the art of explaining complicated concepts in a simple but direct style. His ability to simplify technical concepts, and his one-of-a-kind presentation style, explain his unique position as one of the premier educators and *Code* experts in the United States. In addition to the materials he's produced, and the extensive list of companies around the world for whom he's provided training, Mike has written articles that have been seen in numerous industry magazines including, *Electrical Construction & Maintenance* (EC&M), *CEE News, Electrical Design and Installation* (EDI), *Electrical Contractor* (EC), *International Association of Electrical Inspectors* (IAEI News), *The Electrical Distributor* (TED), *Power Quality* (PQ) *Magazine,* and *Solar Pro Magazine.*

Mike resides in Central Florida, is the father of seven children, has five grandchildren, and enjoys many outside interests and activities. His commitment to pushing boundaries and setting high standards has also extended into his personal life. He's an 8-time National Barefoot Waterskiing Champion, has set many world records in that sport, and has competed in three World Barefoot Waterskiing Tournaments. In 2015, he started a new career in competitive mountain bike racing and continues to find ways to motivate himself mentally and physically.

What distinguishes Mike is his commitment to living a balanced lifestyle; placing God first, family, career, and self.

Special Acknowledgments

My Family. First, I want to thank God for my godly wife who's always by my side and my children, Belynda, Melissa, Autumn, Steven, Michael, Meghan, and Brittney.

My Staff. A personal thank you goes to my team at Mike Holt Enterprises for all the work they do to help me with my mission of changing people's lives through education. In particular my daughter Belynda, who works tirelessly to ensure that in addition to our products meeting and exceeding the educational needs of our customers, we stay committed to building life-long relationships with them throughout their electrical careers.

The National Fire Protection Association. A special thank you must be given to the staff at the National Fire Protection Association (NFPA), publishers of the *NEC*—in particular, Jeff Sargent for his assistance in answering my many *Code* questions over the years. Jeff, you're a "first class" guy, and I admire your dedication and commitment to helping others understand the *NEC*. Other former NFPA staff members I would like to thank include John Caloggero, Joe Ross, and Dick Murray for their help in the past.

ABOUT THE MIKE HOLT TEAM

Illustrator—Mike Culbreath

Mike Culbreath devoted his career to the electrical industry and worked his way up from apprentice to master electrician. He started in the electrical field doing residential and light commercial construction, and later did service work and custom electrical installations. While working as a journeyman electrician, he suffered a serious on-the-job knee injury. As part of his rehabilitation, Mike completed courses at Mike Holt Enterprises, and then passed the exam to receive his Master Electrician's license. In 1986, with a keen interest in continuing education for electricians, he joined the staff to update material and began illustrating Mike Holt's textbooks and magazine articles.

Mike started with simple hand-drawn diagrams and cut-and-paste graphics. When frustrated by the limitations of that style of illustrating, he took a company computer home to learn how to operate some basic computer graphic software. Upon realizing that computer graphics offered increased flexibility for creating illustrations, Mike took every computer graphics class and seminar he could to help develop his computer graphic skills. He's now worked as an illustrator and editor with the company for over 30 years and, as Mike Holt has proudly acknowledged, has helped to transform his words and visions into lifelike graphics.

Originally from South Florida, Mike now lives in northern lower Michigan where he enjoys hiking, kayaking, photography, gardening, and cooking; but his real passion is his horses. Mike loves spending time with his children (Dawn and Mac) and his grandchildren Jonah, Kieley, and Scarlet.

Special Acknowledgments—I would like to thank Eric Stromberg, an electrical engineer and super geek (and I mean that in the most complimentary manner because I think this guy is brilliant), for helping me keep our graphics as technically correct as possible. I would also like to thank all of our students for the wonderful feedback they provide that helps us improve our graphics.

I also want to give a special thank you to Cathleen Kwas for making me look good with her outstanding layout design and typesetting skills; to Toni Culbreath who proofreads all of my material; and to Dawn Babbitt

who assists me in the production and editing of our graphics. I would also like to acknowledge Belynda Holt Pinto, our Director of Operations, Brian House for his input (another really brilliant guy), and the rest of the outstanding staff at Mike Holt Enterprises, for all the hard work they do to help produce and distribute these outstanding products.

And last but not least, I need to give a special thank you to Mike Holt for not firing me over 30 years ago when I "borrowed" one of his computers and took it home to begin the process of learning how to do computer illustrations. He gave me the opportunity and time needed to develop my computer graphic skills. He's been an amazing friend and mentor ever since I met him as a student many years ago. Thanks for believing in me and allowing me to be part of the Mike Holt Enterprises family.

Technical Director—Brian House

Brian House is a licensed unlimited electrical contractor who worked throughout the southeast United States, starting in the early 1990s. In 2000 he began teaching seminars and apprenticeship classes. Since 2010 he's been participating as a member of the Mike Holt video teams, and in 2014 he joined the Mike Holt Enterprises staff as technical director. Brian is a permanent addition to the technical writing team at Mike Holt Enterprises. He played a key role by assisting in the re-writing and editing of the textbooks for the 2017 *NEC* series, coordinating the content and the illustrations, and assuring the technical accuracy and flow of the information presented. He continues to teach seminars and is actively involved in developing apprenticeship curriculum.

Brian and his wife Carissa have shared the joy of four children and many foster children during 19 years of marriage. When not mentoring youth at work or church, he can be found racing mountain bikes with his kids or fly fishing on Florida's Intracoastal Waterway.